Occupational Medicine

Construction Safety and Health

Guest Editors:

Knut Ringen, DrPH
Jane L. Seegal, MS
The Center to Protect Workers' Rights
Washington, DC

Anders Englund, MD
Department of Health and Social Affairs
National Board of Occupational Safety and Health
Solna, Sweden

Laura Welch, MD
James L. Weeks, ScD, CIH
Division of Occupational and Environmental Medicine
George Washington University
Washington, DC

Volume 10/Number 2
HANLEY & BELFUS, INC.

April–June 1995
Philadelphia

STATE OF THE ART REVIEWS

Publisher: HANLEY & BELFUS, INC.
210 South 13th Street
Philadelphia, PA 19107
(215) 546-4995
Fax (215) 790-9330

OCCUPATIONAL MEDICINE: State of the Art Reviews is included in *Index Medicus, MEDLINE, BioSciences Information Service, Current Contents* and *ISI/BIOMED.*

OCCUPATIONAL MEDICINE: State of the Art Reviews   (ISSN 0885-114X)
April–June 1995   **Volume 10, Number 2**   (ISBN 1-56053-180-0)

OCCUPATIONAL MEDICINE: State of the Art Reviews is published quarterly by Hanley & Belfus, Inc., 210 South 13th Street, Philadelphia, Pennsylvania 19107. Second-class postage paid at Philadelphia, PA, and at additional mailing offices.

POSTMASTER: Send address changes to OCCUPATIONAL MEDICINE: State of the Art Reviews, Hanley & Belfus, Inc., 210 South 13th Street, Philadelphia, PA 19107.

The 1995 subscription price is $86.00 per year U.S., $96.00 outside U.S. (add $40.00 for air mail).

Occupational Medicine: State of the Art Reviews
Vol. 10, No. 2, April–June 1995

CONSTRUCTION SAFETY AND HEALTH
Knut Ringen, DrPH, Anders Englund, MD
Laura Welch, MD, James L. Weeks, ScD, CIH
Jane L. Seegal, MS
Editors

CONTENTS

reviewed that relate to mortality include those resulting from falls from heights, contact with electricity, reversing vehicles, collapsing trench walls, and being struck by falling or moving objects.

Physical factors that contribute to musculoskeletal disorders in construction workers are described, and the clinical findings associated with muscular, tendon, articular, spinal, and peripheral nerve entrapment disorders are reviewed. Psychosocial factors and individual factors such as the worker's age, smoking habits, and endurance are considered.

This chapter focuses on the primary identified respiratory hazards in construction, including respiratory tract cancers, pulmonary and pleural fibrosis, airway diseases, inhalation injuries, and respiratory infection. An extensive table identifies the exposure limits specified by NIOSH, OSHA, and ACGIH for more than 30 substances.

The most hazardous chemicals used in construction, including materials with transdermal effects, carcinogens, embryotoxins, mutagens, and neurotoxins, are discussed here. These include solvents, primers and adhesives, wood dust, plastic woods, sealing agents, wood protectants, insulation, and products used for structural engineering.

Ways to prevent lead poisoning and regulations intended to eliminate exposures to lead are the topics here. Lead registries and other studies are described that were designed to evaluate the extent of the problem and to address the lack of routine blood-lead monitoring in the industry.

In their review of the available information on hazards such as noise, vibration, and heat and cold, the authors conclude that implementation of appropriate programs could help to prevent hearing loss, prevent vibration-related disease, and protect construction workers in both hot and cold environments.

Risk factors and controls for work-related musculoskeletal disorders, related organizational and psychosocial factors, interventions to improve ergonomics at the work site, the role of new technologies, and ways to use education, regulation, and engineering to implement control measures are covered in this chapter.

Using information from the U.S. government and the scientific literature, the authors identify preventive strategies for specific types of injuries and categorize features of employers and workers that are associated with low injury rates. They conclude that safe working conditions are possible and are related to the attitudes of workers and management.

This chapter describes, evaluates, and illustrates generic and conventional industrial hygiene methods for controlling occupational hazards affecting construction workers. Case studies that identify and control exposure to asbestos, lead, crystalline silica, and additives to cement are discussed.

Topics related to medical surveillance covered here include surveillance as prevention, types of medical monitoring programs, regulatory requirements for monitoring workers, health maintenance and promotion, and surveillance for ailments common to construction, such as musculoskeletal disorders, noise-induced hearing loss, lung disease, and dermatitis.

The construction industry has one of the highest proportions of workers without health insurance. The authors review the two types of insurance systems that are generally used to cover the cost of health care for construction workers in the U.S.: health and welfare funds and workers' compensation. Recent developments in health care delivery in the U.S. are discussed, as are the more comprehensive occupational medicine services offered in France, Germany, The Netherlands, and Sweden.

The editors conclude this issue with a discussion of the factors that are fueling change in the construction industry. They call for a new occupational safety and health standard for construction and cite the need for an industrywide approach to construction that views the industry as a whole rather than a collection of separate entities.

CONTRIBUTORS

Toni Alterman, PhD
Senior Research Epidemiologist, Surveillance Branch, Division for Surveillance, Hazard Evaluations, and Field Studies, National Institute for Occupational Safety and Health, Cincinnati, Ohio

Ki Moon Bang, PhD, MPH
Chief, Surveillance Section, Epidemiological Investigations Branch, Division of Respiratory Disease Studies, National Institute for Occupational Safety and Health, Morgantown, West Virginia

Jean-Louis Bélard, MD, DES
Visiting Scientist, Division of Safety Research, National Institute for Occupational Safety and Health, Morgantown, West Virginia; formerly, Secretary, Ergonomics and Human Factors Technical Coordination Group, French Ministry of Defense

Richard Braddee
Safety and Occupational Health Specialist, Trauma Investigation Section, Surveillance and Field Investigations Branch, Division of Safety Research, National Institute for Occupational Safety and Health, Morgantown, West Virginia

Carol Burnett, MS
Research Epidemiologist, Surveillance Branch, Division of Surveillance, Hazard Evaluations, and Field Studies, National Institute for Occupational Safety and Health, Cincinnati, Ohio

Thomas M. Cook, PhD, PT
Associate Professor and Director, Biomechanics/Ergonomics Laboratory, University of Iowa, Iowa City, Iowa

Göran Engholm, MSc
Avdelningsdirektör, Socialstyrelsen (National Board of Health and Welfare), Stockholm, Sweden; National Institute of Occupational Health, Umeå, Sweden; formerly, chief epidemiologist, Bygghälsan, the Swedish Construction Industry's Organization for Working Environment, Occupational Safety and Health

Anders Englund, MD
Director, Department of Health and Social Affairs, Arbetarskyddsstyrelsen (National Board of Occupational Safety and Health), Solna, Sweden; formerly, medical director, Bygghälsan, the Swedish Construction Industry's Organization for Working Environment, Occupational Safety and Health

John F. Finklea, MD, DrPH
Senior Medical Adviser, U.S. Centers for Disease Control and Prevention, on detail to the Center to Protect Workers' Rights, Washington, DC; formerly, director, National Institute for Occupational Safety and Health

David E. Fosbroke, MSF
Statistician, Injury Surveillance Section, Surveillance and Field Investigations Branch, Division of Safety Research, National Institute for Occupational Safety and Health, Morgantown, West Virginia

William E. Halperin, MD, MPH
Director, Division of Safety Research, National Institute for Occupational Safety and Health, Morgantown, West Virginia; formerly Associate Director for Surveillance, Division of Surveillance, Hazard Evaluations, and Field Studies, National Institute for Occupational Safety and Health

Frank J. Hearl, SMChE, PE
Chief, Environmental Investigations Branch, Division of Respiratory Disease Studies, National Institute for Occupational Safety and Health, Morgantown, West Virginia

Eva Holmström, DrMedSci
Regional Manager, Malmö, Sweden, for Bygghälsan, the Swedish Construction Industry's Organization for Working Environment, Occupational Safety and Health

Eckardt Johanning, MD, MSc
Department of Environmental and Occupational Medicine, Mt. Sinai Medical Center, and Medical Director, Eastern New York Occupational Health Program, New York City and Latham, New York

Suzanne Kisner
Statistician, Injury Surveillance Section, Surveillance and Field Investigations Branch, Division of Safety Research, National Institute for Occupational Safety and Health, Morgantown, West Virginia

Norbert Kluger, DiplGeogr
Arbeitsgemeinschaft der Bau-Berufsgenossenschaften, Frankfurt, Germany

Nina Lalich, MSPH
Chief, Illness Effects Section, Surveillance Branch, Division of Surveillance, Hazard Evaluations, and Field Studies, National Institute for Occupational Safety and Health, Cincinnati, Ohio

Doug McVittie
Manager, Technical Services, Construction Safety Association of Ontario, Toronto, Canada

James Melius, MD, DrPH
Medical Director and Scientific Director, Center to Protect Workers' Rights, Washington, DC; formerly, Director, Division of Occupational Health and Environmental Epidemiology, New York State Department of Health

Ulrich Moritz, MD, PhD
Professor Emeritus, Rehabilitation Center, Rehabilitation, University Hospital, Lund, Sweden

Ana Maria Osorio, MD, MPH
Chief, Division of Environmental and Occupational Disease Control, State of California Department of Health Services, Emeryville, California

Earl Pollack, ScD
Senior Statistical Adviser, Center to Protect Workers' Rights, Washington, DC; formerly Chief of Biometry, National Cancer Institute

Laura Punnett, ScD
Associate Professor, Department of Work Environment, University of Massachusetts at Lowell, Lowell, Massachusetts

Knut Ringen, DrPH, MHA, MPH
Director, Center to Protect Workers' Rights, Washington, DC

Cynthia Robinson, PhD
Senior Research Epidemiologist, Surveillance Branch, Division of Surveillance, Hazard Evaluations, and Field Studies, National Institute for Occupational Safety and Health, Cincinnati, Ohio

Robert Roscoe, MS
Epidemiologist, Surveillance Branch, Division of Surveillance, Hazard Evaluations, and Field Studies, National Institute for Occupational Safety and Health, Cincinnati, Ohio

Pekka Roto, MD, MIH
Medical Officer, Tampere Regional Institute of Occupational Health, Tampere, Finland

Reinhold Rühl, DrRerNat
Head, Gefahrstoff-Informationssystem der Berufsgenossenschaften der Bauwirtschaft, Frankfurt, Germany

Scott Schneider, CIH
Ergonomics Program Director, Center to Protect Workers' Rights, Washington, DC

Jane L. Seegal, MA, MS
Editorial Consultant, Center to Protect Workers' Rights, Washington, DC

Paul Seligman, MD
Acting Deputy Assistant Secretary for Health, U.S. Department of Energy, Washington, DC; formerly, Chief, Medical Section, Surveillance Branch, Division for Surveillance, Hazard Evaluations, and Field Studies, National Institute for Occupational Safety and Health, Cincinnati, Ohio

John Sestito, JD, MS
Assistant Chief, Surveillance Branch, Division of Surveillance, Hazard Evaluations, and Field Studies, National Institute for Occupational Safety and Health, Cincinnati, Ohio

Frank Stern, MS
Senior Epidemiologist, Industrywide Studies Branch, Division of Surveillance, Hazard Evaluations, and Field Studies, National Institute for Occupational Safety and Health, Cincinnati, Ohio

Nancy Stout, EdD
Acting Chief, Surveillance and Field Investigations Branch, Division of Safety Research, National Institute for Occupational Safety and Health, Morgantown, West Virginia

Patricia A. Sullivan, MS
Epidemiologist, Epidemiological Investigations Branch, Division of Respiratory Disease Studies, National Institute for Occupational Safety and Health, Morgantown, West Virginia

Gregory R. Wagner, MD
Director, Division of Respiratory Disease Studies, National Institute for Occupational Safety and Health, Morgantown, West Virginia

James L. Weeks, ScD, CIH
Associate Professor, Division of Occupational and Environmental Medicine, George Washington University, Washington, DC

Laura Welch, MD
Associate Professor of Medicine and Division Director, Division of Occupational and Environmental Medicine, George Washington University, Washington, DC

PUBLISHED ISSUES
(available from the publisher)

1995 ISSUES

**Effects of the Indoor Environment
on Health**
Edited by James M. Seltzer, MD
University of California School of Medicine
San Diego, California

Construction Safety and Health
Edited by Knut Ringen, DrPH,
Laura Welch, MD, James L. Weeks, ScD, CIH,
and Jane L. Seegal, MS
Washington, DC
and Anders Englund, MD
Solna, Sweden

Firefighters
Edited by Peter Orris, MD
Cook County Hospital
Chicago, Illinois
and Richard M. Duffy, MSc
International Association of Fire Fighters
Washington, DC
and James Melius, MD, DrPH
Center to Protect Workers' Rights
Washington, DC

Occupational Hearing Loss
Edited by Thais C. Morata, PhD,
and Derek E. Dunn, PhD
National Institute for Occupational Safety
    and Health
Cincinnati, Ohio

1994 ISSUES

Occupational Skin Disease
Edited by James R. Nethercott, MD
University of Maryland
Baltimore, Maryland

Occupational Safety and Health Training
Edited by Michael J. Colligan, PhD
National Institute for Occupational
    Safety and Health
Cincinnati, Ohio

Reproductive Hazards
Edited by Ellen B. Gold, PhD, B. L. Lasley,
PhD, and Marc B. Schenker, MD, MPH
University of California
Davis, California

Tuberculosis in the Workplace
Edited by Steven Markowitz, MD
Mount Sinai School of Medicine
New York, New York

1993 ISSUES

The Mining Industry
Edited by Daniel E. Banks, MD
West Virginia University
Morgantown, West Virgina

De Novo Toxicants
Edited by Dennis J. Shusterman, MD, MPH
California EPA, Berkeley, California
and Jack E. Peterson, PhD, CIH
Alpine, California

Spirometry
Edited by Ellen A. Eisen, ScD
University of Massachusetts
Lowell, Massachusetts

Women Workers
Edited by Dana M. Headapohl, MD
St. Patrick's Hospital
Missoula, Montana

Ordering Information:
Subscriptions for full year and single issues are available from the publishers—
Hanley & Belfus, Inc., 210 South 13th Street, Philadelphia, PA 19107
Telephone (215) 546-7293; (800) 962-1892. Fax (215) 790-9330.

PREFACE

Construction workers suffer more than their share of work-related deaths in many industrialized countries, including the United States. Occupational safety and health issues in construction are in many ways more pressing than in other industries.

The industry's rates of occupational death, injury, and illness are high, even given the obvious risks—of work with heavy machinery, on scaffolding hundreds of feet above ground, in trenches or pipes, or on hazardous-waste sites. Unfortunately, reliable data about many of the hazards and outcomes, including occupational illness, are lacking.

Until the late 1980s, safety and health research in the construction sector was mostly limited to a few European countries, including Sweden. There, beginning in the early 1970s, Bygghälsan, the Swedish Construction Industry's Organization for Working Environment, Occupational Safety, and Health, conducted a preventive medical program and longitudinal study of health outcomes among more than 200,000 construction workers; many of the findings and data are published in this volume (chapter 2 and annex).

Despite the extensive research in Sweden, more research has been needed—among other things, to account for differences in populations, work tasks, and organization in other countries. That picture is changing. Epidemiologic and applied intervention research are increasing, especially in the United States, and interested organizations are beginning to exchange information internationally.

Labor, management, and public health professionals believe that better information and an emphasis on improved safety and health can help prevent injuries and illnesses, reducing the costs—financial and human. This emphasis is needed among policymakers, at all levels of construction management, throughout the workforce, and among health care researchers and providers.

The information in this volume applies to all aspects of safety and health in the construction industry. This volume has been prepared anticipating that its readers will represent a broad spectrum of the health professions. The emphasis, however, is on providing preventive and occupational medicine.

The editors would like to thank John Finklea, James Melius, John Moran, Earl Pollack, Scott Schneider, and Pam Susi for reviewing some chapters and Sean Hartig, Marcia Akresh, Jennifer Harley, Lisa Hatch, Kimberly Lockhart, and Patricia Sullivan Quinn for their help with production.

KNUT RINGEN, DrPH
ANDERS ENGLUND, MD
LAURA WELCH, MD
JAMES L. WEEKS, ScD, CIH
JANE L. SEEGAL, MS
GUEST EDITORS

KNUT RINGEN, DrPH
ANDERS ENGLUND, MD
LAURA WELCH, MD
JAMES L. WEEKS, ScD, CIH
JANE L. SEEGAL, MS

WHY CONSTRUCTION IS DIFFERENT

From The Center to Protect
  Workers' Rights
Washington, DC (KR, JLS)
  and
Division of Occupational and
  Environmental Medicine
George Washington University
Washington, DC (LW, JLW)
  and
Department of Health and Social
  Affairs
National Board of Occupational
  Safety and Health
Solna, Sweden (AE)

Reprint requests to:
Jane L. Seegal, MS
The Center to Protect Workers'
  Rights
111 Massachusetts Ave. NW
Washington, DC 20001

Construction workers build, repair, renovate, modify, and demolish structures: houses, office buildings, temples, factories, hospitals, roads, bridges, tunnels, stadiums, docks, airports, and more. In the United States, they also clean hazardous waste sites. The work ranges from fully mechanized activities to hard physical labor. It often must be done in extreme heat or cold; in windy, rainy, snowy, or foggy weather; or at night. Sometimes the work sites are isolated locations; at other times, they are in the midst of heavy traffic.

Construction differs markedly from most other types of manufacturing in the extent of the safety and health risks to workers. The unique organization of the work exacerbates the risks.

Incidence of Injuries and Illness

In industrialized nations, construction is consistently ranked among the most dangerous occupations. Among industrial sectors in the United States, the death rate from work-related traumatic injuries in construction is exceeded only by such rates for mining or for agriculture, forestry, and fishing (see chapter 3).[13]

Data from a study of 180,000 death certificates for men ages 16–64 in California over 3 years show that construction trades were five of the 10 occupations with the highest standardized mortality ratios. Based on data from that study, we estimate that members of construction trades who die during their working years die an average of 8–12 years earlier than members of some low-risk white-collar occupations.[3]

OCCUPATIONAL MEDICINE: State of the Art Reviews—
Vol. 10, No. 2, April 1995. Philadelphia, Hanley & Belfus, Inc.

255

Because construction generally involves a larger proportion of the work force than other high-risk occupations, construction's risks endanger a larger population. For instance, in the United States, construction represents 5–6% of the work force but has 15% of the work-related deaths from injuries—more than any other sector.[13] * The construction sector in Japan is 10% of the work force but has 42% of the work-related deaths; in Sweden, the numbers are 6% and 13%, respectively.[1,7]

The sector also has a disproportionate share of lost-time injuries, those serious enough to require restricted work or time off to recover—9% of all such injuries in the United States, according to the Bureau of Labor Statistics (BLS) (personal communication) (see chapters 4 and 11). The rate of these injuries remained essentially unchanged in 1975–1990, but there appears to be a new trend. BLS reports lost-time injury rates for the U.S. construction industry have declined in 1990–1993, from 6.6 to 5.4 per 200,000 hours.

Many of the serious ailments in construction are not induced by acute trauma but, instead, develop incrementally. Although these musculoskeletal disorders are not fatal, they are significant in terms of their cost and the numbers of workers they affect (see chapters 5, 9, and 10). Work-related musculoskeletal disorders include low back pain and carpal tunnel syndrome.

Several illnesses have been linked to construction trades, among them the pneumoconiosis of the tunnel builder and the welder, asbestosis of the building demolition worker, skin allergies of the mason, and kidney problems from the painter's and the roofer's exposure to solvents. Some illnesses may be acute, such as lead poisoning suffered by the bridge rehabilitation worker and heat stress of the hazardous waste clean-up worker (from wearing moon suits). In addition, there are physiologic impairments: white finger (Raynaud's syndrome) of the jackhammer operator or noise-induced hearing loss (chapters 2, 6-9).[2]

In general, chronic work-related illnesses are underreported and even unrecognized. Among the reasons for this are the mix of causes of most illnesses, the difficulty characterizing exposures to occupational hazards, and the long latencies between initial exposure to a disease-causing agent and the first appearance of symptoms (see chapter 13).

In New York State, for instance, the Mount Sinai School of Medicine estimated that 3,700 people died yearly in 1979–1982 of occupational cancers. Although the deaths in 1979 included 80 caused by mesothelioma, the workers' compensation board accepted just three cancer deaths as work-related for each of the years. The study also concluded that the low figure reflected a general failure of the medical system to recognize occupational illness.[10]

Work Organization and Industry Characteristics

The logistics of constructing a factory or road or renovating a structure are unlike those needed to manufacture a jeep or blue jeans. The organization of the work and work environment are complex and constantly changing.

First, several employers may work on a large construction site simultaneously: the general contractor and subcontractors who do electrical wiring, finish concrete flooring, deliver and install marble exteriors, or install roofing. Second, a worker's location on a site may change regularly in relation to other workers; therefore, the

---

* The National Institute for Occupational Safety and Health, using the National Traumatic Occupational Fatalities data base for 1980–89, reports a death rate from injuries of 25.6 per 100,000 full-time equivalents for construction.[8] The U.S. Bureau of Labor Statistics reports a death rate of 14 per 100,000 workers for 1993.[14]

worker's potential exposure as a bystander to such hazards as welding fumes or dusts also changes. Third, as the work develops—for instance, as a building's walls are erected or as the weather changes—the ambient conditions such as ventilation and temperature can change markedly.

Fourth, unlike in an industrial setting where a worker may have one employer for years, construction workers may have four, five, or more employers in a year. Although some major construction projects take a few years, they often are short-lived, and construction workers typically are hired from project to project. Many trades work only briefly on a site; roofers or plasterers, for instance, may have only a few days' employment on a new building.

Clearly, construction workers are regularly working themselves out of a job. With unemployment between projects and with interruptions because of bad weather, the average worker may put in 1,500 or fewer hours yearly in construction. In contrast, a 40-hour work week with 2 weeks of vacation adds up to 2,000 hours yearly.

The uncertainties of employment and the hazards mean that many workers are discouraged from making construction a career. Many construction workers who can find other work do so. Others are forced to leave as a result of injuries or disease. As a result, the work force includes a large proportion of inexperienced, temporary, and transient workers. Although construction work often must be done in teams, it is difficult to develop effective, safe teamwork under such conditions.

Like the work force, the universe of contractors is marked by high turnover and populated mainly by small operations. Of the 1.9 million construction contractors identified by the 1990 U.S. Census, only 28% had any employees. Just 136,000 (7%) had 10 or more employees (John T. Dunlop, personal communication). As in some other industries, an increasing proportion of contractors in the U.S. consists of workers hired as "independent contractors" by employers seeking to evade customary tax and benefit obligations. BLS estimates that 9% of the U.S. work force is self-employed,[6] but in construction the figure may be as high as 25%.[4] In the U.S., relatively few contractors—mainly the ones with a large number of workers—belong to trade organizations.

The Costs

Estimates for the cost of injuries in construction in the U.S. range from $10 billion to $40 billion annually;[12] at $20 billion, the cost per construction worker would be $3,500 yearly. One cost indicator, workers' compensation premiums for three trades—carpenters, masons, and structural iron workers—averaged 28.6% of payroll nationally in mid 1994.[13] Premium rates vary enormously, depending on trade and jurisdiction. Premiums for $100 of payroll in roofing cost $18.09 in Indiana and $51.96 in Texas.[13] In addition to workers' compensation, there are liability insurance premiums and other indirect costs, including reduced work crew efficiency, clean-up (from a cave-in or collapse, for instance), or overtime necessitated by an injury. These indirect costs can exceed the workers' compensation claim for an injury by several multiples.[5,9]

Implications for Safety and Health

On the work site, unlike on an assembly line, a worker moving about makes many decisions that affect safety and health, such as how to lift heavy steel rods or whether to test a confined space for dangerous gases or vapors before entering it.

Efforts to implement well-coordinated safety programs are hampered by the lack of comprehensive employer organizations and the fact that most workers in the U.S. are not tied to a single employer or union. Preventive safety and health programs are best promoted industrywide through umbrella groups. For instance, labor-management organizations were the vehicles for safety and health programs in the Federal Republic of Germany, the Netherlands, Sweden, and Ontario, Canada.

A dearth of small firms in industry forums means that such firms are often left unaware of the likely payoffs in reduced suffering and costs that can result from improved safety and health programs. Even if small firms do want to implement preventive programs, such companies may not have enough of a profit margin to support investing up front in training, personal protective equipment, ergonomically designed tools, or other improvements. Yet it is at small work sites and among the self-employed that the highest injury rates appear to occur.[11,14]

Because of the rarity of long-term worker employment by individual contractors, the construction union is the only work-related institution with which many workers are affiliated. The building trades unions know that improved safety and health are essential in order to offer their membership an improved quality of life, but they represent only a portion of the work force. About 25% of the construction workers in the United States are unionized; the percentage is much higher for non-residential construction, certain trades, certain localities, the public sector, and large projects.

On-again, off-again work adds to the health risks, including the emotional toll of uncertainty about getting another job. Relocating often or commuting long distances to secure work adds to the stress. In addition, in the U.S., where there is no universal health insurance, intermittent employment and the high cost of health insurance mean that many construction workers and their families do not have health care coverage. Even when construction workers do put in the 30 or 60 days needed to qualify for insurance coverage on a job—if coverage is available—they often cannot afford to maintain coverage from the time that job ends until they are eligible for coverage on another project.

Because of a combination of factors, construction workers in the U.S. tend not to maintain long-term relationships with individual health providers. This lack of continuity, in turn, means that preventive care is neglected and many changes in an individual's health are not noticed and caught early, when they can be most easily cured (see chapter 14).

For workers who do have health care coverage, episodic employment, frequent changes of employer, and continuous changes in work site exposures and ambient conditions limit the clinician's or the researcher's ability to trace the individual's work history or exposures to hazards.

REFERENCES

1. Arbetarskyddsstyrelsen (National Board of Occupational Safety and Health), Sweden (personal communication).
2. Burkhart G, Schulte PA, Robinson C, et al: Job tasks, potential exposures, and health risks of laborers employed in the construction industry. Am J Ind Med 24: 413-425, 1993.
3. California Department of Health Services: California Occupational Mortality 1979-81. Sacramento, California Dept. of Health Services, March 1987.
4. Commission on the Future of Worker-Management Relations: Fact Finding Report. Washington, DC, U.S. Dept. of Labor, May 1994.
5. Hinze J: Indirect Costs of Construction Accidents. Austin, TX, Construction Industry Institute, 1991.
6. Jack TA, Zak MJ: Results from the First National Census of Fatal Occupational Injuries, 1992. Washington, DC, Bureau of Labor Statistics, December 1993.
7. Japan Construction Safety and Health Association (personal communication).

8. Kisner SM, Fosbroke DE: Injury hazards in the construction industry. J Occup Med 36:137-143, 1994.

9. Levitt RE, Samelson NM: Construction Safety Management. 2nd ed. New York, Wiley & Sons, 1993.

10. Markowitz S, Fisher E, Fahs M, et al: Occupational disease in New York State: A comprehensive re-examination. Am J Ind Med 16:417-436, 1989.

11. Marsh B: Chance of getting hurt is generally far higher at smaller companies. Wall Street Journal, February 3, 1994, p A1.

12. Meridian Research: Worker protection programs in construction. Silver Spring, MD, Meridian Research, 1994 (OSHA Contract J-9-F-1-0019).

13. Powers MB: Cost fever breaks. Engineering News-Record 233(13):40-41, 1994.

14. Toscano G, Windau J: The changing character of fatal work injuries. Monthly Labor Review. Washington, US Dept. of Labor, October 1994, pp 17-28.

15. Workplace Hazard and Tobacco Education Project: Construction Workers' Guide to Toxics on the Job. Berkeley, CA, California Public Health Foundation, 1993.

GÖRAN ENGHOLM, MSc
ANDERS ENGLUND, MD

MORBIDITY AND MORTALITY PATTERNS IN SWEDEN

From the Department of Provincial
    and Regional Health and
    Medical Care
National Board of Health and
    Welfare
Stockholm, Sweden
    and
National Institute of Occupational
    Health
Umeå, Sweden (GE)
    and
Department of Health and Social
    Affairs
National Board of Occupational
    Safety and Health
Solna, Sweden (AE)

Reprint requests to:
Göran Engholm, MSc
Avdelningsdirektör
Department of Provincial and
    Regional Health and Medical
    Care
National Board of Health and
    Welfare
P.O. S-106 30 Stockholm
Sweden

Construction workers in most countries are an ill-defined group. More often than not, most of the workers have only temporary jobs in and out of the industry. For certain tasks that require special skills, a core of craftspeople is able to make a lifetime career of an occupation, including carpenters, bricklayers, machine operators, rockblasters, and asphalt pavement workers. However, for some groups of workers, particularly asphalt pavement workers, the work tends to be seasonal. Concrete workers are a less specialized and more mobile group; in some countries, they are labeled helpers and in some countries their ranks include a large proportion of women. In Sweden, besides the professions in the home building and civil engineering sectors, specialists such as electricians, insulators, painters, pipefitters/plumbers, and sheet metal workers belong to the general construction trades, as do supervisors and foremen.

Statistics on the mortality of members of such groups, based on national registries, have been presented over the years from countries such as Denmark, the United Kingdom, and the United States.[3,5,6] Such data usually reflect the occupation listed at time of death. Because of the intermittent employment of workers in construction, however, this data may not be the most reliable source for describing mortality patterns. These statistics might be more reliable for acute and immediate conditions and less so for chronic ones, such as cancer, which occur at a late age. There are a number of studies on well-defined groups of special craftsmen, such as insulators,[7] painters,[4] and sheet metal workers.[8] Only a few studies address the incidence of cancer in construction workers, including a census-based Danish study[3] and reports on painters and plumbers from Sweden.[1]

In general, little qualitative or quantitative information is available on exposures. Often, possible excesses of deaths or cancers can only be related to job categories representing a wide range of exposures. Knowledge about the typical tasks of the respective crafts, proportion of those tasks, and changes of work practices and materials used over time is necessary when judging observed excess risks.

There are several conditions for which the source of occupational exposure can be discovered only by examining the workers, obtaining their work and medical histories, and performing certain medical tests. This is especially true for musculoskeletal disorders, bronchitis, and other forms of impaired respiratory function, including allergic reactions. It is also the case for skin diseases and impaired hearing capacity (see chapters 5, 6, and 9).

A STUDY FROM SWEDEN

Population and Methods

In Sweden in the late 1960s, the employers and unions in the construction industry agreed to set up a comprehensive and nationwide occupational health service program covering all the trades (Bygghälsan). Since then and up to the end of 1992, a medical check-up every 2–3 years was one component of the Bygghälsan program. Although the program was voluntary, 85–90% of eligible workers participated at least once. Since 1993, however, the program has lost its comprehensive character and turned into a fee-for-service consultancy program. The prospective follow-up for mortality and cancer incidence continues but is now carried out by the National Institute of Occupational Health.

In addition to keeping traditional medical records with the medical history and results of blood pressure, spirometry, and audiometry tests, Bygghälsan recorded information on job history, including specific exposures and smoking habits, in computer files. An epidemiologic monitoring program was established as part of the overall program.[2] The monitoring included follow-up of the examinees for mortality and incidence of cancer. The availability of a unique personal identification—the 10-digit social security number—used in the Bygghälsan computer files and in various national registries facilitated this work. The follow-up was done by computer record linkage to the national cancer registry, the national register of deceased subjects, and registers of migrants and of the current population. The monitoring program also included three historical cohorts of painters, insulators, and plumbers.

Virtually all people enrolled in the monitoring program were followed successfully. Loss to follow-up was less than one in 1,000. Observed numbers of deaths or cancers have primarily been compared with expected numbers based on age, gender, and calendar-specific rates for the whole Swedish population (standardized mortality ratio, SMR, and standardized incidence ratio, SIR). Because the Bygghälsan examinees, even 10–15 years after their first check-up, showed mortality rates considerably lower than that of the general population, an additional internal comparison was made: each occupational group of examinees was compared with all other groups combined, which is expressed as relative risk (RR).

The group of all Bygghälsan examinees comprises 226,648 people first examined from 1971 to 1979. They were followed for mortality through 1988 and for the incidence of cancer through 1987. The number of person-years at risk in the mortality follow-up was 3,136,523. The average length of follow-up was 13.8 years, and the maximum length, 17.3 years. Median age during follow-up was 43.4 years.

The historical cohorts include 30,600 painters, 1,700 insulators, and 18,400 plumbers. The painter cohort consists of all people who, at any time in 1966–1972, were members of the painters' union. The insulator and plumber cohorts include all people receiving certificates of skill in 1965–1972. Many of these workers also belong to the cohort of examinees. A comparison between the members of these three trades who were and were not examined was made in the hope that the results would shed some light on selection mechanisms.

Mortality and Cancer Incidence

FINDINGS FOR ALL EXAMINEES

A total of 18,659 deaths were observed among the Bygghälsan examinees. The age and calendar-period adjusted expected number of deaths was 26,128, which means that the SMR was 0.74. The low SMR, often seen as a manifestation of the so-called healthy worker effect, has no correspondence to a low incidence of cancer. The total number of cancers reported to the cancer registry was 9,940, with an expected number of 10,500, which gives an SIR of 0.95 (see Annex, page 453).

Almost half of the deaths were due to vascular diseases (SMR 0.74). For all cancers, the SMR was 0.88. The only causes of death for which the SMR was elevated were pleural tumors (SMR 1.36) and work-related accidents (SMR 1.30).

The relatively low risk for vascular diseases suggests a selection bias. It is possible that workers with vascular disease may have been excluded from hiring for construction work or may have been less prone to attend Bygghälsan check-ups, because they may have already had a personal physician.

The only sites of cancer for which the SIR was elevated were the pleura (1.56) (virtually all cases were mesotheliomas) and the lip (SIR 1.20). The SIR was markedly low for the larynx (0.82), the esophagus (0.66), and the liver (0.69), which are all cancers associated with excess consumption of alcohol. These results also suggest selection bias, a finding supported by a closer look at three smaller cohorts.

FINDINGS FOR EXAMINEES AND NONEXAMINEES

A comparison between examinees and nonexaminees among the historical cohorts of insulators, painters, and plumbers found that the overall mortality of the nonexaminees was roughly twice that of the examinees. For causes of death associated with excess consumption of alcohol, the SMRs for nonexaminees were two to six times higher than those of the examinees. Among such causes were violent death, cirrhosis of the liver, and alcoholism. For deaths associated with a work exposure, such as a pleural tumor, however, there was no such difference between the nonexaminees and examinees (see Table 4 on page 439).

FINDINGS FOR SELECTED OCCUPATIONS

Several standardized mortality ratios and standardized incidence ratios were found to be excessive for some occupations (Table 1).

Asphalt workers. Among 2,700 road paving asphalt workers who were followed, the number of person-years at risk in the mortality follow-up was almost 38,000. The group was, on average, young; the median age during mortality follow-up was 42.6 years. Accordingly, the expected number of deaths and cancers was small. There were 144 observed deaths and 72 cancers reported to the cancer registry, corresponding to an overall SMR of 0.69 and an overall SIR of 0.82.

TABLE 1.   Occupations with Excess Standardized Mortality Rates (SMRs) and
Standardized Incidence Rates (SIRs) for Selected Causes

Occupation	Significantly Higher SMR	Significantly Higher SIR
Bricklayers	—	Peritoneal tumor
Concrete workers	All causes*, all cancers*, stomach cancer, violent death*, accidental falls	Lip cancer, stomach cancer, larynz cancer*[a], lung cancer[b]
Crane drivers	Violent death*	—
Drivers	All causes*, cardiovascular*	Lip cancer
Insulators	All causes*, lung cancer, pneumoconiosis, violent death*	Peritoneal tumor, lung cancer
Machine operators	Cardiovascular*, other accidents	—
Plumbers	All cancers*, lung cancer, pneumoconiosis	All cancers, pleural tumor, lung cancer
Rock workers	All causes*, cardiovascular*, violent death, other accidents	—
Sheet metal workers	All cancers*, lung cancer, accidental falls	All cancers, lung cancer
Woodworkers/carpenters	—	Nose and nasal sinuses

[a] The relative risk for larynx cancer among concrete workers, compared to carpenters, is three times higher.
[b] The relative risk for lung cancer among concrete workers, compared to carpenters, is almost double.
*Cancers or causes of death marked by an asterisk(*) are significantly higher in comparison to all other occupational groups combined. "Other accidents" includes typical work-related injuries.

As for specific causes of death and specific sites of cancer, the SMR and the SIR were 1.62 and 1.80, respectively, for stomach cancer, and they were 1.98 and 1.55 for kidney cancer. The SMR for traffic accident fatalities was 1.52. The confidence intervals are wide, and none of the excesses are significant at the 5% level.

The all-cause SMR and the all-sites SIR were slightly lower for asphalt workers than for all other groups taken together.

Bricklayers.   Among 7,900 bricklayers who were followed, there were 908 deaths and there were 468 cancers reported to the cancer registry. This corresponded to an SMR of 0.71 and an SIR of 0.88, both of which were significantly lower than expected at the 5% level. The only site with a significantly high SIR was cancer of the peritoneum. Compared to the other groups combined, the RR for mortality from cancer of the esophagus was 2.02, a significant excess.

Concrete workers.   About 31,000 concrete workers, an occupational group that in the U.S. would consist mainly of laborers, were followed. There were 4,153 observed deaths and 2,082 reported cancers, corresponding to an overall SMR of 0.79 and an overall SIR of 0.95. Compared with all other groups taken together, the RR was 1.09 for mortality (significant) and 1.00 for cancer incidence.

The SMR was 0.95 for all cancers, but it was 1.10 compared with all other construction groups, which was significantly higher than expected. For cancer of the stomach, the SMR and the SIR were 1.24 and 1.19, respectively, both significant at the 5% level. For lung cancer, the SMR and the SIR were 1.10 and 1.03, respectively, which is not significant at the 5% level. Compared with the other groups combined, the RR for mortality was 1.23 (significant) and the relative risk for cancer incidence was 1.13 (not significant). For cancer of the lip and cancer of the larynx, the SIRs were 1.83 and 1.17, respectively. The SIR was significant at the 5% level for lip cancer but not for laryngeal cancer. However, at 1.61, the RR for laryngeal cancer mortality compared with the other groups combined was significant. The SMR and SIR for tumors of the pleura were 1.53 and 1.66, respectively, neither of which were significant at the 5% level.

The SMR for accidental falls, 1.43, was a significant excess. Compared to all other groups combined, so were the RR for violent death (1.23), suicide (1.21), drowning (1.85), and accidental falls (1.61).

Drivers. About 3,400 truck drivers, equivalent to teamsters in the U.S., were followed. There were 324 observed deaths and 152 reported cancers, which corresponded to an overall SMR of 0.88 and an overall SIR of 0.93. The mortality rate from all causes was significantly higher for drivers than for all other groups taken together (RR 1.15).

The SMR and the SIR for multiple myeloma were 3.72 and 2.73, respectively, and the SIR for cancer of the lip 3.64. Further, mortality related to ischemic heart disease was significantly higher for drivers than for the other groups taken together (RR 1.37).

Electricians. Among 19,100 electricians, there were 707 observed deaths and 438 reported cases of cancer, corresponding to an SMR of 0.66 and an SIR of 1.00. The SMR and SIR for bladder cancer were 2.30 and 1.33, respectively. Only the SMR was significant at the 5% level. The incidence of liver cancer incidence was significantly higher for electricians than for all other groups taken together.

Glass workers. About 1,500 glass workers were followed; members of the equivalent group in the U.S. install glass and are members of the painters' union. The total number of person-years at risk in the mortality follow-up was about 21,000. The median age is low, 38.0, and, accordingly, the numbers of expected deaths and cancers were small. The observed number of deaths was 89, and the number of cancers reported to the cancer registry was 38, which corresponded to an overall SMR of 0.83 and an overall SIR of 1.04.

In terms of specific causes of death and specific cancer sites, the SMR and SIR for prostate cancer were 2.70 and 1.62, respectively. None were significant at the 5% level but, compared to all other occupational groups combined, the RR, 2.86, was significant. As for cancer of the bladder, the SIR of 2.73 was significant at the 5% level but the SMR of 4.76 was not. However, the bladder cancer mortality was significantly higher in glass workers than in the other groups taken together (RR 6.04). So was the mortality from diseases of the arteries (RR 3.87).

Insulators. Some 1,500 examined insulators—equivalent to asbestos workers in the U.S.—were followed. The total number of person-years at risk in the mortality follow-up was about 20,500. Since the group was young (median age during follow-up 39.3), the expected number of deaths and cancers was small. There were 98 observed deaths and 38 cancers reported to the cancer registry, corresponding to an SMR of 1.01 and SIR of 0.95. Mortality for all causes combined was significantly higher for insulators than for all other groups combined. This is reflected in the high ratios for violent deaths (RR 1.63), including suicides (RR 2.11).

The SMR and the SIR for cancer of the lung in insulators were 2.67 and 2.31, respectively. These excess ratios were both significant at the 5% level, as was the SMR for pneumoconiosis (40.0). The incidence of cancers of the liver and of the peritoneum was significantly higher for the insulators than the other groups taken together. This also applied to comparison with the general population for cancer of the peritoneum.

In the cohort of 1,676 certified insulators, mortality for all causes based on almost 300 deaths and mortality from cancer of the peritoneum, lung, and pleura, and nonmalignant diseases of the respiratory tract were significantly increased compared to the general Swedish male population; the SMR for vascular death was close to expected.

In this subcohort the vascular deaths were about one-third of all deaths (99/279), which is close to 34/98, the proportion in the cohort of examined insulators. In the total cohort of construction examinees, however, the vascular deaths constituted 50%.

With regard to the incidence of cancer, the SIR was increased for all sites combined and for cancers of the lip, peritoneum, lung, and pleura.

Machine operators. About 7,100 machine operators, a group equivalent to operating engineers in the U.S., were followed. The observed number of deaths was 394, and the number of cancers reported to the cancer registry was 204. This corresponded to an SMR of 0.79 and an SIR of 1.06. The SMR for cardiovascular and cerebrovascular death were 0.94 and 1.04, but compared to the other groups combined, the RRs were 1.23 and 1.51, respectively, which were significant excesses. For no other causes or sites were the SMRs and SIRs significantly greater than 1.

Painters. Some 16,400 examined painters were followed, with 1,405 observed deaths and 785 cancers reported to the cancer registry. The SMR was 0.72 and SIR was 0.98. As for specific causes of death, the only significantly elevated SMRs were for nonmalignant respiratory disease and for homicide, which were higher for painters than for the other groups taken together, but this was not so compared to the general population. There are no cancer sites with significantly high SIRs.

In the cohort of some 30,600 members of the painters' union, rates of mortality from all causes, from vascular diseases, and from violent causes were close to the expected levels. SMRs for cancers of the esophagus, rectum, larynx, lung, and pleura, and for chronic bronchitis and other nonmalignant respiratory diseases and accidental falls were significantly increased. The excess mortality in all mentioned causes—including all combined, with the exception of accidental falls—was found only in the subcohorts of men born before the turn of the century.

The cancer incidence in this cohort showed significant excesses for all sites combined, for cancers of the esophagus, rectum, larynx, lung, and pleura. For most of these sites, the excess was limited to workers born before 1909. For an asbestos-related site such as pleura, the excess was seen particularly for the 1900–1919 birth cohort; for alcohol or solvent-related cancer sites, such as the esophagus, the excess was seen in the birth cohort of 1910–1929.

Plumbers. About 16,200 examined plumbers and pipefitters were followed. There were 1,094 observed deaths and 631 reported cancers, corresponding to an SMR of 0.75 and an SIR of 1.04. The SMR and SIR for all cancer sites combined were significantly higher for the plumbers than for the other groups taken together. The SMR and the SIR for lung cancer was 1.42 and 1.34, respectively, and for cancer of the pleura, 3.88 and 6.33 respectively. The SMR for pneumoconiosis was 4.40, which was significant at the 5% level. For plumbers, the RR of 1.81 and 1.62 for pneumonia and liver cirrhosis, respectively, were significantly higher than for all other groups combined.

In the cohort of about 18,400 certified plumbers, mortality from all causes and from vascular causes were close to the expected rate among Swedish men in general. The SMRs for cancer of the esophagus, larynx, lung, and pleura and from chronic bronchitis were significantly increased. With regard to cancer incidence, the SIR was significantly increased for all sites combined, for cancers of the esophagus, peritoneum, larynx, lung, and pleura.

Rock workers. Some 3,200 rock workers were followed, a group equivalent to laborers in the U.S. There were 410 observed deaths and 182 cancers reported to the cancer registry. This corresponded to an overall SMR of 0.96 and an overall SIR of 0.99. Compared to all other groups taken together, the RR for mortality from all causes was 1.30, and for all sites the incidence was 1.05. The SMR and the SIR for prostate cancer were 1.92 and 1.08, respectively, and for brain cancer, 2.05 and 1.68, respectively. Only the high rate of prostate cancer mortality was significant at the 5% level. For liver cancer, the elevated SMR (1.72) and the SIR (1.98) were not significant at the 5% level. Compared to all other groups together, however, the RR was significantly elevated (2.95).

The SMR for alcoholism was 1.62 (not significant) but, compared with all other groups combined, the RR of 3.37 was significantly elevated. The SMR for violent death was 14.54 and, compared to all other groups, the RR was 2.02, both of which were significant. For water transport accidents and "other accidents," typically including work-related accidents, the SMRs were 5.41 and 6.10, respectively. Even compared with the other groups combined, the excess risk was five- to sixfold.

Sheet metal workers. Among about 6,000 sheet metal workers who were followed, there were 294 observed deaths and 175 reported cancers. This corresponded to an SMR of 0.77 and an SIR of 1.12. The SIR and the SMR for all cancer sites were significantly higher for sheet metal workers than for all other groups taken together (RR 1.19 and 1.26, respectively). The SMR and the SIR for lung cancer were 1.70 and 1.59 respectively; the SMRs were 2.25 for brain cancer and 2.42 for accidental falls. These excesses are significant at the 5% level. However, this was not the case for cancer of the pleura, with an SMR of 4.55 and an SIR of 4.76. The SMR for malignant melanoma of the skin was significantly higher for sheet metal workers than for the other groups taken together, but the SIR was not.

Woodworkers or carpenters. Some 44,400 woodworkers and carpenters were followed, with 3,543 observed deaths and 1,891 reported cancers. This corresponded to an SMR of 0.67 and an SIR of 0.87, which were both significantly lower than 1 at the 5% level. Cancer of the nose was the only site for which the SIR was significantly high (2.20) compared with the general population, and there was a fourfold excess compared with the other groups together. For cancers of the esophagus, liver, pancreas, larynx, lung, kidney, and bladder and for melanoma of the skin, the SIR was significantly lower than expected at the 5% level, as was the SMR for lung cancer. The SMR for violent death was also significantly lower than expected.

CONCLUSION

This study of construction workers in Sweden led to the following conclusions.

1. The SMR for mortality from all causes does not deviate from unity in any occupational group but, compared to all other groups combined, the mortality is significantly increased for insulators, rock workers, drivers, and concrete workers.

2. The mortality for all cancers is significantly increased, compared to all other groups combined, for sheet metal workers, plumbers, and concrete workers; and the incidence of all cancers is significantly increased for sheet metal workers and plumbers.

3. The SIR for lip cancer is significantly increased among drivers and concrete workers.

4. The SMR and SIR for stomach cancer are significantly increased in concrete workers.

5. The SIR for peritoneal tumor is significantly increased in insulators and bricklayers and, for pleural tumor, in plumbers.

6. The SIR for cancer of the nose and nasal sinuses is significantly increased in carpenters or woodworkers.

7. The incidence of larynx cancer is significantly higher in concrete workers than in the other occupational groups combined. Compared to the carpenters, the relative risk is three times as high.

8. Lung cancer mortality (SMR) and incidence (SIR) are significantly increased in insulators, sheet metal workers, and plumbers. In addition, the relative risk for lung cancer in concrete workers compared to the other trades is significantly increased and almost twice that of the carpenters.

9. There is no occupation with a significantly elevated SMR for cardiovascular and cerebrovascular disease. However, a significantly increased cardiovascular mortality compared to all other groups combined is seen for drivers, machine operators, and rock workers.

10. The SMR for pneumoconiosis is significantly increased in insulators and plumbers.

11. There is a significantly elevated SMR for violent death in rock workers. Concrete workers, insulators, and crane drivers do have a higher mortality due to violent death than the other occupations combined. The SMR for accidental falls is significantly elevated for concrete workers and sheet metal workers. A significantly increased SMR for "other accidents," which include typical work-related injuries, is found for rock workers and machine operators.

In conclusion, comparisons with the general Swedish male population show a strong healthy worker effect with respect to mortality in this cohort of active construction workers. Therefore, these comparisons fail to discover occupational hazards in the industry. Internal comparisons, however, between the socioeconomically similar occupational subgrous may better identify problem areas. In such comparisons, insulators, rock drillers, and concrete workers show an excess with respect to total mortality. Sheet metal workers and plumbers show increased total cancer mortality and total cancer incidence. For the major cause of death—cardiovascular diseases—excess mortality is found in drivers, machine operators and rock drillers, all of which are jobs with exposure to engine exhaust, stressful demands, and vibrating equipment. The highest risk for fatal work-related injuries is found in concrete workers and sheet metal workers—fall accidents—and in rock drillers and machine operators, findings that well reflect the hazardous character of these jobs. Excess rates of asbestos-associated malignancies such as lung cancer and pleural mesotheliomas are seen predominantly in insulators, plumbers, and sheet metal workers, occupations with the heaviest exposures. However, the rates of cancers of the lung, larynx, and the lip, which in concrete workers is two to three times as high as in carpenters, invites speculations about the role of the concrete dust. The excess incidence of cancers of the nose and the sinus is probably an effect of exposure to wood dust.

REFERENCES

1. Englund A: Cancer incidence among painters and some allied trades. J Toxicol Environ Health 6:1267-1273, 1980.
2. Englund A: Swedish approaches to industry-wide studies: The construction industry. Ann N Y Acad Sci 643:313-315, 1991.
3. Lynge E: Dödlighet og erhverv 1970-75 (Occupational mortality 1970-75). Danmarks Statistik. Statistiske undersögelser No.37. Copenhagen, 1979.
4. Matanoski GM, Stockwell HE, Diamond EL, Haring-Sweeney M: A cohort mortality study of painters and allied tradesman. Scand J Work Environ Health 12:16-21, 1986.
5. Milham S: Occupational mortality in Washington State 1950-71. Washington, DC, US Dept. of Health, Education, and Welfare; National Institute for Occupational Safety and Health, April 1976.
6. Registrar General: Occupational mortality; dicennial supplement for England and Wales 1970-72. London, Her Majesty's Stationery Office, 1978.
7. Selikoff IJ, Churg J, Hammond EC: Asbestos exposure and neoplasia. JAMA 188:142–146, 1964.
8. Zoloth S, Michaels D: Asbestos disease in sheet metal workers: The result of a proportional mortality analysis. Am J Ind Med 7:315-321, 1985.

C.F. ROBINSON, PhD, W. E. HALPERIN, MD, MPH
T. ALTERMAN, PhD, R. W. BRADDEE
C. A. BURNETT, MS, D.E. FOSBROKE, MSF
S. M. KISNER, N. R. LALICH, MSPH
R. J. ROSCOE, MS, P. J. SELIGMAN, MD
J. P. SESTITO, JD, F. B. STERN, MS, N. A. STOUT, EdD

MORTALITY PATTERNS AMONG CONSTRUCTION WORKERS IN THE UNITED STATES

From The National Institute for
   Occupational Safety and Health
Cincinnati, Ohio

Reprint requests to:
Cynthia Robinson, PhD
NIOSH, MS R-18
4676 Columbia Parkway
Cincinnati, OH 45226

Published occupational mortality reports from California, Washington State, and the United Kingdom have suggested that construction industry workers are experiencing elevated mortality for many cancers, respiratory diseases, mental conditions, homicide, and fatal injuries.[7,22,39] This chapter summarizes recent and ongoing national occupational mortality surveillance studies of U.S. construction workers conducted by the National Institute for Occupational Safety and Health (NIOSH).

In the past, mortality data have been useful for characterizing mortality patterns and maintaining surveillance on worker populations. Since the time of William Farr, the British founder of occupational mortality surveillance in the 19th century, death certificate statements of occupation and industry have been used to identify unusual or excess patterns of mortality that may be occupationally related (Table 1).[18] In the United States, occupational mortality surveillance reports generally have been based on findings from state occupational mortality data.

Population-based surveillance assesses magnitude and trends—in this case, in mortality—for given populations. Populations can be defined in categories such as all U.S. residents, all males aged 16–65, all construction workers, or all union

OCCUPATIONAL MEDICINE: State of the Art Reviews—
Vol. 10, No. 2, April 1995. Philadelphia, Hanley & Belfus, Inc.

269

TABLE 1.   Occupational Mortality Surveillance Studies

Geographic Base of Study	Years	Reference
United States	1950	Guralnick, 1963[14]
California	1959–61	Petersen, 1980[37]
England and Wales	1970–72	Registrar General, 1978[38]
Washington State	1950–79	Milham, 1983[23]
Massachusetts	1971–73	Dubrow, 1984[10]
England and Wales	1979–80, 1982–83	Registrar General, 1986[39]
British Columbia	1950–78	Gallagher, 1986[13]
New York State	1980–82	MacCubbin, 1986[19]
California	1979–81	Riedmiller, 1987[40]
Pennsylvania	1983–85	Pennsylvania State Health Data Center, 1987[36]
North Carolina	1984–86	Surles, 1988[50]
Meta-analysis	1950–79	Dubrow, 1983[11]

Note: These reports present cause-specific mortality risks by occupation and industry for working populations.

members in the U.S. Case-based mortality surveillance builds on a reported case of a preventable death and asks how this death could have been prevented. An example is death caused by a fall on a construction site.

CASE-BASED SURVEILLANCE OF OCCUPATIONAL MORTALITY

Using case-based surveillance to identify the population at risk is critical for targeting prevention activities.[45] The Fatality Assessment and Control Evaluation (FACE) project is an example of a case-based mortality surveillance system for construction workers.

Fatality Assessment and Control Evaluation

The FACE project was designed by NIOSH to measurably reduce fatal occupational injuries in construction in the U.S. through a combination of case-based surveillance, on-site investigation, and prevention activities. In the in-house portion of FACE, state agencies in nine states voluntarily notify NIOSH of traumatic occupational fatalities resulting from targeted causes of death, including electrocutions, falls from elevations, confined spaces, and machinery. NIOSH safety professionals investigate the fatalities on-site. Using a case series design, they identify factors contributing to the fatalities and develop recommendations for preventing similar deaths.

In the state FACE program, NIOSH participates in a series of cooperative agreements with state health departments to conduct surveillance, investigation, and prevention activities. The state FACE programs, currently active in 15 states, include multiple-source surveillance systems for identifying all traumatic occupational fatalities occurring in the state. Investigations are then conducted by health and safety professionals for selected causes of death to identify risk and causal factors and to recommend prevention strategies. Data collected are used by NIOSH and the states to prioritize, develop, and evaluate traumatic occupational injury research and prevention programs.

Results of the in-house FACE investigations have been tabulated for 1982–92. During these 11 years, NIOSH investigated 460 fatal injuries; 246 (53.5%) of them were in construction workers, but they were not necessarily representative of all construction fatalities. All but one of the fatally injured construction workers were men (99.6%), and their average age was 33.7. Electrocution was the cause of death of 130 (52.8%) of the construction workers; 67 (27.2%) fell from an elevation to their death; 37 (15.0%) died in confined spaces; and 12 (4.9%) died from other causes.

Each work site investigation results in a FACE summary report that recounts the circumstances of the fatal incident and includes recommendations on how such incidents might be prevented. If a number of similar incidents are investigated, *NIOSH Alerts* are developed. These publications describe a hazardous situation, present scenarios of fatal injuries, recommend methods of prevention, and request assistance in preventing similar incidents. Each alert is disseminated to a targeted population including workers, employers, labor groups, manufacturers, and others who are at risk of, or can affect, the hazards described.

FACE investigations of fatal injuries to construction workers have resulted in *NIOSH Alerts* on preventing the following: fatal falls through skylights and roof openings,[29] electrocutions from contact between cranes and power lines,[34] electrocutions of workers using portable metal ladders near overhead power lines,[30] deaths and injuries from excavation cave-ins,[33] occupational fatalities in confined spaces,[32] fatalities of workers who contact electrical energy,[31] electrocutions during work with scaffolds near overhead power lines,[27] and worker injuries and deaths caused by falls from suspension scaffolds.[26] *NIOSH Alerts* have been translated into Spanish, French, and Chinese and are being used as training aids in several countries. FACE data are also used to target injury prevention efforts at the national, state, and local levels and to support national safety policy including the promulgation of new Occupational Safety and Health Administration standards, such as those for lockout-tagout and confined space entry. (Lockout or tagout occurs when machines or equipment are shut down and locked while servicing or maintenance is performed.) The effectiveness of the FACE program is under evaluation.

Sentinel Health Events (Occupational) for Construction

A list of 50 Sentinel Health Events (Occupational), SHE(O), was published in 1983 based on reports in the scientific literature[42] and was updated in 1991 to include 64 work-related conditions.[24] The sentinel health event was defined as an untimely, unnecessary injury, illness, or death that represented a failure of prevention.[42] Potential connection to employment in a construction trade or activity has been identified for 20 of the 64 work-related conditions (Table 2).

The SHE(O) list does not cover all types of events. Cumulative trauma disorders and fatalities are not included, and the list includes only occupational diseases that have been reported in the published and peer-reviewed scientific literature.[24] The list has potential use for case-based surveillance, when used to link records such as those from a union's pension system with those of a state death registry.[46] Although not yet tried for the construction trades, its potential utility as a surveillance tool has been described.[17,21,51]

POPULATION-BASED SURVEILLANCE OF OCCUPATIONAL MORTALITY

Population-based death data are useful for describing the magnitude of work-related mortality by occupation or industry, particularly for difficult-to-study industrial

TABLE 2. Sentinel Health Events in Construction

Condition	Industry/Process/Occupation	Agent
Asbestosis	Asbestos industries and utilizers	Asbestos
Bronchitis (acute), pneumonitis, and pulmonary edema due to fumes and vapors	Arc welders, boilermakers	Nitrogen oxides Vanadium pentoxide
Chronic or acute renal failure	Plumbers	Inorganic lead
Contact and allergic dermatitis	Cement masons and finishers, carpenters, floorlayers*	Adhesives and sealants, irritants (e.g., cutting oils, phenol, solvents, acids, alkalis, detergents); allergens (e.g., nickel, chromates, formaldehyde, dyes, rubber products).
Extrinsic asthma	Wood workers, furniture makers	Red cedar (plicatic acid) and other wood dusts
Histoplasmosis	Bridge maintenance workers	Histoplasma capsulatam
Inflammatory and toxic neuropathy	Furniture refinishers, degreasing operations	Hexane
Malignant neoplasm of scrotum	Chimney sweeps	Mineral oil, pitch, tar
Malignant neoplasm of nasal cavities	Wood workers, cabinet and furniture makers, carpenters	Hardwood and softwood* dusts Chlorophenols
Malignant neoplasm of trachea, bronchus, and lung	Asbestos industries and utilizers†	Asbestos
Malignant neoplasm of nasopharynx	Carpenter, cabinet maker	Chlorophenols
Malignant neoplasm of larynx	Asbestos industries and utilizers†	Asbestos
Mesothelioma (Malignancy of peritoneum and pleura)	Asbestos industries and utilizers†	Asbestos
Noise effects on inner ear	Occupations with exposure to excessive noise	Excessive noise
Raynaud's phenomenon (secondary)	Jackhammer operator, riveter	Whole body or segmental vibration
Sequoiosis	Red cedar mill workers, wood workers	Redwood sawdust
Silicosis	Sandblasters	Silica
Silicotuberculosis	Sandblasters	Silica + mycobacterium tuberculosis
Toxic encephalitis	Lead paint removal‡	Lead
Toxic hepatitis	Fumigators	Methyl bromide

* Not included in original 1991 table.
† Including construction, renovation and demolition industries.
‡ Lead exposure occurs in at least 23 construction-related industrial/occupational groups, including painting contractors, bridge and highway construction, and demolition work. Extremely high levels of lead exposure have been documented for workers in these groups.[1]
Adapted from Mullan R, Murthy L: Occupational sentinel health events: An up-dated list for physician recognition and public health surveillance. Am J Ind Med 19:775–799, 1991.

TABLE 3.   Years of Data and Numbers of Deaths According to State of Residence for the National Occupational Mortality Surveillance, 1979–90

State	Years	Number of Deaths
Alaska	1987–88	3,527
California*	1979–81	173,445
Colorado	1985–90	139,113
Georgia	1984–90	330,108
Idaho	1988–90	21,025
Indiana	1986–90	235,849
Kansas	1984–90	146,771
Kentucky	1984–90	233,103
Maine	1982–83[†]; 1984–90	96,117
Missouri	1984–86	143,181
Nebraska	1984–85	28,025
Nevada	1984–90	51,653
New Hampshire	1984–90	53,332
New Jersey	1988–90	199,974
New Mexico	1986–90	47,725
New York[‡]	1980–87	350,499
North Carolina	1984–86[†]; 1990	368,839
Ohio	1985–90	571,718
Oklahoma	1985–90	167,255
Pennsylvania[†]	1983–87	590,277
Rhode Island	1979–83[†]; 1984–90	106,431
South Carolina	1984–90	190,398
Tennessee	1985–88	171,358
Utah	1984–90	51,093
Vermont	1986–90	22,263
Washington	1989–90	69,516
West Virginia	1988–90	54,626
Wisconsin	1984–90	279,816
Total number of deaths		4,897,037

* Data provided directly to NIOSH, restricted to ages 15 to 64.
† Data obtained by NIOSH through state cooperative agreements.
‡ Data obtained by NIOSH through state cooperative agreement, restricted to ages 15 to 74.
Note: The PMRs reported for the construction industry in Tables 4–7 are based on NOMS data from 4,897,037 death certificate records from 28 states for one or more years from 1979–1990. The data were provided in part by state vital statistics offices through the Vital Statistics Program of the National Center for Health Statistics, with the support and collaboration of the National Institute for Occupational Safety and Health and from the National Cancer Institute.

settings such as are found in the construction industry. The primary advantage of population-based death data is the availability of data for all sectors of industry and for all race-gender groups, particularly minorities, and the potential to generate rates.

National Occupational Mortality Surveillance

The National Occupational Mortality Surveillance system was developed by NIOSH to evaluate and reduce work-related mortality through surveillance of workers, dissemination of results, and preventive activities (Table 3). The system identifies patterns of excess or unusual mortality by comparing cause-specific proportionate mortality for one occupation with the proportionate mortality experience of all occupations. The age-adjusted proportionate mortality ratio (PMR) is the summary statistic used for the analysis of the data.[23] *

Data from the National Occupational Mortality Surveillance system provide large numbers of deaths that allow estimation of mortality for rare causes of death and for the smaller occupational groups. Analyses of death certificate data have been criticized because of limitations of death certificate statements of usual industry, usual occupation, and diagnosis.[43] And the concept of hypothesis generation or "fishing expeditions" has been critiqued.[8] Mortality surveillance is more than mere publication of death rates, however. It must involve interpretation of elevated PMRs or estimated rates in conjunction with other available data, assessment of the biologic and reasonable plausibility of the elevated rate, recognition of the limitations of the data, and dissemination of the findings to the public health community.

Mortality Patterns for U.S. Construction Workers, 1979–1990

Significantly elevated or reduced age-adjusted PMRs based on data from the National Occupational Mortality System are presented in Tables 4–7 for men and women usually employed in construction. The PMRs are based on death certificate statements of usual industry for 4,897,037 death certificate records from 28 U.S. states from 1979–1990. Age-adjusted PMRs were calculated for each race-gender group by occupation and by industry using a computer program developed by NIOSH.[9] The program calculated PMRs by comparing the proportion of deaths for a specific cause within each occupation or industry group with the proportion of deaths from that cause in all occupations or industries.

PMRs for all causes of death and for all trades[40,41] could not be listed in the tables due to space limitations. Because NIOSH's purpose was to identify increased mortality, most tables show only statistically significant elevated PMRs, PMRs for ischemic heart disease, and the all-cancer PMRs. For a few specific causes of interest, however, elevated PMRs were listed. Because the data did not indicate the circumstances of the traumatic fatalities (ICD 800-999), the authors excluded most PMRs for traumatic fatalities from the tables, except for homicide, suicide, and all traumatic fatalities combined.

Results in Male Construction Workers. Analyses were based on 248,164 deaths among white male construction workers and 37,448 deaths among black male construction workers. PMRs shown for total deaths are for all workers and for those who died before age 65 (usual industry is thought to be reported more accurately when death occurs at a pre-retirement age).

The highest PMRs observed among white men were for occupational lung disease. More than twice as many deaths caused by asbestosis and silicosis were

---

* See the referenced material for limitations of the PMR.

TABLE 4.   Mortality Among White Men Usually Employed in Construction in 28 U.S. States, 1979–90

Cause of Death (ICD)	Under Age 65			Total		
	PMR	Number Observed	95% CI	PMR	Number Observed	95% CI
All deaths	100	100,799	—	100	248,164	—
Pulmonary tuberculosis (011)	127	69	(99-161)	120*	171	(103-139)
All cancer (140-208)	100	24,394	(99-101)	102*	61,122	(102-103)
Cancer of oral cavity and pharynx (141-149)	114*	777	(106-122)	111*	1427	(106-117)
Cancer of larynx (161)	121*	371	(102-134)	122*	826	(114-131)
Cancer of lung (162)	113*	10,549	(112-115)	115*	24,643	(114-117)
Cancer of peritoneum and pleura (mesothelioma) (158, 163)	122	81	(97-152)	135*	207	(117-155)
Cancer of pleura (mesothelioma) (163)	154*	50	(114-203)	163*	139	(137-142)
Mental disorders (290-319)	136*	1438	(130-141)	121*	2687	(117-125)
Ischemic heart disease (410-414)	92*	20,672	(91-93)	94*	61,777	(93-95)
Pneumoconioses and other respiratory diseases (470-478, 494-519)	111*	2572	(107-115)	113*	12,652	(111-114)
Asbestosis (501)	261*	31	(177-370)	256*	115	(211-307)
Silicosis (502)	210*	21	(130-320)	104	43	(75-140)
Chronic liver disease and cirrhosis (571)	118*	3642	(115-121)	114*	4933	(111-117)
Systemic sclerosis (710)	144*	41	(103-195)	132*	61	(101-169)
Traumatic injuries (800-999)	116*	27,315	(115-116)	114*	31,478	(113-115)
Homicide (960-969)	134*	3162	(131-138)	133*	3263	(129-137)

* Indicates the PMR was significantly elevated or reduced at $p < 0.05$.
Note: PMRs reported for the construction industry in Tables 4–7 are based on NOMS data from 4,897,037 death certificate records from 28 states for one or more years (see Table 3 for a listing of number of deaths by state and year). Occupation and industry information was coded by clerks trained in the use of 1980 Bureau of the Census classification system. PMR analyses were restricted to decedents age 15 or more years whose death occurred in-state and who were residents of one of the 28 participating states. (Data are available upon request to authors.) The causes of death were coded according to the Ninth Revision of the ICD classification. ICD codes are in parentheses after each cause-of-death category.[57]

experienced by white men employed in construction compared with men employed in all industries. Elevated PMRs for asbestosis and silicosis were particularly experienced by white men who died before age 65. Mortality from mesothelioma (cancer of the pleura or peritoneum) was significantly elevated for white male construction workers. Other elevated PMRs for site-specific cancer included cancer of the oral cavity and pharynx and larynx among white men and cancer of the oral cavity and pharynx, larynx, and esophagus, among black men.

Occupational diseases are believed to be more common and more severe among minority workers. However, many published studies of occupational disease fail to reveal data or present conclusions regarding minority workers. This may be because of small sample sizes in existing data sets, which may preclude the ability to examine heterogeneity within a given racial group.[12] The NIOSH surveillance data showed that excess mortality has occurred among black construction workers. Future analytic studies should include minority construction workers in sufficient numbers to permit estimates of risk.

TABLE 5.   Mortality Among Black Men Usually Employed in Construction in 28 U.S.
States, 1979–90

Cause of Death (ICD)	Under Age 65			Total		
	PMR	Number Observed	95% CI	PMR	Number Observed	95% CI
All deaths	100	20,489	—	100	37,448	—
Pulmonary tuberculosis (011)	139*	72	(109-175)	119	105	(97-144)
All cancer (140-208)	100	4219	(97-102)	102*	8970	(100-103)
Cancer of oral cavity and pharynx (141-149)	113*	265	(100-128)	113*	351	(101-125)
Cancer of esophagus (150)	130*	407	(118-144)	130*	633	(120-140)
Cancer of larynx (161)	128*	127	(107-153)	126*	197	(109-145)
Cancer of lung	101	1647	(97-105)	106*	3234	(102-109)
Mental disorders (290-319)	131*	699	(121-144)	127*	907	(119-135)
Ischemic heart disease (410-414)	89*	2442	(86-92)	94*	5838	(92-96)
Pneumoconioses and other respiratory disease (470-478, 494-519)	100	380	(90-110)	104	1114	(99-110)
Traumatic injuries (800-999)	116*	5104	(114-118)	115*	5622	(113-117)
Homicide (960-969)	124*	2138	(120-128)	124*	2213	(120-128)

* Indicates the PMR was significantly elevated or reduced at p < 0.05.
Note: PMRs reported for the construction industry in Tables 4–7 are based on NOMS data from
4,897,037 death certificate records from 28 states for one or more years (see Table 3 for a listing of
number of deaths by state and year). Occupation and industry information was coded by clerks trained in
the use of 1980 Bureau of the Census classification system. PMR analyses were restricted to decedents
age 15 or more years whose death occurred in-state and who were residents of one of the 28 participating
states. (Data are available upon request to authors.) The causes of death were coded according to the Ninth
Revision of the ICD classification. ICD codes are in parentheses after each cause-of-death category.[57]

Deaths due to traumatic injuries, homicide, and mental disorders occurred disproportionately among white and black male construction workers. The deaths due
to mental disorders fell primarily into the category of alcohol and drug abuse. The
PMR for systemic sclerosis, a rare connective tissue disorder, was significantly elevated, as were PMRs for pulmonary tuberculosis.

Construction workers may be exposed to many occupational hazards.[44]
Although further research is needed, potential exposures to these hazardous materials may partly explain the elevated PMRs among construction workers. The hazards
they face include potential exposures to known respiratory carcinogens, such as asbestos, silica, and other dusts, that have been associated with lung disease, lung
cancer, and mesothelioma. Additional hazards include hydrocarbons in roofing and
road tars associated with skin cancer,[35] metal fumes associated with lung cancer, solvents[2,3] such as benzene, and resin polymers and neurotoxins[2,3,28] such as lead, arsenic, and mercury that have been associated with mental disorders and other
adverse health outcomes.

The dangers of construction sites are well known for catastrophic outcomes.
High rates of traumatic fatalities, but not homicide, that occurred at work for the
construction industry have been previously documented.[4,25] Elevated PMRs for
homicide may reflect events that occurred after work, regional variations in rates,
other causes, or chance. More frequent use of alcohol and tobacco has been reported
for construction workers,[15] particularly construction laborers.[6,20] However, Singleton

TABLE 6.   Mortality Among White Women Usually Employed in Construction in 28 U.S. States, 1979–90

Cause of Death (ICD)	Under Age 65			Total		
	PMR	Number Observed	95% CI	PMR	Number Observed	95% CI
All deaths	100	2273	—	100	5504	—
All cancer (140-208)	107*	960	(101-114)	111*	1775	(107-115)
Cancer of colon (153)	123	78	(97-153)	117*	179	(101-136)
Cancer of lung (162)	118*	216	(102-134)	121*	385	(110-134)
Cancer of peritoneum or pleura (mesothelioma) (158, 163)	215	3	(44-627)	188	5	(61-439)
Cancer of bone, connective tissue, skin, or breast (170-175)	109	291	(97-122)	112*	441	(102-123)
Cancer of connective tissue (171)	128	11	(64-229)	161	20	(98-249)
Cancer of breast (174-175)	108	225	(95-122)	110	384	(100-122)
Cancer of bladder (188)	106	5	(35-248)	158*	26	(103-231)
Non-Hodgkin's lymphoma (200, 202)	129	35	(90-179)	119	66	(92-151)
Acute myeloid leukemia (205.0)	128	15	(72-211)	140	26	(92-205)
Ischemic heart disease (410-414)	82*	221	(92-94)	87*	997	(82-92)
Pneumoconioses and other respiratory diseases (470-478, 494-519)	93	54	(70-121)	110	201	(95-126)
Chronic liver disease and cirrhosis (571)	77	45	(56-103)	77*	62	(59-99)
Traumatic injuries (800-999)	138*	482	(126-151)	132*	544	(121-144)
Suicide (950-959)	121	107	(99-146)	117	111	(97-142)
Homicide (960-969)	125	50	(93-165)	127	53	(95-166)

* Indicates the PMR was significantly elevated or reduced at p < 0.05.
Note: PMRs reported for the construction industry in Tables 4–7 are based on NOMS data from 4,897,037 death certificate records from 28 states for one or more years (see Table 3 for a listing of number of deaths by state and year). Occupation and industry information was coded by clerks trained in the use of 1980 Bureau of the Census classification system. PMR analyses were restricted to decedents age 15 or more years whose death occurred in-state and who were residents of one of the 28 participating states. (Data are available upon request to authors.) The causes of death were coded according to the Ninth Revision of the ICD classification. ICD codes are in parentheses after each cause-of-death category.[57]

reported excess mortality for lung cancer among construction occupations that persisted after adjustment for lifestyle.[47] Range-finding environmental surveillance and analytic epidemiologic studies based on both hazard assessment and task-specific data are needed to identify potential causative factors of excess mortality and to develop new preventive technologies and work practices.

Results in Female Construction Workers.   The construction industry may be characterized as a traditionally male work force. In the U.S. in 1992, about 9% of construction workers were women; in 1977, about 6.4%.[54] In contrast, 46% of all employees in the U.S. are women. There is evidence that male construction workers may be experiencing a high proportion of work-related mortality. Two reports have examined the mortality of female construction workers. In one study,[7] mortality for female construction workers was not reported to be elevated for California in 1979–81, but the conclusion was based on small numbers of deaths. The other study reported elevated mortality for women in the construction trades.[41]

TABLE 7. Mortality Among Black Women Usually Employed in Construction in 28 U.S. States, 1979–90

Cause of Death (ICD)	Under Age 65			Total		
	PMR	Number Observed	95% CI	PMR	Number Observed	95% CI
All deaths	100	197	—	100	304	—
All cancer (140-208)	112	52	(84-147)	121	81	(96-151)
Digestive cancer (150-159)	126	11	(63-225)	161*	25	(104-238)
Cancer of stomach (151)	165	2	(20-597)	340*	7	(137-701)
Cancer of lung (162)	178	13	(95-305)	203*	21	(125-310)
Ischemic heart disease (410-414)	99	17	(58-159)	93	38	(66-128)
Pneumoconioses and other lung diseases (470-478, 494-519)	95	3	(20-277)	133	7	(53-274)
Chronic liver disease and cirrhosis (571)	74	5	(24-172)	82	6	(930-179)
Traumatic injuries (800-999)	138*	45	(101-185)	145*	50	(107-191)

* Indicates the PMR was significantly elevated or reduced at $p < 0.05$.
Note: PMRs reported for the construction industry in Tables 4–7 are based on NOMS data from 4,897,037 death certificate records from 28 states for one or more years (see Table 3 for a listing of number of deaths by state and year). Occupation and industry information was coded by clerks trained in the use of 1980 Bureau of the Census classification system. PMR analyses were restricted to decedents age 15 or more years whose death occurred in-state and who were residents of one of the 28 participating states. (Data are available upon request to authors.) The causes of death were coded according to the Ninth Revision of the ICD classification. ICD codes are in parentheses after each cause-of-death category.[57]

Among white women usually employed in construction, the highest PMR observed was for mesothelioma, a cancer known to be caused by exposure to asbestos. Both black and white women also experienced excess mortality for other site-specific cancers. Mortality due to cancer of the colon, lung, and bladder were elevated significantly for white female construction workers. PMRs for all digestive cancer sites combined, cancer of the stomach, and cancer of the lung were significantly in excess for black women. Mortality for traumatic injuries was significantly elevated for both white and black women. Additionally, elevated PMRs for suicide and homicide were of borderline statistical significance for white women who died before age 65.

These excesses of mortality for female construction workers suggest hypotheses of association between work and disease that are different for women than for men. The new cancer sites observed in excess among women employed in the construction industry include cancer of the colon, stomach, bladder, and the borderline elevated sites of connective tissue and breast. These sites of cancer have not previously been reported for women construction workers[40] and may reflect differences in tasks, causes, or health status that are gender-specific. They, therefore, should be further evaluated using analytic studies to determine causes, evaluate the effectiveness of protective equipment and work practice, and to develop new prevention strategies.

National Traumatic Occupational Fatalities Surveillance

The National Traumatic Occupational Fatalities Surveillance System was developed to fill the gap in the knowledge of work-related injury deaths in the U.S. by providing a census of occupational injury deaths for all U.S. workers.[4,49]

Data for use in this surveillance system are obtained from all 50 states, New York City, and the District of Columbia. They provide death certificates to NIOSH

TABLE 8.   Percentage Distribution of Fatal Occupational Injuries in the Construction Industry by Occupation Division and Cause of Death, National Traumatic Occupational Fatality Data, 1980–89[16]

Occupation Division	Falls	Electrocutions	Motor Vehicle	Machines	Struck by Falling Object	Other	Total
			(Percent)				
Crafts	17.1	9.7	4.5	4.3	3.0	9.7	48.3
Laborers	5.5	3.5	4.5	3.6	2.9	7.1	27.1
Transport operatives	0.4	1.0	3.5	3.8	0.8	2.3	11.8
Exec/admin/mgr	1.4	0.7	1.1	1.0	0.5	1.9	6.6
Machine operators	0.7	0.3	0.1	0.4	0.3	0.7	2.5
Other	0.3	0.2	0.6	0.3	0.0	2.3	3.7
Total	25.4	15.4	14.3	13.4	7.5	24.0	100.0

Cause of Death (n = 11,417)

Note: The National Traumatic Occupational Fatality data contain variables useful for describing characteristics of victims as well as injury circumstances, including demographic, employment, and cause-of-death variables. Employment information was coded from the "usual industry" and "usual occupation" entries on the death certificate. Occupation narratives were coded into 11 major divisions of occupation according to the 1980 Bureau of the Census classification scheme[52]; industry narratives were coded into the 10 standard industrial divisions according to the Standard Industrial Classification (SIC) Manual, 1987.[57] The industry division for construction, including major SIC groups 15, 16, and 17, were used for this analysis.

for workers age 16 or older for whom an external cause of death was noted (ICD Ninth Revision E800-999[57]) and for whom the certifier entered a positive response to the "Injury at Work?" item. The data base contains data from 1980–1989.

Fatality rates for the construction industry were calculated as average annual deaths per 100,000 full-time civilian workers[16] using annual average employment data from the Bureau of Labor Statistics' Employment and Earnings[5] and the Bureau of the Census' County Business Patterns.[53] Fatality rates were calculated for the nation, for age groups, and for occupation divisions (Table 8).

Males accounted for 99% of the traumatic deaths in construction. Although 47% of the fatalities were in construction workers younger than 35, workers 65 and older had the highest fatality rate (Fig. 1). About 88% of all fatalities were in white workers, 9% in blacks, and 3% in workers of another or unknown race; 7% were of Hispanic ethnicity. Three quarters of the deaths were in workers in two occupation divisions: precision production/craft/repair (48%) and laborers (27%).

When rates of fatal injuries are compared *by occupation division between the construction industry and all industries,* construction workers had higher fatality rates than the general work force in every occupational classification except one: farmers/foresters/fishers (Fig. 2). Laborers had the highest fatality rate in the construction industry: 39.5 per 100,000 workers employed.

The three leading causes of death for construction workers were falls (25%), electrocutions (15%), and motor vehicle-related incidents (14%) (Fig. 3). Table 3 shows the distribution of fatalities among construction workers by occupation division and cause of death. In contrast to the PMR analysis of data from the National Occupational Mortality Surveillance (above), U.S. construction workers were not found to be at elevated risk of work-related homicide. Homicide constituted 2.1% of

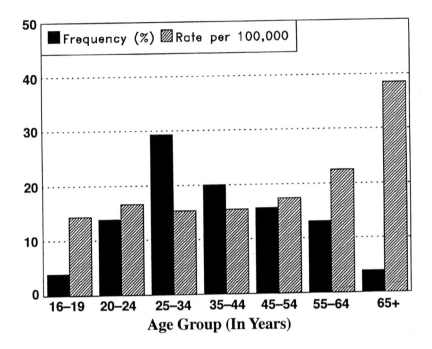

FIGURE 1. Percentage distribution and rate of fatal occupational injuries in the construction industry by age group, NTOF, 1980–89 (n = 11,417).

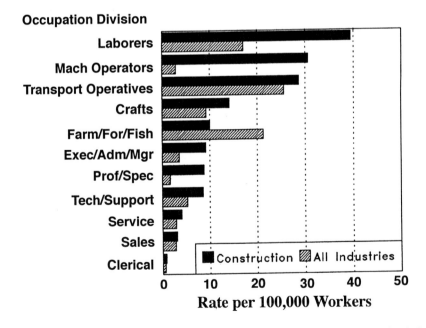

FIGURE 2. Rate of fatal occupational injuries by occupation division—construction industry versus all industries, NTOF, 1980–89.

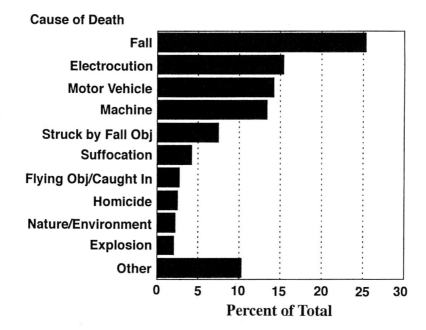

Cause of Death

Percent of Total

FIGURE 3. Percentage distribution of fatal occupational injuries in the construction industry by cause of death, NTOF, 1980–89 (n = 11,417).

construction worker deaths, and the work-related homicide rate for construction
workers was lower than the overall occupational homicide rate for the U.S. labor
force. This suggests that the elevated PMRs for homicide may reflect sociodemo-
graphic differentials in homicide prevalence away from work or methodologic limitations of PMR analyses.

On average, three construction workers die each day from an injury sustained
on the job. For the 1980s, the fatal occupational injury rate of 25.6 per 100,000
workers in the construction industry was more than 3.5 times the occupational fatality rate for all industries in the U.S.[25] This compares to an "experimental rate" of
fatal construction injuries in 1992 of 14 per 100,000 workers employed, reported by
the Bureau of Labor Statistics from the Census of Fatal Occupational Injuries.[55]
(Cause-of-death distribution by industry is not available from CFOI.)

Intervention measures to prevent fatal occupational injuries among construction workers should focus on the occupations of laborers and machine operators and
on incidents caused by falls, electrocutions, motor vehicles, and machinery. Surveillance based on task-specific data and analytic epidemiologic studies is needed to
determine causative factors, to evaluate the effectiveness of existing protective
equipment and practices, and to develop new technologies and work practices that
better protect the lives of construction workers.

UNION MEMBERS MORTALITY STUDY

NIOSH, in collaboration with nine of the AFL-CIO building and construction
trade unions and the Center to Protect Workers' Rights, is conducting union-based
mortality studies for construction union members nationwide.[1] NIOSH has recently

completed the first study, which examined the mortality risks of 11,685 members of the Laborers' International Union of North America who died between 1985 and 1988.[48] Although construction laborers have been included in other studies, this is the first study that has examined the general mortality experience of construction laborers only.[7,47,49]

The NIOSH study of members of the Laborers' International Union N.A. (LIUNA) found statistically significant elevated mortality risks for all cancer, lung cancer, stomach cancer, and cancer of the thyroid gland. The proportionate cancer mortality ratios for these cancers were elevated among both white and nonwhite men, regardless of length of union membership, in most 10-year categories of age-at-death above 40 and for the three largest LIUNA regions examined. The study also observed 20 mesothelioma deaths, which indicated that some LIUNA members had been previously exposed to asbestos. Statistically significant elevated risks also were observed for deaths from transportation injuries, falls, and other types of injuries. The deaths due to injuries were most often observed among members who had the shortest amount of time within the union, were younger, and first entered the union after 1955. Other studies that have included construction laborers have observed similar findings, with the exception of the excess risk of thyroid cancer.

CONCLUSION

This chapter has described previously published studies (Table 1) and current NIOSH mortality surveillance studies for workers in the construction industry. The FACE and SHE(O) projects exemplify case-based surveillance. The FACE program conducts on-site investigations of traumatic fatalities for the purpose of measurably reducing fatalities across the nation. The SHE(O) list identifies work-related conditions that have been reported in the peer-reviewed scientific literature for construction workers.

The goals of the NIOSH population-based mortality surveillance studies have been to describe magnitudes, trends, and risks in the mortality of construction workers. The National Traumatic Occupational Fatality system provides a census of occupational injury death rates for all U.S. workers and has reported falls, electrocutions, and motor vehicle-related deaths to be the leading causes of fatalities for construction workers. Data from the National Occupational Mortality Surveillance System have identified patterns of excess mortality among male and female U.S. construction workers in 1979–1990. The nine ongoing construction union-based PMR studies will estimate the magnitudes and trends in mortality for construction trade union members in the 1980s and early 1990s. As surveillance programs interface, opportunities emerge for prevention and intervention to reduce illness and injury rates for all workers.

REFERENCES

1. Anonymous: Lead Exposure in Construction; Interim Final Rule. Department of Labor. Fed Reg 58:26590–26649, 1993.
2. Baker EL, Letz RE, Eisen EA, et al: Neurobehavioral effects of solvents in construction painters. J Occup Med 30:116–123, 1988.
3. Baker EL, Fine LJ: Solvent neurotoxicity: The current evidence. J Occup Med 28:126–9, 1986.
4. Bell CA, Stout NA, Bender TR, et al: Fatal occupational injuries in the United States, 1980 through 1985. JAMA 263:3047–3050, 1990.
5. Bureau of Labor Statistics: Employment and earnings, household data annual averages, Vols 23–37. Washington, DC, U.S. Govt. Printing Office, 1981–1990.
6. Burkhart G, Schulte P, Robinson C, et al: Job tasks, potential exposures, and health risks of laborers employed in the construction industry. Am J Ind Med 24:413–425, 1993.

7. California Department of Health Services: California occupational mortality, 1979–1981. Sacramento, CA, CDHS Health Demographics Section, March 1987
8. Cole P: The hypothesis generating machine [commentary]. Epidemiology 4:271–273, 1993.
9. Dubrow R, Spaeth S, Burnett CA, et al: Proportionate mortality ratio analysis system—Version IV. Draft documentation. Cincinnati, NIOSH, 1994.
10. Dubrow R, Wegman D: Occupational characteristics of cancer victims in Massachusetts. Cincinnati, Dept. of Health and Human Services, 1994, NIOSH publication 84-109.
11. Dubrow R, Wegman D: Setting priorities for occupational cancer research and control: Synthesis of the results of occupational disease surveillance studies. J Natl Cancer Inst 71:1123–1142, 1983.
12. Friedman-Jimenez G: Occupational disease among minority workers: A common and preventable public health problem. AAOHN J 37:64–70, 1989.
13. Gallagher R, Threlfall W, Band P, et al: Occupational mortality in British Columbia 1950–1978. Ottawa, Cancer Control Agency of British Columbia, April 1986.
14. Guralnick L: Mortality by occupation and cause of death among men 20 to 64 years of age, United States, 1950. Washington, DC, Public Health Service, National Vital Statistics Division, 1963, Vital Statistics—special reports 53, No. 1-5).
15. Harford T, Brooks S: Cirrhosis mortality and occupation. J Stud Alcohol 53:463–468, 1992.
16. Kisner SM, Fosbroke DE: Injury hazards in the construction industry. J Occup Med 36:137–143, 1994.
17. Lalich N, Schuster L: An application of the sentinel health event (occupational) concept to death certificates. Am J Public Health 77:1310–1314, 1987.
18. Langmuir AD: William Farr: Founder of modern concepts of surveillance. Int J Epidemiol 5:13–18, 1976.
19. MacCubbin P, Herzfeld P, Therriault G: Mortality in New York State, 1980–1982: A report by occupation and industry. Albany, NY, New York State Department of Health, 1986, monograph 21.
20. Mandell W, Eaton W, Anthony J, Garrison R: Alcoholism and occupations: A review and analysis of 104 occupations. Alcohol Clin Exp Res 16:734–746, 1992.
21. Mathias CGT, Sinks TH, Seligman PJ, Halperin WE: Surveillance of occupational skin diseases: A method utilizing workers' compensation claims. Am J Ind Med 17:363–370, 1990.
22. Milham SJ: Occupational mortality in Washington State 1950–1979. Cincinnati, Dept. of Health and Human Services, 1983, NIOSH publication 83-116.
23. Monson RR: Occupational Epidemiology. 2nd ed. Boca Raton, FL, CRC Press, 1990.
24. Mullan R, Murthy L: Occupational sentinel health events: An up-dated list for physician recognition and public health surveillance. Am J Ind Med 19:775–799, 1991.
25. Jenkins EL, Kisner SM, Fosbroke DE, et al: Fatal injuries to workers in the United States, 1980–1989: A decade of surveillance. Cincinnati, Dept. of Health and Human Services, 1993, NIOSH publication 93-108.
26. National Institute for Occupational Safety and Health: Scaffold Falls. Cincinnati, Dept. of Health and Human Services, 1992, NIOSH publication 92-108.
27. National Institute for Occupational Safety and Health Alert: Request for assistance in preventing electrocutions during work with scaffolds near overhead power lines. Cincinnati, Dept. of Health and Human Services, 1991, NIOSH publication 91-110.
28. National Institute for Occupational Safety and Health: Preventing lead poisoning in construction workers. Cincinnati, Dept. of Health and Human Services, 1991, NIOSH publication 91-116.
29. National Institute for Occupational Safety and Health Alert: Request for assistance in preventing worker deaths and injuries from falls through skylights and roof openings. Cincinnati, Dept. of Health and Human Services, 1990, NIOSH publication 90-100.
30. National Institute for Occupational Safety and Health Alert: Request for assistance in preventing electrocutions of workers using portable metal ladders near overhead power lines. Cincinnati, Dept. of Health and Human Services, 1989, NIOSH publication 89-110.
31. National Institute for Occupational Safety and Health Alert: Request for assistance in preventing occupational fatalities of workers who contact electrical energy. Cincinnati, Dept. of Health and Human Services, 1987, NIOSH publication 87-103.
32. National Institute for Occupational Safety and Health Alert: Request for Assistance in Preventing Occupational Fatalities in Confined Spaces. Cincinnati, Dept. of Health and Human Services, 1986, NIOSH publication 86-110.
33. National Institute for Occupational Safety and Health Alert: Request for assistance in preventing deaths and injuries from excavation cave-ins. Cincinnati, Dept. of Health and Human Services, 1985, NIOSH publication 85-110.
34. National Institute for Occupational Safety and Health Alert: Request for assistance in preventing electrocutions from contact between cranes and power lines. Cincinnati, Dept. of Health and Human Services, 1985 NIOSH publication 85-111.

D. J. McVITTIE

FATALITIES AND SERIOUS INJURIES

From the Construction Safety
  Association of Ontario
Toronto, Ontario
Canada

Reprint requests to:
D. J. McVittie
Manager, Technical Services
Construction Safety Association
  of Ontario
74 Victoria Street
Toronto, Ontario M5C 2A5
Canada

The construction industry has long been recognized as having a relatively high rate of fatal
and disabling injuries compared with most fixed
industries. Data from the U.S. Census of Fatal
Occupational Injuries indicates that construction
laborers have a fatality rate of 34 per 100,000
workers at risk. This compares with a rate of 3
per 100,000 machine operators, assemblers, and
inspectors in manufacturing industries. The
work-related death rate reported by U.S. Bureau
of Labor Statistics (BLS) for all construction is
14 per 100,000 workers, compared with 4 for
manufacturing.[7]

However, when the statistics from the BLS
are adjusted to compare full-time equivalents instead of workers, the U.S. construction death rate
is higher—about 18.6 per 100,000 full-time equivalents. Construction workers generally work no
more than 1,500 hours annually, while workers in
other manufacturing work about 2,000 hours.

Dramatic construction disasters are well documented and publicized. Examples are the collapse
of the partially constructed L'Ambience Plaza
building in Bridgeport, Conn., where 28 construction workers were killed,[3] or the 1978 collapse of
a cooling tower under construction in Saint Marys,
West Virginia, that killed 51 construction workers.

In addition, rates for coverage established by
workers' compensation boards or insurance carri-
ers tend to reflect the hazards in this industry,
with rates for construction generally being much
higher than for occupations or sectors such as office work and light manufacturing. The Workers'
Compensation Board of Ontario's assessment rates
for construction for 1994 averaged (in Canadian
dollars) $7.81 per $100 of payroll compared to an
average of $3.86 per $100 for manufacturing.[8]

This chapter defines some of the problems related to work-related deaths and serious injuries in construction. The information is presented with a view to assisting in the targeting of the major problems and identifying intervention strategies to reduce the incidence of these unfortunate and unnecessary events. The primary sources of data for the observations presented here were the fatal accident investigation reports from the Ontario Ministry of Labour, Occupational Health and Safety Division, and the Accident Causal Data System compiled from injury reports filed with the Workers' Compensation Board of Ontario, Canada. Some comparative statistics from the U.S. also are presented.

FATAL ACCIDENTS

Differing types of fatal injuries occur across all parts of the construction industry. The injuries occur on all kinds of projects, ranging from large petrochemical and industrial projects to minor repair and maintenance tasks on single-family residences. They have occurred with large and small employers and have affected every trade. Because of limitations in data available about the size of trade groups and the distribution of activity by type of project, it is difficult to determine relative injury risks for different trades or types of projects. It is possible, however, to identify problems that have resulted in fatalities and that continue to present serious risks to construction workers.

The major recurrent types of fatalities in construction in Ontario and the U.S. are falls from heights, electrocution or contact with power lines, being struck by or caught between objects or equipment, including reversing vehicles, and trench or excavation wall collapse (Table 1).

Causes of the remaining fatalities are widely distributed and inconsistent from year to year. They include fire and explosion, compensable motor vehicle accidents, and asphyxiation in confined spaces.

Falls from Heights

Falls from heights account for most of the fatal accidents in construction (Table 2). This is true for both Ontario and the United States. In a detailed review of 63 fatal accidents involving falls that occurred in Ontario's construction industry, 53 (84%) occurred in situations where there was an obvious fall hazard—for instance,

TABLE 1.   Distribution of Fatalities from Injuries in Construction, Ontario[2] and the United States[4]

Classification	Ontario (n = 146) 1988–92	United States (n = 3,496) 1985–89
Fall to different elevation	40%	30%
Electrical contact	15	17
Struck by	10	23*
Reversing vehicles	8	—
Caught between	10	18*
Trench cave-in	6	—
Other[†]	11	10

* OSHA data base combines deaths resulting from "struck by" with "reversing vehicles" and deaths daused by "trench cave-in" with "caught between."
[†] "Other" includes fires, explosions, motor vehicle accidents (at work), and asphyxiation.

TABLE 2. Working Surface from Which Fatal Falls Occurred in Construction, Ontario[2] and the United States[5]

Surface	Ontario (n = 63) 1989–92	United States (n = 1,148) 1985–89
Skeletal structure*	25%	14%
Unfinished floor	24	10
Roof	18	26
Suspended scaffold	13	2
Scaffold	11	19
Ladder	6	6
Other†	3	23

* Skeletal structure includes structural steel/precast concrete structural framework, roof trusses, transmission towers/antennae, and similar open structures.
† "Other" includes mobile equipment and water towers.

working on partially completed structures or suspended work platforms—and the fatality could have been prevented if personal fall protection (safety harnesses or belts) had been in use.

In many cases, safety harnesses were readily available on site but were not in use or were not being used properly at the time of the accident. Only one case involved the failure of a fall arrest system and, in that case, the worker had fastened his safety harness to a hoisting line instead of the lifeline.

Eight others (13%) were the result of unguarded or poorly guarded floor openings where personal fall protection would not normally have been required or indicated.

In other cases, an opening in the floor was covered by an unsecured piece of plywood or other material. Fatal accidents have occurred when the covering was dislodged accidentally or when the victim picked up the sheet of material to use for some other purpose and, unaware that there was an opening beneath the sheet, walked directly into the opening.

Data from Ontario and the U.S. show slightly differing distributions of working surfaces from which fatal falls occur (see Table 2).

The reasons for the differences between the Ontario and U.S. data are not readily evident. Part of the difference may rest in how the data in the "other" category in the U.S. statistics are distributed and or in incomplete reporting of details of the accident. These differences may be worth further investigation to obtain a better understanding of the job-site conditions and work practices that lead to fatalities.

Electrocution or Power Line Contacts

The category of electrocution and power line contacts includes fatalities from accidental contact with overhead power lines, working directly on "live" electrical apparatus, and using defective or ungrounded electrical tools.

One of the most common situations in this class occurs when a worker moves a conductive item such as an aluminum ladder, crane boom, or scaffold and inadvertently makes contact with an energized overhead powerline. In the 44 fatalities occurring in Ontario in 1983–1992, 27 (61%) were the result of power line contact. Fourteen cases (32%) were the result of work on energized electrical systems, and 3 cases (7%) were related to defective or improperly grounded portable electrical tools. This is consistent with U.S. data, in which 65% of electrocution fatalities resulted from contact with overhead power lines, 12% from portable tools and cords, and 23% from other sources, including work on energized systems.[8]

Contact with Equipment

Being struck by or caught between objects or equipment represents a diverse group of risks. Depending on the perspective of the person classifying the data, it is possible to classify many accidents in one or another subpart. For this chapter, they are treated as one set of risks. As with other types of fatal accidents, no particular type of project, occupation, or activity appears to predominate in "struck by" accidents.

Data from 64 fatal accidents of this type in 1983–1992 showed that in 37 cases (58%) the victim was directly engaged in moving the material, tool, or equipment involved in the activity. Unanticipated movement, a miscalculation of the effort required, or equipment failure were common factors contributing to these accidents.

In 17 cases (26%), the victim was a bystander with no direct involvement in the activity that resulted in the accident. In the remaining 10 cases (16%) there was insufficient information to determine the involvement of the victim in the events preceding the accident.

Reversing vehicles are a common hazard on many construction projects. Unfortunately, they have led to several fatalities because of site congestion or large "blind spots" behind a vehicle where a driver has no clear view of the intended path of travel. Although several different types of vehicles and mobile equipment have been involved in this type of fatality, dump trucks are involved most commonly (Tables 3 and 4).

Collapses or Cave-ins

Unshored or improperly supported or sloped trenches and excavations continue to present a serious risk of fatal injury in construction. Excavations in unstable soils that are loose, overly wet, or, in some cases, overly dry, are dangerous situations that require support systems or proper sloping to prevent collapse. Trench boxes or liners can be used when sloping or shoring is not feasible. Tremendous forces are generated by collapsing soil walls because of the weight of the soil (more than 2,700 pounds per cubic yard), which makes survival unlikely if a worker is trapped or buried by the collapse.

Even relatively shallow trenches—less than 6 or 7 feet—have collapsed and buried workers in them (Table 5). In some cases, changing environmental conditions such as recent rainfall or sudden thawing can change the stability of soils and increase the risk of a cave-in.

TABLE 3. Type of Vehicle or Equipment in 22 Fatalities Involving Reversing Vehicles in Construction, Ontario, 1981–90[2]

Vehicle or Equipment Type	Percentage of Total
Dump truck	68
Other truck	9
Bulldozer	9
Scraper	5
Tractor, loader, or hackhoe	5
Pavement grinder	5

Note: U.S. data did not identify this subclass of fatality. Vehicle-related accidents of this type are included in the "struck by" classification and "caught in/between" classifications.

TABLE 4. Type of Project Involved in Reversing-vehicle Fatalities, Ontario, 1981–90[2]

Type of Project	Percentage of Total (n = 22)
Road	65
Parking lot	5
Building excavation	5
Sewer or watermain	5
Airport runway	5
Hospital	5
Low-rise residential	5
Commercial building	5

SERIOUS INJURIES

With the similarity in construction practices, materials, equipment, and work force in the U.S. and Ontario, it is not surprising that the injury problems identified in the Ontario data are similar to those in the U.S. In this chapter, serious injuries, also known as lost-time injuries, are defined as those resulting in at least 1 day away from work. Such injuries are accepted by the Workers' Compensation Board of Ontario. Where possible, comparisons are made with U.S. data drawn from state workers' compensation boards and the Army Corps of Engineers.[6,7]

Some variations in definitions need to be considered in examining some of the data. Ontario and some states in the U.S. have a 1-day waiting period before injured workers are eligible for compensation. Other states have waiting periods of up to 7 days. In the U.S., lost-time injuries generally include those necessitating restricted activity. Depending on the state, some types of injuries may be underrepresented because short-duration claims from minor strains and sprains may not be fully represented in the summarized data.

Given the lack of a universal definition for the number of injuries and for differences in determining the number of worker-hours or person-years of exposure, this chapter does not attempt to establish rates of specific injuries or relative risks for individual trades or activities. The distribution of types of accidents in Ontario and the U.S. is listed in Table 6.

The problems that result in the greatest number of injuries are different than those that cause deaths. While "falls to a different elevation" and "struck by" accidents are prevalent in both sets, "reversing vehicles," "trench cave-ins," and "electrocution"—all of which tend to be fatal—are replaced in the injury category by "overexertion," "slips, trips, and falls," and "struck against" classifications.

Since the mid 1970s, the Construction Safety Association of Ontario (CSAO) has been capturing and coding accident causal data from Workers' Compensation Board injury reports in order to compile a construction industry accident causal data base. Most of the readily available injury data address the part of body injured, the type of injury, and identifying characteristics of the employer and the injured worker.

TABLE 5. Trench Depth in 239 Construction Fatalities, United States, 1984–89[4]

Trench Depth	Percentage of Total
5–9 feet	38
10–14 feet	41
15–20 feet	16
Deeper than 20 feet	5

Table 6.   Distribution of Nonfatal Construction Injuries by Type of Accident, Ontario[2] and United States[5]

Classification	Ontario* (n = 53,865) (1987–89)	United States† (n = 359,765) (1985–88)
Overexertion	28%	24%
Struck by object	20	22
Falls to different elevation	20	14
Slips, trips, and falls to same elevation	7	7
Struck against object	6	8
Other‡	19	25

* The Ontario data reflect multiple coding: the injury of a worker struck by something who then fell to another level would be listed in two classifications.
† U.S. data are limited to 10 states: Louisiana, Michigan, Maryland, Indiana, Missouri, Mississippi, Kentucky, Iowa, Oregon, and California.
‡ "Other" includes not reported, stepped on an object, burns, and welding flash.

By examining the source injury reports, CSAO is able to capture additional information about type of construction project, type of construction activity, specific worker activity, working surface, type of equipment, materials and tools involved, and other pertinent causal information. In addition to the coded information, a large data field is provided to allow for a full text description of the injury event.[1] This kind of detail is needed in order to determine the likely causes of the particular injuries. For example, although it is valuable to know what parts of the body are being injured by construction workers, it is more important to know what the workers were doing, the type of construction service that was being provided, the job-site conditions that prevailed, and other information in order to target prevention efforts effectively.

As part of its technical service to Ontario's construction industry, CSAO has conducted numerous analyses of its injury data for trade and industry groups. From these analyses, three major injury problems are evident: manual materials handling (lifting, carrying, pushing, and pulling), direct installation (laying block, erecting steel, connecting electrical services, installing flooring), and in-transit activities (movement on the job, such as climbing, descending, and walking).

Although the relative proportions within each problem category differ from one trade to another, these classifications have been useful in addressing specific problems in each trade or industry sector as well as the general risk factors that are likely to affect all trades on a project, such as on-site access and materials handling. For example, in data from more than 1,000 lost-time injuries incurred by electricians and related apprentices in Ontario in 1988, approximately 32% were related to materials handling, 31% to direct installation activities, and 18% to on-site movement. For the remaining 18%, information on worker activity was not available.

Manual Materials Handling

Given the high labor content of most construction tasks, the prevalence of injures related to lifting, carrying, and moving tools or materials is not unexpected. It is surprising, however, that many workers in the industry assume that the major injury hazard in any given trade relates primarily to the specialized skill portion of the work. In actuality, workers in many trades spend proportionally far more of their time performing materials-handling tasks than the special skill functions of their craft.

TABLE 7. Distribution of Injuries Involving Electricians and Apprentice Electricians, Ontario, 1988[2]

Type of Injury	Number (n = 1,037)	Percentage of Total
Overexertion	304	28.4
Fall to different elevation	169	15.8
Struck against stationary object	81	7.6
Particle in eye	74	6.9
Struck by moving object	59	5.5
Slip, trip, or fall same level	103	9.9
Electrical contact	34	3.2
Electrical flash	19	1.8
Others	194	18.7

For example, there is a fairly widespread belief that the major injury for electricians relates to electrical contact. However, a much larger proportion of electricians are injured while lifting, carrying, or moving tools and materials (Table 7). For electricians to get to the point where contact with live electrical circuits becomes a likely concern, the crew must first unload their tools and materials, get the materials to the work area, erect scaffolds or ladders, lift and install the conduit, run the pulling line, and pull electrical wire or cable. Only when electricians do the actual terminations and tie the new circuit into the existing service do they generally run into problems with energized circuits. On new construction projects, where most of the power distribution is provided by temporary wiring and extension cords, there may not be any "live" permanent circuits to pose a problem until much of this work is done.

In some trades, such as bricklaying and installing reinforcing steel, most of the work is a specialized form of manual materials handling. Much has been done to develop and introduce materials-handling tools or equipment, such as cranes, lift trucks, dollies, and mobile hoists. Often, however, the terrain or the job-site conditions preclude or limit widespread use of mechanized materials handling equipment. Efforts are needed to examine different work practices, improve housekeeping and materials handling systems, and improve lifting techniques used by construction workers.

Direct Installation

Direct installation comprises the most diverse group of risk factors. It includes all of the specialized tasks that are generally not included in the other defined groups. Typical injuries in this group are cuts, eye injuries, and muscle strains. The activities are quite varied, ranging from installing drywall and piping, to erecting walls, painting, and stripping formwork. Depending on which trades are being examined, the tasks can be numerous and diverse. For instance, carpenters and their allied trades may perform a variety of construction: cutting and hammering, installing drywall and acoustical ceilings, and erecting and dismantling scaffolding. Similarly, some of the mechanical trades have diverse functions, including welding, cutting, tightening, installing, removing, bending, and testing.

It is difficult to generalize about the primary problems with this set of risk factors, because each trade group tends to have different problems as a result of trade-specific tasks. It is not uncommon to find a large number of injuries to carpenters resulting from cutting or hammering, because both tasks are common to carpentry work. On the other hand, it is not common to find many cutting or hammering injuries in painters, who do not have these tasks as part of their normal work activity.

A detailed review of each trade group is needed to identify the injury risk factors. Once this is done, preventive efforts can be targeted to the most appropriate areas.

In-transit Injuries

The third readily definable group of risk factors common to all trades includes activities such as walking, climbing, descending, and dismounting. Given the onsite mobility of most trades, much time is spent getting from one place to another. In northern climates, the effect of ice and snow presents an obvious risk factor that leads to numerous slips and falls that result in injuries.

Apart from weather, there are problems with rough, uneven terrain on many projects, especially in sewer and watermain work, in excavations, and around the unfinished exterior of most buildings. The stair and ladder climbing that is common to most vertical construction projects also presents the risk of serious injuries from loss of footing or loss of grip.

Getting up into or down from the cabs of large vehicles and or mobile equipment is often awkward and difficult. The prevalence of knee and ankle injuries to truck drivers and equipment operators clearly shows that jumping down from the cab is a risky activity. Improved access such as larger and better-placed steps and handholds and the use of "three-point-contact" (two hands and one foot or two feet and one hand) at all times while mounting and dismounting equipment can greatly reduce the number and severity of these injuries.

Housekeeping Problems

Surprisingly, almost 25% of all accidents in Ontario's construction industry are related to poor housekeeping on site. This factor directly affects all three major injury categories. Typical injuries include slips and trips due to waste materials, debris, general clutter, and ice, snow, and other slippery surfaces. Poor housekeeping has an effect on the ability to use scaffolds and ladders properly, often resulting in overreaching or improper setup of the equipment and thereby affecting both the direct installation and in-transit classes of injuries. In addition, poor housekeeping and materials management greatly limit the usefulness of materials handling equipment such as dollies, lift trucks, or other assistive devices. Multiple handling of items, with the attendant overexertion problems, are compounded when poor housekeeping practices require materials and equipment to be moved several times before installation.

One major feature of the housekeeping problem on most projects is that it receives insufficient attention. As a result, site clean-up and materials management are simply not carefully managed or controlled, and the facilities for storing or moving waste materials are inadequate. Many subcontractors or crews leave their waste materials behind for someone else to clean up, and a spiralling effect is started whereby problems with garbage and debris seem to grow exponentially.

In addition to the numerous run-of-the-mill injuries that result from poor housekeeping, there are problems with the storage of flammable, corrosive, or toxic materials that can lead to serious property damage, personal injury, or both if adequate controls are not in place. Although these events are rare, they can be catastrophic, and their relatively low frequency may be due more to good luck than good management practices.

SUMMARY

The construction industry has major fatality problems relating to falls from heights, electrical contact, reversing vehicles, trench wall collapses, and workers being struck by falling or moving objects.

Serious-injury problems relate to housekeeping, manual materials handling, direct installation activities, and on-site in-transit activities. They vary from one construction trade to another and from one type of project to another. Each of the these problems can be reduced through the application of better site management, better training, and improved work practices. In some instances, changes in materials, tools, or equipment can be beneficial in reducing the incidence of fatal or serious injuries.

REFERENCES

1. Construction Safety Association of Ontario: Accident Causal Data System Coding Manual. Toronto, Construction Safety Association of Ontario, 1992.
2. Ministry of Labour, Fatal Accident Investigation Reports, Ontario [unpublished data].
3. National Bureau of Standards: Investigation of L'Ambience Plaza Building Collapse in Bridgeport Connecticut. Gaithersburg, MD, National Bureau of Standards. 1988, report #NBSIR 3640.
4. Occupational Safety and Health Administration: Analysis of Construction Fatalities—The OSHA Database 1985-89. Washington, DC, U.S. Dept. of Labor, 1990.
5. Occupational Safety and Health Administration: Construction Accidents: The Workers' Compensation Database—1985-88. Washington, DC, U.S. Dept. of Labor, 1992.
6. Office of Construction and Engineering, OSHA: Construction Lost-Time Injuries: The U.S. Army Corps of Engineers Data Base 1984-1988. Washington, DC, U.S. Dept. of Labor, 1992.
7. Toscano G: Fatal work injuries—Results of the 1992 National Census. Monthly Labor Review, October 1993, pp 39–48.
8. Workers' Compensation Board of Ontario: Table of Assessment Rates for 1994. Toronto, Canada, Workers' Compensation Board of Ontario, 1994.

EVA HOLMSTRÖM, DrMEDSci
ULRICH MORITZ, MD, PhD
GÖRAN ENGHOLM, MSc

MUSCULOSKELETAL DISORDERS IN CONSTRUCTION WORKERS

From Bygghälsan
Malmö, Sweden (EH)
and
Lund, Sweden (UM)
and
National Board of Health and
Welfare
Stockholm, Sweden
and
National Institute of Occupational
Health
Umeå, Sweden (GE)

Reprint requests to:
Eva Holmström, DrMedSci
Bygghälsan
Höjagatan 21
S-21233 Malmö, Sweden

Cross-sectional studies, based on questionnaires, reveal a high prevalence of musculoskeletal complaints described as pain, ache, and discomfort among construction workers.[24,40] Similar complaints have been reported in other professional groups[15,21,52,67,89,103] and populations in industrialized countries.[1,10,14,47,57,76,92,111]

Besides causing individual suffering, musculoskeletal disorders result in absenteeism and early retirement pensions, which entail heavy costs for companies and governments.[7,29,66,94] In a Swedish study, early retirements due to these disorders were more common among construction workers than other men.[83] During 1988–1989, 72% of all sick leaves longer than 4 weeks in the construction industry in Sweden were due to musculoskeletal disorders.[62]

These symptoms may be caused by tissue changes[30] induced by mechanical stress in work tasks. In addition, psychological and social factors can be expected to intensify pain and suffering, especially in chronic cases (see chapter 10).

PHYSICAL FACTORS

Overall, the data suggest that extreme work postures and work with the muscles being static contribute to the occurrence of low back and musculoskeletal symptoms in construction workers.

Comparisons between Construction Workers and Office Workers

An interview survey conducted in Sweden studied the relationship between work and musculoskeletal disorders. Carpenters, bricklayers, concrete workers, plumbers, and machine and crane operators had a significantly increased standardized morbidity ratio for musculoskeletal diseases compared with Swedish men,[82] indicating that construction work is a risk factor. Another survey, based on questionnaire reports from 87,391 male Swedish construction workers, showed that musculoskeletal symptoms were much more prevalent among all groups of construction workers than among male office workers (Figs. 1–4).[24] All calculations were adjusted for age. The construction workers comprised 20 occupational groups.

Investigations in Finland have shown that neck and shoulder symptoms, lumbago, nonspecific low back pain, and sciatica were more prevalent among machine operators and carpenters than sedentary workers.[87,102] Construction workers also have an increased relative risk for herniated disk, with an odds ratio of 2.4, compared to office workers.[35]

A study of bricklayers and rockblasters found that physical workload contributed to the development of radiographic osteoarthritis of the acromioclavicular joint, and exposure to vibration contributed to the development of shoulder tendinitis.[97] Vingård reported that, compared with blue-collar workers less exposed to risks, construction workers have a significantly increased risk ratio for osteoarthritis of the knee and hip, with relative risks of 1.4 and 1.7, respectively.[109,110]

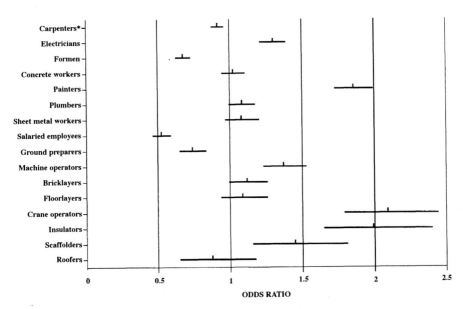

FIGURE 1.   Neck pain symptoms: Prevalence by occupation as reported for preceding 12 months by Bygghälsan examinees. Age-adjusted odds ratios (95% CI) in comparison with carpenters.
* Carpenters' odds ratio is in comparison with all others combined.
Note: Carpenters (n = 19,677) were used as a reference group because they are the largest group in construction and their work includes a variety of tasks—static and dynamic—that use different postures.
From Engholm G, Englund A: Ohälsa, belastningar och arbetsmiljöproblem inom byggbranschen (Health, workload and working environment problems in the construction industry). Bygghälsan HK, Danderyd, Sweden, 1993 (in Swedish).

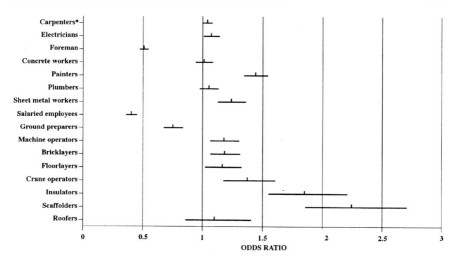

FIGURE 2. Shoulder symptoms: Prevalence by occupation as reported from preceding 12 months by Bygghälsan examinees. Age-adjusted odds ratios (95% CI) in comparison with carpenters.
* Carpenters' odds ratio is in comparison with all others combined.
Note: Carpenters (n = 19,677) were used as a reference group because they are the largest group in construction and their work includes a variety of tasks—static and dynamic—that use different postures.
From Engholm G, Englund A: Ohälsa, belastningar och arbetsmiljöproblem inom byggbranschen (Health, workload and working environment problems in the construction industry). Bygghälsan HK, Danderyd, Sweden, 1993 (in Swedish).

Few prospective studies of musculoskeletal disorders have been carried out, particularly concerning construction workers. A clear association between severe low back disorders such as sciatica and herniated disk and heavy work was proved in prospective studies, where heavy work was defined as construction work of some kind.[34,35,88] Nonspecific low back pain had no such apparent association with heavy work in prospective studies.[88]

Comparisons between Occupational Groups in Construction

Occupational groups in construction are exposed to various kinds of physical workload, involving different parts of the body. There are differences in reported pain localization among the occupational groups, which may indicate pain resulting from differing pain-provoking mechanical stresses.

In a Swedish survey of construction workers, the prevalence of neck symptoms was highest in crane operators, followed by insulators and painters, respectively (Fig. 1).[24] Finnish investigations comparing machine operators and carpenters showed that machine operators have an increased age-adjusted relative risk for more persistent neck symptoms.[102]

The Swedish survey found that shoulder symptoms occurred most frequently among scaffolding erectors, insulators, and painters (Fig. 2).[24] In another study, hand/wrist symptoms were experienced frequently by about half of a group of electricians.[48]

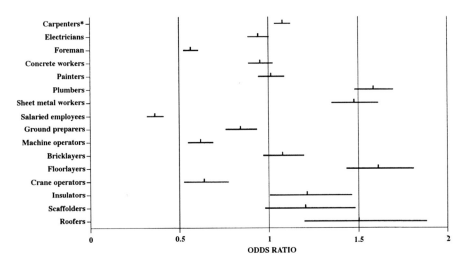

FIGURE 3.   Knee symptoms: Prevalence by occupation as reported for preceding 12 months by Bygghälsan examinees. Age-adjusted odds ratios (95% CI) in comparison with carpenters.
* Carpenters' odds ratio is in comparison with all others combined.
Note: Carpenters (n = 19,677) were used as a reference group because they are the largest group in construction and their work includes a variety of tasks—static and dynamic—that use different postures.
From Engholm G, Englund A: Ohälsa, belastningar och arbetsmiljöproblem inom byggbranschen (Health, workload and working environment problems in the construction industry). Bygghälsan HK, Danderyd, Sweden, 1993 (in Swedish).

Of 20 occupational groups, carpet and floor layers had the highest prevalence of knee symptoms, followed by plumbers and roofers (Fig. 3).[24]
A Finnish work analysis of carpet and floor laying and painting showed that carpet and floor layers kneeled, on average, 42% of the time in the observed work tasks. Among painters, kneeling was rare.[59] One clinically verified knee disorder, bursitis in the front of the knee, was more frequent among carpet and floor layers than painters,[59,100] suggesting kneeling and squatting as contributory factors. Ultrasonography showed thickening of the prepatellar or superficial infrapatellar bursa in 49% of the carpet and floor layers and in 7% of the painters.[58] In addition, radiographic changes of the patella were more common among carpet and floor layers than among painters.
With regard to nonspecific low back pain and lumbago, Finnish and Swedish studies found no differences between concrete reinforcement workers and painters or between machine operators and carpenters.[24,87,88] However, Burdorf et al. reported an increased age-adjusted odds ratio of 2.8 for concrete workers producing prefabricated concrete elements, compared to a control group of maintenance engineers.[11] The authors concluded that the average time spent in a bent or twisted position contributed to the prevalence of back pain. Roofers, carpet and floor layers, and scaffolding erectors had an increased prevalence of low back symptoms compared to carpenters (Fig. 4).[24] Concrete reinforcement workers ran a greater risk of sciatica compared with house painters, a fact that could be explained by the increased time spent working while bent forward.[88]

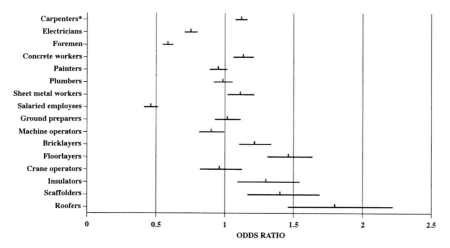

FIGURE 4. Lower-back symptoms: Prevalence by occupation as reported for preceding 12 months by Bygghälsan examinees. Age-adjusted odds ratios (95% CI) in comparison with carpenters.
* Carpenters' odds ratio is in comparison with all others combined.
Note: Carpenters (n = 19,677) were used as a reference group because they are the largest group in construction and their work includes a variety of tasks—static and dynamic—that use different postures.
From Engholm G, Englund A: Ohälsa, belastningar och arbetsmiljöproblem inom byggbranschen (Health, workload and working environment problems in the construction industry). Bygghälsan HK, Danderyd, Sweden, 1993 (in Swedish).

Manual Materials Handling and Use of Machines

Construction workers are exposed to physical workload through heavy manual materials handling, strenuous work postures or movements, static muscle contractions, and vibration.[12,18,90,106]

Frequent handling of construction materials was not associated with any striking increase in prevalence rates of neck-shoulder or low back pain.[24,44,45] This is in accord with Leino's results concerning musculoskeletal disorders in blue collar workers.[67] The conclusion may be that manual handling of construction materials is hazardous because of a variety of factors—such as heaviness, cumbersome size, or extreme lifting conditions—and that the overall risk is similar in different trades.

However, frequent use of machines, especially hand-held ones, was associated with increased prevalence of low back pain and neck and/or shoulder trouble;[44,45] this finding may be explained by the association between hand-held machine tools and a long time spent working in static postures or an increased work pace. Use of a powered screwdriver compared with a manual one, for instance, increases the work pace.[81]

Working with the hands above shoulder level has been shown to increase neck and shoulder pain with a dose-response relationship.[45] The same thing has been noted for low back pain and stooping[24,27,44,84] and kneeling.[44]

Vibration

Long-term exposure to vibration affects the circulatory, nervous, and musculoskeletal systems with symptoms such as vibration white finger and numbness and pain in the arms and hands.[33] A study of concrete workers and safety engineers found that the concrete workers had significantly increased relative risks for numbness during the night, decreased grip force, increased clumsiness, and vibration white finger.[31] An association also has been found between the prevalence of shoulder symptoms and years working with vibrating tools.[31]

Several studies have shown a link between seated whole-body vibration and an increased incidence of low back pain.[17,26,35,46,55] However, as Hulshof et al. have reported, no clear exposure-response relationship between whole-body vibration and low back pain has been found. Similarly, a recent investigation of the long-term exposure to whole-body vibration in bus and truck drivers could not prove a vibration dose-response relationship.[72] In construction specifically, Hilfert et al. reported an increased prevalence of back pain earth-moving equipment workers compared with construction workers not exposed to vibration.[39] These studies may be confounded by other risk factors; workers exposed to whole-body vibration mostly are bus or truck drivers or motor vehicle operators and, as such, are exposed to other physical risk factors. Burdorf et al. found exposure to whole-body vibration—from working with vibrotables—to be a contributory factor for elevated prevalence of low back pain among concrete workers.[11] Crane operators exposed to whole-body vibration received disability pensions resulting from intervertebral disk disorders more often than controls, with a risk ratio of 2.28.[8] Further research is needed in this area.

SPECIFIC DISORDERS: CLINICAL FINDINGS AND TISSUE PATHOLOGY

A key shortcoming of epidemiologic studies that use questionnaires is that they do not usually provide a clinical diagnosis. To determine the prevalence of musculoskeletal conditions rather than just symptoms, studies should look at the prevalence of specific clinical diagnoses using a standard case definition. In the few investigations that have combined epidemiologic studies with clinical examination,[41,56,80] the correspondence between reported symptoms and clinical findings has varied. However, detailed physical examination correlated well with current back pain and functional impairment reported on a concurrent questionnaire in a study of construction workers.[41]

Muscular Disorders

Symptoms may arise from different tissues of the muscle-tendon unit, including muscle belly, myotendon junction, tendon, tendon sheath, and tendon insertion.[74] Work-induced muscular symptoms may be due to strain causing delayed muscle soreness, especially after repeated eccentric contractions. Histologic examination reveals Z-line streaming and degenerative changes in the sarcomeres.[25,74] Experimental studies show complete remodeling to normal within 2 weeks. There are no clinical studies on the effect of repeated heavy eccentric loading over an extended time in a work situation.

Muscular symptoms may also be caused by local ischemia, resulting in impaired muscle function and pain.[30] Persistent degenerative changes of type 1 fibers with moth-eaten and ragged red fibers have been demonstrated after prolonged static, repetitive loading of the trapezius muscles in women with chronic myalgia.[63] Moth-eaten and ragged red fibers also have been found in back muscles of patients operated on for lumbar disk herniation.[112] In these cases, the mitochondrial myopathies may be caused by chronic protective muscle spasm impairing microvascular blood flow.

Compared to the less painful side, blood flow has been shown to be reduced in the upper part of the trapezius muscle during rest and during isometric contraction in patients with chronic trapezius myalgia.[64] The reduction of blood flow was related to the intensity of pain and persisted despite long-term absence from the static load at work.

In contrast to the histologic changes observed in muscles of patients with rheumatic diseases such as rheumatoid arthritis or polymyositis, patients with work-induced myalgia do not show infiltration of inflammatory cells and muscle fiber destruction to any significant extent. Patients with true inflammatory histologic changes and destruction of muscle tissue complain less often of muscle pain and tenderness as typically described by myalgic patients, except in acute and severe cases. This suggests that muscle pathology alone does not explain the nature of work-related pain. Central nervous system mechanisms involving motor control[23] and afferent central interaction[91] may play a more important role.

Tendon Disorders

The myotendinous junction is not as strong as its associated tendon.[74] Muscular strain may thus cause a structural failure in this region of the muscle-tendon unit. Delayed-onset muscle soreness is partly localized to the junction and may represent a work-related disorder.[74] Inflammation of the paratenon and adjacent muscle tissue (peritendinitis) is thought to be caused by mechanical strain or trauma.[61] Biopsies indicate the existence of edema and accumulation of fibrin in addition to vascular changes.

Strain may also cause tendinitis and tenosynovitis.[61] Compressive loads and shear forces are added when the loaded tendons turn corners, for instance, during wrist deviation.[75,101] The idea that tendinitis and tenosynovitis are caused by ergonomic factors such as high-force repetitive and stereotyped work has been suggested[93] but not convincingly demonstrated.[108]

Disturbance of circulation and nutrition of the tendons seems to be an important factor for degenerative changes in the tendon.[30] Zones of avascularity have been demonstrated in the supraspinatus tendon, the biceps brachii tendon, and the upper part of the infraspinatus tendon.[85] During aging, degenerative changes and microruptures are found especially in these areas. Humeral compression of the rotator cuff against the coracoacromial arch and constant tension on the supraspinatus tendon from working with elevated arms has an ischemic effect and may be the major cause of supraspinatus tendinitis.[36] A high intramuscular pressure (mean about 80 mm Hg) has been demonstrated in the supraspinatus muscle early in shoulder abduction, even without hand load, indicating impaired muscle blood flow in this muscle and, consequently, in its tendon, already at low shoulder load.[49,50] Vibration exposure also increases the risk for shoulder tendinitis.[96]

Articular Disorders

Joint symptoms may be caused by degenerative or inflammatory changes. Articular dysfunction also may be due to ligament or meniscal lesions. Some degenerative changes are part of normal aging. Early signs of degeneration are fibrillation and increased hydration of the cartilage followed by proteoglykan loss and a reduced number of chondrocytes. These age-related degenerative changes are not necessarily followed by a decrease of the thickness of the joint cartilage,[78] which is the diagnostic criterion of osteoarthritis. The joints most often affected by primary arthrosis after age 60 are the hip, knee, distal interphalangeal and acromioclavicular joints, and the carpometacarpal joint of the thumb. The ankle, wrist, elbow, and humeroscapular joint rarely show signs of osteoarthritis under normal conditions.

Osteoarthritis of the knee has been linked to mechanical factors such as heavy physical work, prior knee injury, and obesity. This was confirmed in a study of severe osteoarthritis in patients age 55 and older who were treated with total knee arthroplasty.[60] Patients with osteoarthritis were two to three times more likely than controls to have performed moderate to very heavy work. The odds ratio for patients reporting significant knee injury was 4.6; obesity at age 40 (body mass index >25) gave an odds ratio of 5.3.

Laborers having worked in the heavy shipyard industry for decades also have been shown to have a higher prevalence of radiologic knee osteoarthritis than white-collar workers.[69] The same samples were analyzed with regard to the relation between labor and coxarthrosis.[68] Coxarthrosis occurred in about 3%, with no difference between the two samples. A random population sample drawn from the records of the town where the shipyard was located showed a somewhat lower prevalence, 1.6%. The difference was not significant. However, if hospitalization and hip surgery are chosen as dependent variables, the correlation between exposure and coxarthrosis is more apparent,[16,109] suggesting that heavy work may be a risk factor for more serious disease.

Exposure to vibration among rock blasters has been shown to be an additional risk factor for osteoarthritis of the acromioclavicular joint, but vibration alone was a weaker risk factor than years of manual work and total weight lifted during working life.[97] There is also evidence that work with pneumatic percussive tools such as chipping hammers and scalers may cause premature elbow and wrist osteoarthritis, but the prevalence appears to be low.[28] Strong dynamic and static joint loading and repetitive hand-arm movements typical for manipulation of these tools play an additional important etiologic role.

Osteophytes as the only radiologic finding are not sufficient evidence for the diagnosis of osteoarthritis; they are usually considered to be a sign of aging[19,37] and do not necessarily precede narrowing of the joint space.[20] An increased prevalence of osteophytes has been observed, however, in joint structures exposed to heavy mechanical stress. Osteophytes in the cranial and caudal margins of the patellar joint surface were significantly more common among carpet and floor layers working in kneeling postures than among painters (58 and 41% respectively), while narrowing of the joint space (1–2%) showed no difference between the groups.[59]

Osteophytosis of the knee was related to knee pain in carpet and floor layers (RR 1.4) but not in painters. The mean age was 39 at the time of examination. Similar observations were reported by Wickström et al., who compared concrete reinforcement workers and painters (mean age 41.5).[107] Predominant radiologic findings were insertion periostitis and osteophytes in the femeropatellar joint and osteophytes in the femorotibial joint. Narrowing of the joint space was observed in 2% and subchondral sclerosis in only 1–2%. The prevalence was the same in concrete reinforcement workers and in painters, but the concrete reinforcement workers with radiologic signs had more severe symptoms.

It can be concluded that repetitive heavy loading of extremity joints and prior injuries accelerate cartilage destruction, especially when combined with exposure to vibration. In addition, reactive bone tissue changes such as osteophytes may also be work-related. The severity of pain and stiffness depends not only on the degree of radiologic change but also on the mechanical stress to which the joint is exposed.

Disorders of the Spine

Examination of lumbar spines removed at autopsy has shown that degenerative changes of the intervertebral disk are present in the intervertebral disks of all people by middle age.[104] By the third decade, the nuclei have lost much of their turgescence, with marked increase of collagen in the nucleus. After the middle years, the distinction between annulus and nucleus is largely lost, and the disk height is reduced. Splits and clefts are frequently found in the tissue of the disk. Vascular ingrowth around the margins of the cleft indicating a repair reaction suggests that the clefts may extend into the annulus by a tearing process rather than tissue breakdown caused by degeneration.[104]

Changes in the disk are often accompanied by osteophyte formation on the margins of the vertebral bodies and remodeling changes in the apophyseal joints. Although osteophytes may be related to degeneration of the disk, they are probably also caused by other factors, such as ligamentous stress.[105]

Osteoarthritis of the apophyseal joints is frequently seen at one or two levels above and below severely affected disks, even if the disks at these levels show only minor degenerative changes.[104] This indicates that degeneration of the intervertebral disk may have a mechanical impact on apophyseal joints in adjacent vertebral segments.

There is a significant relationship between cervical and lumbar disk degeneration in men and women,[65] indicating that disk degeneration is a constitutional disorder, possibly influenced by hereditary factors.[105] However, occupational work load plays a definite role, at least in men. Radiologic findings indicating disk degeneration have been shown to be more frequent in men who do heavy manual work.[2,65,105]

A radiographic study of concrete reinforcement workers and house painters showed that disk space narrowing in the lumbar spine occurred about 10 years earlier in the concrete workers and osteophytes about 5 years earlier than in the painters.[86] The pattern of degenerative changes was similar in the two groups. Height, relative weight, and smoking did not affect occurrence of the degenerative changes, although age was significantly related to disk space narrowing and osteophytes. Earlier back accidents did not significantly influence the prevalence of degenerative changes. Retrospectively, moderate-to-severe degenerative changes in both groups were associated with increased risk of sciatic pain but not with the occurrence of lumbago or nonspecific back pain.[88] This conforms with Lawrence's finding of a significant association in men between a history of incapacitating back-hip-sciatic pain and advanced x-ray changes of disk degeneration in the lumbar spine.[65] Neurologic signs of nerve root involvement present at the time of examination were found in only 5% of the workers with moderate-to-severe disk degeneration.

Kelsey did not find convincing evidence that heavy manual work causes a greater risk for acute herniated lumbar disk specifically.[54] The case-control study indicated a higher risk for sedentary occupations, particularly those requiring prolonged driving of motor vehicles. On the other hand, hospitalization for herniated lumbar disk was found to be highest among blue-collar workers in industry (RR 2.1–2.9), construction workers (RR 2.3), and forest workers (RR 3.0) compared to white-collar workers.[35] The study confirms an increased risk for motor vehicle drivers (RR 2.8).

It can be concluded that mechanical loading enhances the degenerative process. While disk space narrowing appears to be related to work factors, involvement of apophyseal joints and osteophytes alone does not reflect the influence of occupational work load on the lumbar spine.[73]

Peripheral Nerve Entrapment

The viability of nerve fibers depends on nutrition provided by the intraneural circulation and on the intracellular axonal bidirectional transport of essential products. Compression or stretching of the nerve interferes with these essential functions.[70] Underlying diseases such as diabetes mellitus and metabolic neuropathies increase the vulnerability of the nerves.

Certain anatomic configurations of skeletal and muscular structures expose nerves to increased risks. These anatomic locations, called entrapment points, are the carpal tunnel and Guyon's canal (ulnar tunnel) at the wrist, the cubital tunnel and tendinous bands of the pronator teres muscle and of the origin of flexor digitorum superficialis at the elbow level, and the arcade of Frohse. Proximal entrapment points of the upper extremity are the coracoid process and the origin of the pectoralis minor muscle, the space between the first rib and the clavicle, and the scalenus muscles.

Until now, the main interest has been in carpal tunnel syndrome. In a review of relevant studies, Stock concluded that there is strong evidence of a causal relationship between repetitive, forceful work and nerve entrapment of the median nerve.[98] Most of these investigations, however, had significant limitations in exposure and outcome measurements. Epidemiologic studies on carpal tunnel syndrome usually include other groups of workers than construction workers.[32] Therefore, no definite conclusion can be drawn concerning the impact of repetitive, forceful work and vibration exposure in construction work. Clinical experience indicates that other nerve structures might be involved in construction workers, i.e., the brachial plexus (E. Holmström, unpublished observations).

WORK ORGANIZATION AND PSYCHOSOCIAL FACTORS

Knowledge about the influence of work organization and psychosocial factors on musculoskeletal disorders in construction workers is limited. Male office workers have reported stressful work and difficulty relaxing during leisure time more often than construction workers.[24] At the same time, the male office workers had a significantly lower prevalence of musculoskeletal symptoms in all areas of the body than construction workers.[24] These results suggest a stronger influence of physical factors than psychosocial factors on the occurrence of musculoskeletal disorders in construction workers.

There have been investigations associating job dissatisfaction, measures of job stress, and psychological symptoms with musculoskeletal disorders or symptoms in construction workers. Job dissatisfaction showed some association with neck and shoulder symptoms in carpenters, machine operators, and sedentary workers in a Finnish study.[102] A significant association between low back pain and job dissatisfaction was found in a Swedish investigation, but only in workers younger than 29.[40]

In an investigation of almost 1,800 construction workers, 21% scored high on a stress index.[44] The stress index included four questions about "rushing even when you have plenty of time," "pushing oneself under pressure," "finding it difficult to relax," and "looking upon the job as a mental strain." There was a clear relationship between low back pain and high scores on the stress index, with an age-standardized prevalence rate ratio of 1.6 (95% CI 1.4–1.8) for low back pain and 3.1 (95% CI 2.3–4.0) for severe low back pain. Stress was associated with 5-year prevalence of sciatic pain in concrete reinforcement workers and painters.[88] The prevalence rate ratio for neck and shoulder pain was 3.4 (95% CI 2.6–4.2) at high scores on the stress index.[45] A high score on the stress index, together with increased age, further increased the prevalence rate of neck-shoulder pain.[45] Because this study was cross-sectional, however, it cannot be used to determine if a high stress index predicts musculoskeletal symptoms or vice versa.

The support index from the same study, comprising questions about psychological support from supervisors and fellow workers, did not show any relationship to low back symptoms, severe low back pain, or neck-shoulder pain. This was quite the opposite the results from an extensive study by Bigos et al. regarding low back injury in aircraft employees.[6]

Psychological and psychosomatic symptoms have been associated with low back and neck-shoulder pain.[40] This accords with Biering-Sörensen's prospective study indicating that people with recurring and first-time low back trouble were more likely to have psychosocial health problems.[4]

A significant increase in the prevalence rate of both low back pain and severe low back pain was found among construction workers with high scores on a demand or stress index in combination with low scores on a resource index.[40,43] This combination is called "the high strain corner" in Karasek's model, considering the demands and resources at the same time.[53] The lowest prevalence rates of low back pain were found among workers with low scores on the demand or stress index in combination with high scores on the resource index.[40] These results accorded with Karasek's results regarding coronary heart disease symptoms.[53] A balance between demands and resources seems to be key to reducing the prevalence of low back symptoms.

INDIVIDUAL FACTORS

Age

Age is a strong risk factor for musculoskeletal disorders in construction workers (Fig. 5).[24] When a group of workers younger than 29 was used as a reference group, the odds ratios for elbow, neck, or shoulder disorders in 50- to 59-year-olds were 6.0 (95% CI 5.5–6.5), 4.0 (95% CI 3.8–4.2), and 4.7 (95% CI 4.4–4.9) respectively. Upper back, lower back, hand, and foot disorders in the same age groups were also significantly related to age.

Age was reported as a strong risk factor for neck and shoulder symptoms in a Finnish study of carpenters, machine operators, and sedentary workers.[87] A significant association between the 12-month prevalence of sciatic pain and age was found in machine operators, carpenters, and sedentary workers.[87] Lumbago and nonspecific low back pain were only associated with age in machine operators.

Smoking

Smoking habits showed weak associations with neck-shoulder pain in a Swedish study of construction workers.[40] A strong association between smoking and severe low back pain was seen in construction workers, with the prevalence rate ratio 2.7 (CI 95% 2.0–3.4).[44] Dimberg, however, found a close correlation between smoking and sick leave taken for neck and upper extremity symptoms in older blue collar workers.[22] He also found an association between smoking and complaints from the neck and hands, reported in a questionnaire. Smoking habits as a risk factor for low back pain have been reported by several authors,[5,21,99] but Boshuizen et al. found a relationship between smoking and back pain only in occupations that require physical exertion.[9]

No relationship between smoking habits and sciatic pain was seen in concrete reinforcement workers and house painters.[88] Frymoyer found that patients with

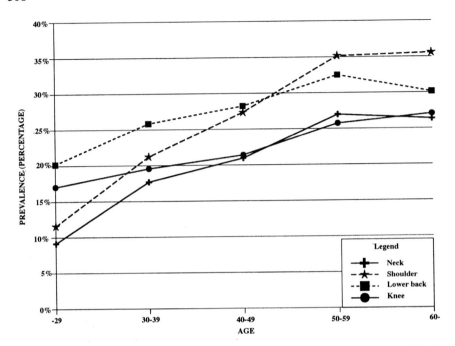

FIGURE 5. Reported pain at four body sites: Prevalence as reported for preceding 12 months by Bygghälsan examinees, by age (percentage).
From Engholm G, Englund A: Ohälsa, belastningar och arbetsmiljöproblem inom byggbran-schen (Health, workload and working environment problems in the construction industry). Bygghälsan HK, Danderyd, Sweden, 1993 (in Swedish).

severe low back pain consumed more tobacco than people with or without moderate low back pain.[26] Smoking habits could not exclusively be a manifestation of pronounced pain, because, in construction workers, there was a significant relationship only between smoking and severe pain in the lower back but not between smoking and pain in the neck and shoulder region.[40] The interactive effects of age, smoking, and heavy work on the musculoskeletal system need to be further studied.

Height and Weight
        Anthropometric factors have been suggested as a risk for the development of musculoskeletal disorders.[71,94] Hildebrandt did not regard height and weight as "generally accepted" risk factors for low back pain.[38] Biering-Sörensen found people with previous low back trouble to be taller and heavier than those with no history of low back trouble, but height and weight were of no prognostic value.[3] Increased height and weight in men were, however, predictors for herniated lumbar disks.[34]

Leisure Time
        Retrospective studies have shown a significant association between back injuries and poor physical fitness.[13] In construction workers, more frequent leisure time activity was related to healthy lower backs[43] and severe low back pain was related to less leisure time activity.[44] A combination of high exposure to load lifted and high exposure to sport activities that engage the arms was a risk factor for osteoarthritis

TABLE 1. Key Disorders and Documented Associated Work Postures, Psychosocial Factors, or Trades

Disorder	Work Posture, Psychosocial Factor, or Trade	Reference
(Excess of) musculo-skeletal problems	Carpenters, bricklayers, concrete workers, plumbers, machine- and crane-operators	24,* 82*
Neck symptoms	Crane operators, electricians, insulators, painters	24*
	Machine operators	24,* 102*
Neck, shoulder symptoms	Machine operators, carpenters	102*
Neck, shoulder pain	Using hand-held machines, hands above shoulder level, reported high psychological stress	45
Shoulder symptoms	Using vibrating tools	31*
Shoulder symptoms	Scaffolding erectors, insulators, painters, crane operators	24*
Shoulder tendinitis	Rockblaster	96*
Radiographic acromio-clavicular joint osteo-arthritis	Bricklayers, rockblasters	97*
Acromioclavicular joint osteoarthritis	Heavy manual work, vibration exposure	97
Hand or wrist	Electricians, insulators, scaffolding erectors, sheet metal workers	24,* 48*
Elbow and wrist osteoarthritis	Using pneumatic, percussive tools (chipping hammers, scalers)	28
Nerve entrapment of median nerve (carpal tunnel syndrome)	Repetitive, forceful work	98
Disk degeneration	Heavy manual work	2, 65, 86,* 105
Herniated disk	All construction	35*
Herniated lumbar disk	Heavy manual work, motor vehicle drivers	54*
Low back pain	Using hand-held machines	44
	Stooping	24, 27, 44, 84
	Kneeling	44
	Reported high psychological stress	40,44
	High demand and low resources	40,43
Nonspecific low back pain	Concrete workers (prefab.)	11*
	Roofers, carpet and floor layers, scaffolding erectors	24*
Nonspecific low back pain	Machine operators, carpenters	87*
Sciatica	Concrete reinforcement workers	88*
Hip (coxarthrosis)	Heavy manual work	68
Knee, hip osteoarthritis	All construction	109,* 110*
Knee osteoarthritis	Heavy manual work	60, 69
Radiological knee osteoarthritis	Heavy shipyard industry (laborers)	69*
Knee symptoms	Carpet and floor layers, plumbers, roofers	24*
Thickening of prepatellar or superficial infra-patellar bursa	Carpet and floor layers	58
Bursitis (front of knee)	Carpet and floor layers	59, 100

* Comparative study (vs. male population, vs. office workers or vs. other construction workers)

of the acromioclavicular joint and for shoulder tendinitis.[95] A corresponding result was found concerning osteoarthritis of the hip.[109]

Muscle Strength and Endurance

Diminished back muscle strength in a group of concrete reinforcement workers was associated with a history of sciatica, and diminished abdominal muscle strength was associated with a history of lumbago.[79] The abdominal muscle test performance was, however, influenced by the individual's spinal mobility capacity. Retrospectively but not prospectively, Riihimäki et al. found a reduced isometric back muscle strength in concrete reinforcement workers with sciatic pain.[88] Results from the same investigation showed no association between isometric abdominal muscle strength and sciatic pain. In a Swedish study of construction workers, a group with a clinically defined low back disorder showed a shorter trunk extensor endurance time compared to a group with healthy lower backs and to a group with a nonspecific low back disorder.[42] This accords with the findings of Nicolaisen and Jörgensen.[77] Jörgensen et al. found a significant decrease of the isometric endurance of the trunk extensors in bricklayers during a working day.[51]

Key disorders and documented associated work postures, psychosocial factors, or trades are listed in Table 1.

CONCLUSION

Review of the literature indicates that long-time exposure to heavy and repetitive work may cause or accelerate normal degenerative processes. Psychosocial factors play an important role, especially imbalance between demands and resources. Individual factors such as smoking may be an additional contributing factor.

REFERENCES

1. Allander E: Hur vanliga är sjukdomar i rörelseorganen? (What is the prevalence of work-related musculoskeletal disorders?) In Svenska Läkarsällskapets Handlingar: Rörelseorganens Belastningssjukdomar (Work-Related Musculoskeletal Disorders). Stockholm, Spri, 1985, pp 69–73 (in Swedish).
2. Andersson GBJ: Epidemiologic aspects on low-back pain in industry. Spine 6:53–60, 1981.
3. Biering-Sörensen F: Physical measurements as risk indicators for low-back trouble over a one-year period. Spine 9:106–119, 1984.
4. Biering-Sörensen F, Thomsen C: Medical, social and occupational history as risk indicators for low-back trouble in a general population. Spine 11:720–725, 1986.
5. Biering-Sörensen F, Thomsen CE, Hilden J: Risk indicators for low back trouble. Scand J Rehabil Med 21:121–157, 1989.
6. Bigos S, Battie' M, Spengler D, et al: A prospective study of work perceptions and psychosocial factors affecting the report of back injury. Spine 16:1–6, 1991.
7. Bigos SJ, Spengler DM, Martin NA, et al: Back injuries in industry: A retrospective study, II. Injury factors. Spine 11:246–251, 1986.
8. Bongers PM, Boshuzien HC, Hulshof CTJ, Koemester AP: Back disorders in crane operators exposed to whole-body vibration. Int Arch Occup Environ Health 60:129–137, 1988.
9. Boshuizen HC, Verbeek JHAM, Broersen JPJ, Weel ANH: Do smokers get more back pain? Spine 18:35–40, 1993.
10. Bredkjaer SR: Musculoskeletal diseases in Denmark. The Danish health and morbidity survey 1986–87. Acta Orthop Scand Suppl 62(suppl 241):10–12, 1991.
11. Budorf A, Govaert G, Elders L: Postural load and back pain of workers in the manufacturing of prefabricated concrete elements. Ergonomics 34: 909–918, 1991.
12. Bygghälsan: Miljübeskrivning av sysselsättningar inom byggbranschen (Occupational environmental description of construction work). Danderyd, Sweden, Bygghälsan, 1977 (in Swedish).
13. Cady LD, Bischoff DP, O'Connell ER, et al: Strength and fitness and subsequent back injuries in firefighters. J Occup Med 21:269–272, 1979.
14. Chaffin DB, Andersson GBJ: Occupational Biomechanics. John Wiley & Sons, New York, 1984.

15. Cook T, Zimmermann C: A symptom and job factor survey of unionized construction workers. In Kumar S (ed): Advances in Industrial Ergonomics and Safety IV. London, Taylor & Francis, 1992, pp 201–206,

16. Croft P, Cooper C, Wickham C, Coggon D: Osteoarthritis of the hip and occupational activity. Scand J Work Environ Health 18:59–63, 1992.

17. Damkot DK, Pope MH, Lord J, Frymoyer JW: The relationship between work history, work environment and low-back pain in men. Spine 9:395–399, 1984.

18. Damlund M, Göth S, Hasle P, Munk K. Low back strain in Danish semi-skilled construction work. Appl Ergonomics 17:31–39, 1986.

19. Danielsson LG: Incidence and prognosis of coxarthrosis. Acta Orthop Scand Suppl 66, 1964.

20. Danielsson LG, Hernborg JS: Clinical and roentgenologic study of knee-joints with osteophytes. Clin Orthop 69:301–312,1970.

21. Deyo RA, Bass J: Lifestyle and low-back pain. The influence of smoking and obesity. Spine 14:501–506, 1989.

22. Dimberg L: Symptoms from the neck, shoulders and arms in an industrial population and some related problems [doctoral thesis]. Department of Orthopaedics, University of Gothenburg, Sahlgren Hospital, Gothenburg, Sweden, 1991.

23. Edwards RHT: Hypotheses of peripheral and central mechanisms underlying occupational muscle pain and injury. Eur J Appl Physiol 57:275–281, 1988.

24. Engholm G, Englund A: Ohälsa, belastningar och arbetsmiljöproblem inom byggbranschen (Health, workload and working environment problems in the construction industry). Bygghälsan HK, Danderyd, Sweden, 1993 (in Swedish).

25. Fridén J, Sjöström M, Ekblom B: A morphological study of delayed muscle soreness. Experientia 37:506–507, 1981.

26. Frymoyer JW, Pope MH, Clements JH, et al: Risk factors and low-back pain. An epidemiologic survery. J Bone Joint Surg 65A:213–218, 1983.

27. Frymoyer JW, Pope MH, Costanza MC, et al: Epidemiologic studies of low-back pain. Spine 5:419–423, 1980.

28. Gemne G, Saraste H: Bone and joint pathology in workers using hand-held vibrating tools. Scand J Work Environ Health 13:290–300, 1987.

29. Haddad G: Analysis of 2932 workers' compensation back injury cases. The impact on the cost to the system. Spine 12:765–69, 1987.

30 Hagberg M: Occupational musculoskeletal stress and disorders of the neck and shoulder: A review of possible pathophysiology. Int Arch Occup Environ Health 53:269–278, 1984.

31. Hagberg M, Jacobsson B, Landström U, et al: Förekomst av och relativa risker för muskuloskeletala besvär och neurologiska symtom i händerna hos betongarbetare (Prevalence and odds ratios for musculoskeletal and neurological symptoms in hands of concrete workers) Arbete och Hälsa 3:1–23, 1987 (in Swedish with English summary).

32. Hagberg M, Morgenstern H, Kelsh M: Impact of occupations and job tasks on the prevalence of carpal tunnel syndrome. Scand J Work Environ Health 18:337–345, 1992.

33. Hammarskjöld E: Exposure to cold, vibration or muscular fatigue—its effect on the reproducibillity of work movements [doctoral thesis]. The Department of Physical Medicine and Rehabilitation, Karolinska Institute, Stockholm, Sweden, 1992.

34. Heliövaara M. Incidence and risk factors of herniated lumbar intervertebral disc or sciatica leading to hospitalization. J Chron Dis 40:251–258, 1987.

35. Heliövaara M: Occupation and risk of herniated lumbar intervertebral disc or sciatica leading to hospitalization. J Chron Dis 40:259–264, 1987.

36. Herberts P, Kadefors R: A study of painful shoulder in welders. Acta Orthop Scand 47:381–387, 1976.

37. Hernborg JS, Nilsson BE: The relationship between osteophytes in the knee joint, asteoarthritis and aging. Acta Orthop Scand 44:69–74, 1973.

38. Hildebrandt VH: A review of epidemiological research on risk factors of low back pain. In Buckle PW (ed): Musculoskeletal Disorders at Work. London, Taylor & Francis, 1987, pp 9–16.

39. Hilfert R, Köhne G, Toussaint R, Zerlett G: Probleme der Ganzkörperschwingungsbelastung von Erdbaumaschinenführern (Problems of whole body vibrations in excavator operators). Zentralbl Arbeitsmed 31:199–206, 1981.

40. Holmström E: Musculoskeletal disorders in construction workers related to physical, psychosocial and individual factors [doctoral thesis]. The Department of Physical Therapy, University of Lund, Lund, Sweden, 1992.

41. Holmström E, Moritz U: Low-back pain—correspondence between questionnaire, interview and clinical examination. Scand J Rehabil Med 23:119–125, 1991.

42. Holmström E, Moritz U: Trunk muscle strength and back muscle endurance in construction workers with and without low back disorders. Scand J Rehabil Med, 24:3–10, 1992.
43. Holmström E, Lindell J, Moritz U: Healthy lower backs in the construction industry in Sweden. Work Stress 7:259–271, 1993.
44. Holmström E, Lindell J, Moritz U: Low back and neck/shoulder pain in construction workers; physical and psychosocial risk factors. Part 1: Relationship to low back pain. Spine 17:663–671, 1992.
45. Holmström E, Lindell J, Moritz U: Low back and neck/shoulder pain in construction workers; physical and psychosocial risk factors. Part 2: Relationship to neck/shoulder pain. Spine 17:672–677, 1992.
46. Hulshof C, Veldhuijzen van Zanten B: Whole-body vibration and low back pain. A review of epidemiologic studies. Arch Occup Environ Health 59:205–220, 1987.
47. Hulth A: Hur vanliga är sjukdomar i rörelseorganen? (What is the prevalence of work-related musculoskeletal disorders?). In Svenska Läkarsällskapets handlingar: Rörelseorganens belastningssjukdomar (Work-related musculoskeletal disorders), Stockholm, Spri, 1985, pp 74–83.
48. Hunting KL, Welch LS, Cuccherini BA, Selger LA: Musculoskeletal symptoms among electricians. Am J Ind Med 25:149–163, 1994.
49. Järvholm U, Palmerud G, Herberts P, et al: Intramuscular pressure and electromyography in the supraspinatus muscle at shoulder abduction. Clin Orthop 245:102–109, 1989.
51. Jörgensen K, Jensen B, Kato M: Fatigue development in the lumbar paravertebral muscles of bricklayers during the working day. Int J Ind Ergonomics 8:237–245, 1991.
52. Kamwendo K: Neck and shoulder disorders in secretaries—Prevalence, risk factors, and neck school intervention [doctoral thesis]. The Department of Physical Therapy, University of Lund, Lund, Sweden, 1991.
53. Karasek RA, Theorell T: Healthy Work. Stress, Productivity, and the Reconstruction of Working Life. New York, Basic Books, 1990.
54. Kelsey JL: An epidemiological study of the relationship between occupations and acute herniated lumbar intervertebral discs. Int J Epidemiol 4:197–205, 1975.
55. Kelsey JL, Golden AL: Occupational and workplace factors associated with low back pain. Occup Med State Art Rev 3:7–16, 1988.
56. Kemmlert K, Kilbom Å: Musculoskeletal discomfort in neck/shoulder and the association with the work situation. Arbete och Hälsa 17, 1988 (in Swedish with English summary).
57. Kilbom Å, Hagberg M: Arbetsrelaterade muskuloskeletala sjukdomar—riskyrken och riskfaktorer. (Work-related musculoskeletal diseases—high risk jobs and risk factors). Arbete och Hälsa 19, 1990 (in Swedish with English summary).
58. Kivimäki J: Occupationally related ultrasonic findings in carpet and floor layers' knees. Scand J Work Environ Health 18:400–402, 1992.
59. Kivimäki J, Riihimäki H, Hänninen K: Knee disorders in carpet and floor layers and painters. Scand J Work Environ Health 18:310–316, 1992.
60. Kohatsu ND, Schurman DJ: Risk factors for the development of osteoarthrosis of the knee. Clin Orthop 261:242–246, 1990.
61. Kurppa K, Waris P, Rokkanen P: Peritendinitis and tenosynovitis. A review. Scand J Work Environ Health 5(suppl 3):19–24, 1979.
62. Labour Market Insurances: Stockholm, Folksam Insurance Company, 1989 (unpublished data).
63. Larsson SE, Bengtson A, Bodegård L, et al: Muscle changes in work-related chronic myalgia. Acta Orthop Scand 59:552–556, 1988.
64. Larsson SE, Bodegård L, Henriksson KG, Öberg PÅ: Chronic trapezius myalgia. Morphology and blood flow studied in 17 patients. Acta Orthop Scand 61:394–398, 1990.
65. Lawrence JS: Disc degeneration. Its frequency and relationship to symptoms. Ann Rheum Dis 28:121–138, 1969.
66. LeBlanc FE: Scientific approach to the assessment and management of activity-related spinal disorders. A monograph for clinicians. Report of the Quebec Task Force on Spinal Disorders. Spine (European edition) 12(suppl 1):12–15, 1987.
67. Leino P: Physical loading and mental stress as determinants of musculoskeletal disorders [doctoral thesis]. The Department of Public Health, University of Tampere, Tampere, Finland, 1989.
68. Lindberg H, Danielsson LG: The relation between labor and coxarthrosis. Clin Orthop 191:159–161, 1984.
69. Lindberg H, Montgomery F: Heavy labor and the occurrence of gonarthrosis. Clin Orthop 214:235–236, 1987.
70. Lundberg G, Dahlin LB: Structure and function of peripheral nerves. In Gelberman RH (ed): Operative Nerve Repair and Reconstruction. Vol 1, Philadelphia, JB Lipincott, 1991, pp 3–18.

71. Lundgren N, Kuorinka J, Jonsson B, et al (eds): Arbetsrelaterade Sjukdomar i Rörelseorganen - Förekomst, Orsaker och Förebyggande. En Kunskapsöversikt (Work-Related Musculoskeletal Disorders—Occurrence, Causes and Prevention. A State of the Art Review). Nord, Copenhagen, Nordiska Ministerrådet, 1990.
72. Magnusson M, Booney R, Wilder DG, et al: Investigation of long-term exposure to whole body vibration. A two center screening. In Hagberg M, Kilbom Å (eds): Book of Abstracts, International Scientific Conference on Prevention of Work-related Musculoskeletal Disorders, Arbete och Hälsa 17, 1992.
73. Magora A, Schwartz A: Relationship between the low back pain syndrome and X-ray findings. 1. Degenerative osteoarthritis. Scand J Rehabil Med 8:115–125, 1976.
74. Moore JS: Function, structure, and responses of compartments of the muscle-tendon unit. Occup Med State Art Rev 7:713–740, 1992.
75. Moore A, Wells R, Ranney D: Quantifying exposure in occupational manual tasks with cumulative trauma disorder potential. Ergonomics 34:1433–1453, 1991.
76. Nachemson AL: Spinal disorders. Overall impact on society and the need for orthopaedic resources. Acta Orthop Scand Suppl 62(suppl 241):17–22, 1991.
77. Nicolaisen T, Jörgensen K: Trunk strength, back muscle endurance and low back trouble. Scand J Rehabil Med 17:121–127, 1985.
78. Nilsson BE, Danielsson LG, Hernborg JS: Clinical feature and natural course of coxarthrosis and gonarthrosis. Scand J Rheumatol Suppl 43:13–21, 1982.
79. Nummi J, Järvinen T, Stambej U, Wickström G: Diminished dynamic performance capacity of back and abdominal muscles in concrete reinforcement workers. Scand J Work Environ Health 4(suppl 1):39–46, 1978.
80. Ohlsson K, Attewell RG, Johnsson B, et al: Assessment of neck/upper extremity disorders by questionnaire and clinical examination. Ergonomics 37:891–897, 1994.
81. Ortengren R. Cederqvist T, Lindberg M, Magnusson B: Workload in lower arm and shoulder when using manual and powered screwdrivers at different working heights. Int J Ind Ergonomics 8:225–235, 1991.
82. Ostlin P: Sambandet Mellan yrke och Sjukdomar i Rörelseorganen - en Studie Baserad på Intervjuuppgifter från SCBs Undersökningar av Levnadsförhållanden (ULF). In Arbeten utsatta for Särskilda Hälsorisker; Sjukdomar i Rörelseorganen, Belastningsskador. Bilaga C. (Work related to special health risks: Musculoskeletal diseases, Work-related injuries), Kartläggningsgruppens rapport till arbetsmiljökommissionen. Gotab, Stockholm, 1989 (in Swedish).
83. Peterson W, Lindell J: Sjukfrånvaro och Sjukskrivningar bland Byggnadsarbetare (Sick-leave and early retirement in the construction industry). Danderyd, Bygghälsans Forskningsstiftelse, 1981 (in Swedish).
84. Punnett L, Lawrence JF, Keyserling WM, et al: Back disorders and nonneutral trunk postures of automobile assembly workers. Scand J Work Environ Health 17:337–346, 1991.
85. Rathburn JB, Macnab I: The microvascular pattern of the rotator cuff. J Bone Joint Surg 52B:540–553, 1970.
86. Riihimäki H: Radiographically detectable degenerative changes of the lumbar spine among concrete reinforcement workers and house painters. Spine 15:114–119, 1990.
87. Riihimäki H, Tola S, Videman T, Hänninen K: Low-back pain and occupation. A cross-sectional questionnaire study of men in machine operating, dynamic physical work and sedentary work. Spine 14:204–209, 1989.
88. Riihimäki H, Wickström G, Hänninen K, Luopajärvi T: Predictors of sciatic pain among concrete reinforcement workers and house painters—a five-year follow-up. Scand J Environ Health 15:415–423, 1989.
89. Rundcrantz BL: Pain and discomfort in the musculoskeletal system among dentists [doctoral thesis]. The Department of Physical Therapy, Lund University, Lund, Sweden, 1991.
90. Saari J, Wickström G: Load on the back in concrete reinforcement work. Scand J Work Environ Health 4(suppl 1):13–19, 1978.
91. Sessle BJ: Central nervous system mechanisms of muscular pain. In Fricton JR, Awad E (eds): Advances in Pain Research and Therapy. Vol 17. New York, Raven Press, 1990, pp 87–105.
92. Sievers K, Klaukka T: Back pain and arthrosis in Finland. How many patients by the year 2000? Acta Orthop Scand Suppl 62(suppl 241):3–5, 1991.
93. Silverstein BA, Fine LJ, Armstrong TJ: Hand wrist cumulative trauma disorders in industry. Br J Ind Med 43:779–784, 1986.
94. Socialstyrelsen redovisar: Att förebygga sjukdomar i rörelseorganen (To prevent musculoskeletal diseases). Socialstyrelsen redovisar 14, Allmänna förlaget, Stockholm, 1987 (in Swedish).

95. Stenlund B: Shoulder tendinitis and osteoarthrosis of the acromioclavicular joint and their relation to sports. Br J Sports Med 27: 125–128, 1993.
96. Stenlund B, Goldie I, Hagberg M, Hogstedt C: Shoulder tendinitis and the relation to heavy manual work and exposure to vibration. Scand J Work Environ Health 19:43–49, 1993.
97. Stenlund B, Goldie I, Hagberg M, et al: Radiographic osteoarthrosis in the acromioclavicular joint resulting from manual work or exposure to vibration. Br J Ind Med 49:588–593, 1992.
98. Stock S: Workplace ergonomic factors and the development of musculoskeletal disorders of the neck and upper limbs: A meta-analysis. Am J Ind Med 19:87–107, 1991.
99. Svensson HO, Andersson GBJ: Low-back pain in forty to forty-seven year old men: Work history and work environment. Spine 8:272–276, 1983.
100. Thun M, Tanaka S, Smith AB: Morbidity from repetitive knee trauma in carpet and floor layers. Br J Ind Med 44:611–620, 1987.
101. Tichauer ER: Some aspects of stress on forearm and hand in industry. J Occup Med 8:63–71, 1966.
102. Tola S, Riihimäki H, Videman T, et al: Neck and shoulder symptoms among men in machine operating, dynamic physical work and sedentary work. Scand J Work Environ Health 14:299–305, 1988.
103. Törner M: Musculo-skeletal stress in fishery causes, effects and preventive measures [doctoral thesis]. The Division of Occupational Orthopaedics, University of Gothenburg, Sahlgren Hospital, Gothenburg, Sweden, 1991.
104. Vernon-Robert B, Pirie CJ: Degenerative changes in the intervertebral discs of the lumbar spine and their sequelae. Rheumatol Rehabil 16:13–21, 1977.
105. Wickström G: Effects of work on degenerative back disease. Scand J Work Environ Health 4(suppl 1): 1–12, 1978.
106. Wickström G, Niskanen T, Riihimäki H: Strain on the back in concrete reinforcement work. Br J Ind Med 42:233–239, 1985.
107. Wickström G, Hanninen K, Mattsson T, et al: Knee degeneration in concrete reinforcement workers. Br J Ind Med 40:216–219, 1983.
108. Viikari-Juntura E: Tenosynovitis, peritendinitis and the tennis elbow syndrome. Scand J Work Environ Health 10:443–449, 1984.
109. Vingård E: Work, sports, overweight and ostearthrosis of the hip. Epidemiological studies [doctoral thesis]. The Department of Orthopaedics, Karolinska Institute, and Department of Occupational Health, Karolinska Hospital, Stockholm, Sweden. Arbete och Hälsa 25, 1991.
110. Vingärd E, Alfredsson L, Goldie I, Hogstedt C: Occupation and osteoarthrosis of the hip and knee: A register based cohort study. Int J Epidemiol 20:1025–1031, 1991.
111. Young LV, Nemecek JR, Higgs PE, Ball DJ: Cumulative trauma disorders: An overview of the problem. J Occup Rehabil 2:139–156, 1992.
112. Zhu XZ, Parnianpour M, Nordin M, Kahanovitz N: Histochemistry and morphology of erector spinae muscle in lumbar disc herniation. Spine 14:391–397, 1989.

PATRICIA A. SULLIVAN, MS
KI MOON BANG, PhD, MPH
FRANK J. HEARL, SMChE, PE
GREGORY R. WAGNER, MD

RESPIRATORY DISEASE RISKS IN THE CONSTRUCTION INDUSTRY

From the Division of Respiratory
  Disease Studies
National Institute for Occupational
  Safety and Health
Morgantown, West Virginia

Reprint requests to:
Patricia A. Sullivan, MS
Division of Respiratory Disease
  Studies
NIOSH—Room 234
1095 Willowdale Road
Morgantown, WV 26505-2888

HAZARDOUS EXPOSURES IN THE CONSTRUCTION INDUSTRY

Construction workers are exposed to a variety of potentially hazardous agents. Substances that may pose risks to the respiratory system include asbestos, silica, dust, synthetic vitreous fibers, cadmium, chromates, formaldehyde, resin adhesives, cobalt, metal fumes, creosote, gasoline, oils, diesel fumes, paint fumes and dusts, pitch, sealers, solvents, wood dusts and wood preservatives, and excessive cold.[92]

In 1992, the Occupational Safety and Health Administration (OSHA) proposed permissible exposure limits (PEL) for the construction industry.[72] Agents for which OSHA PELs were proposed based on their potential to induce lung cancer or nonmalignant respiratory effects are presented in Tables 1–3. OSHA noted that, for some of the listed substances, the potential for significant exposure in construction is limited. It is also probable that substances of importance to some construction trades workers are not included on the OSHA list.

For convenience, we have referred to the construction industry or to construction workers as if there is a unity of work activities and exposures. In reality, construction has as much diversity as manufacturing. The construction environment is dynamic, with frequent adoption of new processes and materials—and resultant potential for new toxic exposures. Although this chapter focuses on the primary identified respiratory hazards,

TABLE 1.   Construction Exposures Identified by OSHA as Potentially Resulting in
Respiratory Effects[72]

Lung Cancer	
Arsenic, inorganic (measured as AS)	Coal tar pitch volatiles
Asbestos	Formaldehyde
Beryllium	Zinc chromates
Chromic acid and chromates	
Nonmalignant Respiratory Effects	
Aluminum (pyro powders)	Mica, respirable dust containing < 1% quartz
Asphalt fumes	Mineral wool fiber
Bismuth telluride (Se-doped)	Nickel (soluble compounds)
Carbon black	Nitrogen oxide
Chlorine dioxide	Oxygen difluoride
Chromium (II) compounds (as Cr)	Ozone
Chromium metal (as Cr)	Paraquat, respirable dust
Coal dust	Silica
Cotton dust	Soapstone
Ethyl acrylate	Sulfur dioxide
Ferrovanadium dust	Sulfur tetrafluoride
Fibrous glass	Talc (containing no asbestos)
Grain dust (oat, wheat, barley)	Tin oxide
Graphite, natural, respirable < 1% quartz	Trimelitic anhydride
Indium and compounds	Wood dust
Iron oxide (dust and fumes)	Yttrium
Methylene bis (4-Cyclohexylisocyanate)	

construction-related activities may result in excessive exposure to virtually any substance found in the industrial workplace. Because exposure to respiratory hazards is widespread in the construction workplace, the health professional should automatically consider the workplace as a source for otherwise unexplained respiratory illness.

Compliance monitoring data gathered by OSHA for the construction industry over the past several years give an idea of the level of exposure prevalent in the industry (Table 4). Review of these data indicates that, with the exception of asbestos, comparatively few samples are taken for agents that pose known respiratory risk.

SURVEILLANCE OF RESPIRATORY DISEASE

Surveillance data indicate the nature and magnitude of health risk in the construction industry.

Morbidity

Surveillance data on respiratory disease incidence or prevalence among construction workers are limited. The Department of Labor's Bureau of Labor Statistics collects occupational injury and illness data from the nation's private industry in accordance with a provision of the Occupational Safety and Health Act of 1970. BLS data from 1991 indicate that incidence rates of employer-reported dust disease of the lung and respiratory conditions due to toxic agents were 4 and 21 per 100,000

TABLE 2.   Substances for which Proposed Limits Are Based on Avoidance of Cancer[1,72]

Chemical Name	NIOSH Recommended Exposure Limits*	Current OSHA Permissible Exposure Limits in Construction and Maritime†	1994–95 ACGIH TLV‡[1]
Arsenic, inorganic (measured as As)	2 µg/m³ Ceiling (15-min)§	10 µg/m³ TWA	0.01 mg/m³ TWA (arsenic and soluble compounds)
Asbestos	100,000 Fibers/m³ (Fibers > 5 µm long)	0.2 fiber/cm³ TWA 1 fiber/cm² STEL	TLV varies with specific form, A1
Beryllium and compounds	Do not exceed 0.5 µg/m³§	0.003 mg/m³ TWA‖	0.002 mg/m³ TWA, A2
Chromic acid and chromates	1 µg/m³ TWA (for carcinogenic hexavalent chromium compounds);§ 25 µg/m³ TWA 50 µg/m³ ceiling (15-min) (for noncarcinogenic hexavalent chromium compounds, which include chromic acid)	0.1 mg/m³ TWA	0.05 mg/m³ TWA (measured as Cr)
Coal tar pitch volatiles	0.1 mg/m³ TWA (cyclohexane extractable fraction)§	0.2 mg/m³ TWA	0.2 mg/m³ TWA, A1
Formaldehyde	0.016 ppm TWA (8-hour) 0.1 ppm Ceiling (15-min)	1 ppm TWA 2 ppm STEL	0.3 ppm Ceiling, A2
Zinc chromates	1 µg/m³ TWA§		0.01 mg/m³ TWA, A1 (measured as Cr)

* NIOSH time-weighted-average (TWA) limits are for 10 hour/day, 40 hour/week exposures unless otherwise specified, and its ceilings are peaks not to be exceeded for any period of time unless a duration is specified in parentheses.
† OSHA's Permissible Exposure Limits (PELs) do not currently apply to agriculture; OSHA's TWA limits are for 8-hour exposures; its short-term exposure limits (STELs) are for 15 minutes, unless otherwise specified, and its ceilings are peaks not to be exceeded for any period of time.
‡ The American Conference of Governmental Industrial Hygienists sets threshold limit values (TLVs). The TLV-TWA is for an 8-hour exposure; the "Ceilings" are peaks not to be exceeded for any period of time during a working shift. A1 = confirmed human carcinogen; A2 = suspected human carcinogen.
§ NIOSH considers this substance a potential human carcinogen and recommends that exposures be reduced to the lowest feasible concentration.
‖ The OSHA standard for beryllium is based only on respiratory effects, not on its potential carcinogenicity.

construction workers, respectively.[94] Respiratory conditions accounted for 14.3% of approximately 7,000 reported occupational illness cases among construction workers.

We estimated the prevalence rate of reported respiratory conditions based on a national probability sample of construction workers from data collected through the National Health Interview Survey in 1988.[90] Of 42,487 respondents, 1,785 white men indicated that they had work experience in the construction industry. Prevalence rates of respiratory conditions among these construction workers were compared with those found among other workers who participated in the survey (Table 5). Prevalence rates and rate ratios vary by respiratory condition. (The rate ratio is the ratio of the rate among construction workers compared to the rate among other workers who participated in the survey.) Prevalence rates per 1,000 white male construction workers range from 1.7 for lung cancer to 25.8 for emphysema. The rate ratio of

TABLE 3.   Substances for which Proposed Limits Are Based on Avoidance of Respiratory Effects[1,72]

Chemical Name	NIOSH Recommended Exposure Limits*	OSHA Permissible Exposure Limits†	1994-95 ACGIH Threshold Limit Values‡	Species	Comments
Aluminum (pyro powders)			5 mg/m³ TWA		
Asphalt fumes	5 mg/m³ ceiling (15-min) (total particulate)		5 mg/m³ TWA		
Bismuth telluride (Se-doped)			5 mg/m³ TWA	Dogs, rats, rabbits	Granulomatous lesions in lungs seen after 6 months of exposure
Carbon black	3.5 mg/m³ TWA; if PAHs are present, 0.1 mg/m³ TWA	3.5 mg/m³ TWA	3.5 mg/m³ TWA		
Chlorine dioxide		0.1 ppm TWA	0.1 ppm TWA, 0.3 ppm STEL		
Chromium (II) compounds (as Cr)	0.5 mg/m³ TWA	0.5 mg/m³ TWA	0.5 mg/m³ TWA		
Chromium (III) compounds (as Cr)	0.5 mg/m³ TWA	0.5 mg/m³ TWA	0.5 mg/m³ TWA		
Chromium metal (as Cr)	0.5 mg/m³ TWA	1 mg/m³ TWA	0.5 mg/m³ TWA		
Coal dust, < 5% quartz		2.4 mg/m³ TWA	2 mg/m³ TWA	Humans	Calculated estimate of 10% probability of developing pneumoconiosis with fibrosis after 35 years of exposure to coal dust
Coal dust, > 5% quartz		$\dfrac{10\ \text{mg/m}^3}{\%\ SiO_2 + 2}$	0.1 mg/m³ TWA (as quartz)		
Cotton dust	200 µg/m³ TWA lint-free cotton dust	1 mg/m³ TWA	0.2 mg/m³ TWA		
Ethyl acrylate		25 ppm TWA, Skin	5 ppm TWA, 15 ppm STEL		
Ferrovanadium dust	1 mg/m³ TWA, 3 mg/m³ STEL	1 mg/m³ TWA, 3 mg/m³ STEL	1 mg/m³ TWA		
Fibrous glass	5 mg/m³ TWA total fibrous glass		10 mg/m³ TWA		

(Continued on following page)

TABLE 3. Substances for which Proposed Limits Are Based on Avoidance of Respiratory Effects *(Cont.)*

Chemical Name	NIOSH Recommended Exposure Limits*	OSHA Permissible Exposure Limits†	1994-95 ACGIH Threshold Limit Values‡	Species	Comments
Grain dust (oat, wheat, barley)			4 mg/m³ TWA	Humans	Chronic bronchitis, shortness of breath, reduced pulmonary function, increased incidence of respiratory symptoms
Graphite, natural, respirable < 1% quartz		15 mppcf TWA	2 mg/m³ TWA	Humans	Anthracosilicosis, similar to that seen in coal miners
Indium and compounds		0.1 mg/m³ TWA	0.1 mg/m³ TWA	Rats	Widespread alveolar edema following exposure to In_2O_2
Iron oxide (dust and fumes)		10 mg/m³ TWA	5 mg/m³ TWA		
Methylene bis(4-Cyclohexylisocyanate)			0.005 ppm TWA		
Mica, respirable dust containing < 1% quartz		20 mppcf TWA	3 mg/m³ TWA	Humans	Signs and symptoms resembling silicosis and pneumoconiosis in 8 of 57 workers
Mineral wool fiber			10 mg/m³ TWA		
Nickel (soluble compounds)	0.015 mg/m³ TWA§ (inorganic compounds)	1 mg/m³ TWA	0.1 mg/m³ TWA		
Nitrogen dioxide	1 ppm Ceiling (15-min)	5 ppm Ceiling	3 ppm TWA, 5 ppm STEL	Humans	Fatal pulmonary edema
Oxygen difluoride		0.05 ppm TWA	0.05 ppm Ceiling	Laboratory animals	Lethal to a wide variety of laboratory species, causing pulmonary edema and hemorrhage after several hours of exposure

(Continued on following page)

TABLE 3. Substances for which Proposed Limits Are Based on Avoidance of Respiratory Effects *(Cont.)*

Chemical Name	NIOSH Recommended Exposure Limits*	OSHA Permissible Exposure Limits†	1994-95 ACGIH Threshold Limit Values‡	Species	Comments
Ozone		0.1 ppm TWA	0.1 ppm Ceiling	Humans	Significant reduction in pulmonary vital capacity
				Mice	Damage to alveolar tissue
Paraquat		0.5 mg/m³ TWA, Skin	0.1 mg/m³ TWA (respirable) 0.5 mg/m³ TWA (total dust)	Humans	69 accidental deaths from pulmonary injury reported through 1972
Silica—amorphous, diatomaceous earth		20 mppcf	10 mg/m³ TWA		
Silica—amorphous, precipitate, and gel			10 mg/m³ TWA		
Silica—crystalline cristobalite	50 µg/m³ TWA	250/% SiO₂ + 5 (as mppcf)	0.05 mg/m³ TWA	Dogs	Cellular infiltration of lung and fibrotic nodules in pulmonary lymph nodes
Silica—crystalline quartz, respirable	50 µg/m³ TWA	250/% SiO₂ + 5 (as mppcf)	0.1 mg/m³ TWA	Humans	Accelerated loss of pulmonary function beyond effects of aging alone
Silica—crystalline tridymite (as respirable quartz dust)	50 µg/m³ TWA	250/% SiO₂ + 5 (as mppcf)	0.05 mg/m³ TWA	Rats	Most active form of free silica when administered by intratracheal injection
Silica—crystalline tripoli (as respirable quartz dust)	50 µg/m³ TWA	250/% SiO₂ + 5 (as mppcf)	0.1 mg/m³ TWA	Lab animals	Progressive nodular fibrosis
Silica, fused		250/% SiO₂ + 5 (as mppcf)	0.1 mg/m³ TWA (respirable dust)		
Soapstone—total dust		20 mppcf TWA	6 mg/m³ TWA		
Soapstone—respirable dust			3 mg/m³ TWA		
Sulfur dioxide	0.5 ppm TWA	5 ppm TWA	2 ppm TWA, 5 ppm STEL	Humans	Accelerated loss of pulmonary function

(Continued on following page)

TABLE 3. Substances for which Proposed Limits Are Based on Avoidance of Respiratory Effects *(Cont.)*

Chemical Name	NIOSH Recommended Exposure Limits*	OSHA Permissible Exposure Limits†	1994-95 ACGIH Threshold Limit Values‡	Species	Comments
Sulfur tetrafluoride			0.1 ppm Ceiling	Rats 4 hrs/day/10 days	Emphysema, marked clinical signs of respiratory impairment
Talc (containing no asbestos)		20 mppcf TWA	2 mg/m³ TWA (respirable dust)		
Tin oxide			2 mg/m³ TWA		
Trimelitic anhydride			0.04 mg/m³ Ceiling	Rats	Intra-alveolar hemorrhage (no exposure duration indicated)
Wood dust, hard			1 mg/m³ TWA		
Wood dust, soft			5 mg/m³ TWA 10 mg/m³ STEL		
Yttrium		1 mg/m³ TWA	1 mg/m³ TWA		

* NIOSH time-weighted-average (TWA) limits are for 10 hour/day, 40 hour/week exposures unless otherwise specified, and its ceilings are peaks not to be exceeded for any period of time unless a duration is specified in parentheses.

† OSHA's Permissible Exposure Limits (PELs) do not currently apply to agriculture; OSHA's TWA limits are for 8-hour exposures; its short-term exposure limits (STELs) are for 15 minutes, unless otherwise specified, and its ceilings are peaks not to be exceeded for any period of time.

‡ The American Conference of Governmental Industrial Hygienists (ACGIH) sets threshold limit values (TLVs). The TLV-TWA is for an 8-hour exposure; the "Ceilings" are peaks not to be exceeded for any period of time during a working shift. A1 = confirmed human carcinogen; A2 = suspected human carcinogen.

§ NIOSH considers nickel a potential occupational carcinogen.

2.15 suggests an increased risk of asbestosis among construction workers. Rate ratios for lung cancer, emphysema, and chronic bronchitis were each approximately 1.3.

Asthma was reported less frequently by construction workers than by the general population. Since sensitized individuals or those having a significant response to workplace irritants may voluntarily leave the construction workforce, additional research should investigate the potential role of health-related employment migration in reducing the rate of asthma reported by construction workers. Research is also needed to evaluate asthma rates among worker subpopulations in the construction industry; there may be subsets of workers in the construction trades whose elevated risk of asthma is unrecognized when risk is assessed across the entire set of diverse trades.

The trend in incidence rate for employer-reported lung disease among construction workers was stable between 1985 and 1991. In 1985, there were 22 incident cases per 100,000 among 3.6 million construction workers; in 1991, there were 25 incident cases per 100,000 among 4.7 million construction workers.[94]

TABLE 4.   OSHA Compliance Monitoring in the Construction Industry, 1987–1991

	Percent of Samples over the PEL (Number of Samples)					
Substance	SIC 15		SIC 16		SIC 17	
Arsenic and compounds	20.0	(10)	—	—	5.9	(68)
Asbestos, all forms	5.0	(303)	—	—	6.1	(1533)
Beryllium and compounds	2.1	(47)	8.8	(80)	1.3	(159)
Cadmium fume	3.0	(33)	—	—	0.8	(132)
Chromic acid and chromates (as CRO3)	—	—	—	—	7.1	(14)
Coal tar pitch volatiles	—	—	31.6	(19)	68.8	(32)
Cobalt metal, fume and dust	—	—	1.4	(70)	0.9	(108)
Respirable dust, not otherwise regulated	—	—	—	—	23.4	(47)
Formaldehyde	—	—	—	—	3.8	(26)
Iron oxide fume	10.7	(28)	7.1	(112)	8.4	(179)
Manganese and compounds (as Mn)	—	—	2.9	(139)	—	—
Respirable crystalline silica	47.4	(19)	33.0	(69)	38.4	(146)
Sulfur dioxide	—	—	—	—	60.0	(5)
Total dust, not otherwise regulated	25.0	(14)	38.1	(21)	21.6	(97)
Vanadium	4.3	(23)	8.5	(71)	3.8	(105)
Welding fume	—	—	—	—	22.2	(9)
Wood dust, softwood	—	—	—	—	25.0	(4)
Zinc oxide fume	—	—	0.8	(129)	4.0	(249)

Note: SIC 15 consists of building construction, general contractors: SIC 16 is heavy construction except buildings, general contractors; SIC 17 is special trades contractors.
Data source: NIOSH tabulations from compliance-inspection data tape provided by OSHA.

Mortality

Since 1968 the National Center for Health Statistics has prepared data tapes listing both underlying and contributing causes of death: the multiple cause of death listings.[91] Industry and usual occupation codings on death certificates were reported by 25 states during 1985–1990. In this subset of all U.S. death certificates, there were a total of 286 deaths with asbestosis among decedents age 15 and older with industry and occupation coding indicating construction work. The National Institute for Occupational Safety and Health (NIOSH) found that, among construction workers in these 25 states, there were 21,197 deaths from lung cancer; 100 due to coal workers' pneumoconiosis; 74, silicosis; 107, malignant neoplasms of the pleura; and 28, malignant neoplasms of the peritoneum.[67]

The 1984–1986 NIOSH occupational mortality surveillance data from 19 states were analyzed to describe the proportionate mortality ratio (PMR) patterns of construction workers in special trades (Table 6).[77] For 61,682 white male construction workers who died 1984–86, PMRs were significantly elevated for lung cancer (114, 95% CI 111–116), asbestosis (295, 95% CI 189–439), and nonmalignant respiratory disease (119, 95% CI 116–122). Among white men younger than 65, the NIOSH researchers found significantly elevated PMRs for asbestos-related disease. PMRs were 158 for cancer of the nasopharynx, 136 for cancer of the larynx, and 327 for

TABLE 5. Prevalence Rate and Rate Ratio of Self-Reported Respiratory Conditions Among 1,785 White Male Construction Workers Age 15 and Older: National Health Interview Survey, 1988 Occupational Supplement

Respiratory Condition	Prevalance Rate per 1000 Workers	Rate Ratio
Lung cancer	1.7	1.31
Asbestosis	2.8	2.15
Asthma	19.6	0.82
Emphysema	25.8	1.34
Chronic bronchitis	24.1	1.30

Note: The rate ratio is the ratio of the rate in construction workers compared to the rate among other workers who participated in the survey.
Source: NIOSH tabulations from National Health Interview Survey, 1988 Occupational Supplement public use data tape.[90]

silicosis. For white women working in construction, PMRs were 163 (95% CI 126–207) for nonmalignant respiratory disease and 126 (95% CI 100–157) for lung cancer. For black men, PMRs were not significant for any respiratory disease. However, for black women, the PMR for lung cancer was 272 (95% CI 100–593). White male construction and maintenance painters' PMRs for silicosis and lung cancer were 449 and 124, respectively.

RESPIRATORY DISEASES IN CONSTRUCTION

Surveillance data suggest that work in the construction industry is associated with increased risk of respiratory illness and death. The following section reviews the epidemiologic evidence that specific respiratory diseases are associated with work in the construction trades and discusses exposures in these trades that may be associated with respiratory disease.

Although significant health risks exist in the manufacture of construction materials, this chapter will focus only on hazards for pulmonary disease that occur to workers involved in construction operations, such as the building of tunnels, bridges, roads, and buildings.

Respiratory Tract Cancers

LUNG CANCER

Studies from several countries, using a variety of designs, have documented an increased risk of lung cancer among general construction workers.[5,14,20,29,55,70] The evidence for an association between work in the construction trades and lung cancer is consistent with an occupational etiology, even after controlling for smoking.[5,8,46,65,68,77,78] Increased risk also has been identified in special trades.

Painters and plasterers appear to be at increased risk of lung cancer.[46,50,51,55,65,66,70,74] One factor may be cadmium, which is used as a pigment in paint. NIOSH has documented excess risk of lung cancer associated with cadmium exposure[86] and identified the construction industry as one area where OSHA standards are needed to better protect workers.[64] High potential for exposure may occur during unventilated renovation work. In addition, painters and plasterers may be exposed to acetone, acids, alkalis, benzene, chlorinated hydrocarbons, chromates, drying agents, paint strippers, oil base and resin paints, pigments, silica, solvents, thinners, and turpentine, as well as asbestos from spackling compounds and building restoration.[50,55,66,92]

TABLE 6. Proportionate Mortality Ratios for Selected Respiratory Diseases Among White Males in Special Construction Trades, 1984–86 (Observed Number of Deaths)

Condition	Lung Cancer		Non-malignant Respiratory Disease		Pleural Cancer		Silicosis		Asbestosis	
(ICD-9 Code)	(162)		(490-519)		(163)		(502)		(501)	
Brickmasons	120†	(240)	133†	(191)	—	—	—	—	—	—
Carpenters	116†	(1489)	124†	(1278	—	—	—	—	—	—
Painters	124†	(615)	127†	(468)	—	—	449‡	(4)	—	—
Plumbers	110‡	(508)	113‡	(378)	327‡	(5)	—	—	1097†	(8)
Insulation workers	193†	(51)	152‡	(22)	2467†	(2)	—	—	23197†	(9)
Electricians	114†	(626)	110‡	(436)	331‡	(6)	—	—	349	(3)
Operating engineers	120‡	(434)	112	(255)	—	—	—	—	—	—
Roofers	—	—	149†	(67)	—	—	—	—	1873‡	(2)
Structural metal workers	129†	(122)	—	—	—	—	—	—	—	—
Construction laborers	113†	(894)	128†	(685)	—	—	153	(2)	250	(3)

— Data not reported.
  † p < 0.01
  ‡ p < 0.05
Note: n = 61,682
Source: Proportionate mortality ratios based on 1984–1986 NIOSH occupational surveillance data, abstracted from Robinson et al.[77]

Selikoff and Seidman examined 4,951 deaths occurring from 1967–1986 among 17,800 male asbestos insulation workers in the U.S. and Canada and documented a statistically significant increase in lung cancer mortality (SMR = 375).[82] Finkelstein also documented increased risk of lung cancer among insulators.[22]

Sheet metal workers, who may be exposed to asbestos when working near insulators, are at increased risk of lung cancer.[65,101] Structural metal workers also experience an increased risk of lung cancer.[74,77,78]

Ship construction has been associated with an increased risk of lung cancer.[5] Ship construction may involve exposure to asbestos, silica, paint, solvents, wood dust, welding fumes, and volatile petroleum products.

Construction welders may be exposed to filler metals containing cadmium, fluxes containing fluorine compounds, and metal fumes including nickel and chromium. Although a recent NIOSH study did not detect increased risk of lung cancer mortality among mild steel welders in an industrial setting,[87] several other studies have found increased risk of lung cancer among welders in a variety of work settings.[46,51,70,78,83]

Increased risk of lung cancer has been observed among stone masons, bricklayers, and tile setters.[8,65,75] Buiatti et al. found that patients with lung cancer were 6.5 times more likely than controls matched on age and smoking to have worked as bricklayers.[8] Rafnsson and Johannesdottir found a threefold excess risk of lung cancer among masons exposed to hexavalent chromium in cement finishing operations compared with the general population.[75] Masons, bricklayers, and cement finishers may be exposed to cobalt, epoxy resins, pitch, lime, and excessive cold.

Masons also may be exposed to lung carcinogens such as asbestos, silica, nickel, and hexavalent chromium.[75,92]

Other construction trades in which increased risk of lung cancer has been observed include electricians,[51,55,78] carpenters and woodworkers,[74] plumbers and pipefitters,[38,49,51,65,70] and roofers and mastic asphalt workers.[28,51] Roofers are exposed to volatile materials vaporizing from heated asphalt, including polycyclic aromatic hydrocarbons from coal tar pitch and bitumen fumes.[17,51]

Cancer of the Larynx and Oropharyngeal Cancer

Increased risk of cancer of the larynx has been observed among construction workers.[7,49,77] The literature suggests increased risk specifically in painters,[7,14] woodworkers,[7] and insulators.[82]

Few studies have looked at oropharyngeal cancer risk among construction workers. Selikoff and Seidman documented a statistically significant increase in mortality from oropharyngeal cancer (SMR = 173) among 17,800 asbestos insulators.[82]

Merletti et al. observed a statistically significant increased risk of oral or oropharyngeal cancer among construction workers, plumbers, and machinery operators, after controlling for potential confounding by age, education, birthplace, smoking, and alcohol.[52]

Nasal Cancer

Woodworkers, cabinet makers, and furniture makers experience excess risk of nasal cancer.[36,48,56] Carpenters and joiners also appear to be at increased risk of developing nasal cancer.[48,95] Carpenters and cabinet makers may be exposed to wood dust, formaldehyde, solvents, toluene, wood preservative, shellac, stains, bleaches, resin and casein glues, oils, polishes, and insulation agents including asbestos.[92]

Given the rarity of nasal cancer, the evidence for a relationship between nasal cancer and occupational exposure to wood dust is compelling. In a review of the international literature published from 1965–1989 on epidemiology of cancer in woodworkers, Mohtashamipur et al. found that 23% of 5,785 sinonasal cancers occurred among woodworkers.[56] The observed latency for nasal adenocarcinoma ranged from 7–69 years.

Several studies have found an increased risk of nasal cancer among general construction workers.[15,27,48,69,77,79] Although some have suggested that the soft woods used in construction carpentry may not result in the same risk of nasal adenocarcinoma observed in furniture makers exposed to hard woods, Hernberg et al. found an association between epidermoid and anaplastic nasal and sinus paranasal cancer and occupational exposure to soft woods.[34] In a population-based case-control study, Vaughan found that persons with squamous cell nasopharyngeal cancer were more likely to have worked as carpenters, especially in the construction industry.[95] In addition to wood dusts, construction exposures that may explain the observed increased risk include mineral dust, tar, oils, and chromates.[15]

Comba et al. conducted a hospital-based case-control study.[15] Mantel-Haenszel analysis resulted in a statistically significant threefold excess risk for nasal cancer among those ever employed as construction workers; logistic regression analysis controlling for confounding exposures in the wood and leather industries resulted in an odds ratio of 2.3 (90% CI 0.9–5.8).

Hall and Rosenman studied cancer incidence in the construction industries among individuals diagnosed and registered with the New Jersey Cancer Registry in

1979–1980.[27] Industry-specific proportional cancer incidence ratios were significantly elevated for nasopharyngeal cancer among special trades construction workers.

Luce et al. conducted a case-control study examining the relationship between sinonasal cancer and occupation in France.[48] Results are available by histologic type comparing 207 cases with 409 controls. In men, an increased risk of adenocarcinoma was observed among carpenters and joiners (OR = 25.2, 95% CI 14.6–43.6). An excess risk for other histologic types was also observed for carpenters and joiners (OR = 5.8, 95% CI 1.8–18.6) and painters (OR = 4.0, 95% CI 1.2–13.1). An excess risk of squamous cell carcinoma of the nasal sinus was observed among construction workers (OR = 3.7, 95% CI 1.7–8.0), although risk was highest among those employed fewer than 15 years.

Hernberg et al. found that patients with nasal cancer were more likely to have worked in metal welding, frame cutting, and soldering.[34] Exposures associated with nasal cancer included paints and lacquers, chromium and nickel welding fumes, and metal dusts.

MESOTHELIOMA

Reports of mesothelioma among construction workers come from several countries.[3,11,59] Mesothelioma has been observed among construction workers who worked as insulators,[60,82] shipyard construction workers,[14,59,60,88] carpenters,[54] sheet metal workers,[101] construction/maintenance workers,[60] and electricians.[14]

Muscat and Wynder conducted a hospital-based case-control study of 124 histologically confirmed cases of malignant mesothelioma.[60] The individuals were more likely to have worked in construction/maintenance (OR = 8.3; 95% CI 4.6–14.8) or to have self-reported asbestos or insulation exposure (OR = 50.9; 95% CI 21.7–119.8). No relationship between cigarette smoking and mesothelioma was detected.

Pulmonary and Pleural Fibrosis

ASBESTOSIS

Asbestos has been recognized as a respiratory health risk for a number of construction trades.[2,77,85] Occupational exposure to asbestos occurs particularly among plumbers and pipefitters, electricians, sheetmetal workers, and insulators.

Although asbestos is no longer used in new residential or heavy construction, workers in the specialty trades (Standard Industrial Classification [SIC] 17) may continue to be exposed to previously installed asbestos material during maintenance, renovation, addition, or demolition activities. Asbestos-containing fireproofing was sprayed on structural steel and other components of many high-rise buildings in the U.S. before it was banned in 1973.[99,101] Asbestos insulation was sprayed on ductwork. Asbestos cement, associated with fibrotic disease, has been used in roof tiles, roofing panels, wall-board, and domestic and industrial waste tanks.[92] Use of spackle and taping compounds in drywall construction has been associated with asbestos exposure, with especially high exposure during sanding operations.[24,96] Old vinyl flooring also may contain asbestos.

Current asbestos exposure in heavy construction (SIC 16) is most likely to occur during road or bridge renovation and demolition. In the past, some roads were surfaced using material made from asbestos and asphalt, and exposure may continue to occur during the drilling and breaking of such surfaces.

Among building construction, general contractors, and special trades contractors (SIC 15 and 17), asbestos is the substance most frequently sampled by OSHA (*see* Table 4). Compliance sampling reveals that only a small percentage (5.9%) of the asbestos samples collected by OSHA exceed the PEL. The low percentage of samples found in excess of the PEL may be the result of precautions required whenever asbestos-containing materials are encountered in buildings, as well as current requirements to conduct environmental sampling.[19] The move to use alternative man-made and natural mineral fibers is one result of increased regulatory attention focused on asbestos exposure. Man-made mineral fiber exposure may also be associated with respiratory disease.[18]

Several studies have documented an increased prevalence of asbestosis among construction industry workers. Fitzgerald et al. found that residents of two New York counties with pleural changes and parenchymal fibrosis evident on radiography were more likely than the local male population to have been employed for at least 1 year as a construction worker.[25] Kilburn and Warshaw found that the prevalence of asbestosis was 27.4% in construction trades workers.[42]

Asbestosis is common among plumbers and pipefitters,[85] sheet metal workers,[53] and insulators[39] and has been reported among electricians.[35] Selikoff and Seidman documented increased asbestosis mortality among 17,800 Canadian and U.S. insulators.[82] In many studies, increase in prevalence of asbestosis is correlated with length of employment.[2,53,85,99] A prevalence of pleural abnormality as high as 70% has been observed among sheet metal workers with more than 30 years employment.[2,81]

Several studies have suggested that all construction workers may be at risk from asbestos-induced disease resulting from exposure associated with working adjacent to insulation workers.[42] Welch et al. documented a relationship between duration of employment as a sheetmetal worker and pleural and parenchymal disease.[99] Since sheet metal workers do not use asbestos directly, the authors believe their findings suggest that workers in many different construction trades may be at increased risk of asbestos-related disease from working in proximity to insulation workers. Fischbein et al. found that duration of employment as an ironworker was predictive of prevalence of abnormality on chest x-ray.[23] Hodgson et al. documented a 15% prevalence of irregular opacities of at least 1/0 profusion among non-shipyard construction electricians, suggesting widespread exposure to asbestos from concomitant exposure in the construction industry.[35] Electricians with more than 20 years of service had a 25% prevalence of irregular opacities.

SILICOSIS

Occupational exposure to silica occurs in the construction industry among workers employed in concrete removal and demolition work, bridge and road construction, tunnel construction, and concrete or granite cutting, drilling, sanding, and grinding. Sandblasters and rock drillers are at increased risk from exposure to crystalline silica. Those working nearby in other trades on the same construction site may also be at risk from silica-related disease.

More than one third of the respirable crystalline silica compliance measurements taken at construction sites exceed the prevailing exposure limit (*see* Table 4). It is not difficult to understand this observation. Crystalline silica, one of the most abundant minerals in the earth's crust, is present in many construction materials, including stone, the aggregate that becomes concrete, and sand in mortar.[76]

Any construction operation involving cutting or grinding concrete may generate respirable silica dust. A plumber may generate silica dust by cutting a slot in a concrete floor for a pipe to pass between floors of a building. At highway construction sites, concrete pavement is often cut, chipped, or broken, generating respirable silica. Rock drilling, excavation, or tunneling construction projects are likely to be accompanied by silica exposure.[9,63]

In the U.S., sand containing crystalline silica is still used in abrasive blasting operations for maintenance of structures, preparing surfaces for painting, or in forming decorative patterns during installation of building materials. The use of silica for abrasive blasting creates a high potential for silica exposure, both for the operator and for bystanders.[62] Despite the high potential for excessive silica exposure, few compliance samples are collected at construction sites.

OSHA compliance monitoring data suggest that silica exposures within the construction industry continue to exceed recommended limits, and surveillance data[77] based on the small number of silicosis cases recorded on death certificates in the U.S. suggest that some construction trades may be at increased risk for the disease (see Tables 4 and 6). Recently published epidemiologic studies, however, have not focused on documenting silica-related disease within the U.S. construction industry. A number of factors contribute to the difficulty of conducting epidemiologic studies of silicosis among U.S. construction workers, including lack of reporting of silicosis on death certificates, difficulties in quantifying transient exposures, and mobility of the construction workforce.

International studies provide evidence of silicosis risk among construction workers. In Hong Kong, Ng documented an increased SMR for silicosis and tuberculosis mortality among construction workers who died in 1979–1983.[70] Ng et al. documented over-exposure to silica dust, as well as increased prevalence of silicosis and silica tuberculosis among caisson workers in Hong Kong.[71] Pneumatic drilling during caisson construction results in high dust exposures. In China, Nakagawa et al. documented the high prevalence of silicosis among migrant workers employed in tunnel construction, 84% of whom had silicosis based on radiography.[61]

Airway Diseases

BRONCHITIS

Bronchitis has been reported among construction workers exposed to asbestos and man-made mineral fibers, painters using spray applications, and arc welders. In a cross-sectional study of the prevalence of respiratory illness among male construction painters, White and Baker found that use of spray application methods was significantly associated with prevalence of chronic bronchitis.[100]

Hedenstierna et al. found a fourfold excess prevalence of chronic bronchitis among asbestos-exposed construction workers with pleural plaques.[30] Engholm and Von Schmalensee found an association between prevalence of bronchitis and duration of exposure to man-made mineral fibers in construction operations after controlling for smoking, age, and asbestos exposure.[18]

Metal fume exposure may result in respiratory disease, such as asthma, and respiratory symptoms, including wheeze and breathlessness on exertion.[13] Kilburn and Warshaw reported a 20% bronchitis prevalence rate among arc welders who had worked at construction sites.[44]

CHRONIC OBSTRUCTIVE PULMONARY DISEASE

COPD has been reported among tunnel construction workers, construction painters, sheet metal workers, and construction arc welders. Welch et al. screened 12,454 sheet metal workers, finding obstructive disease in 17% and restrictive disease in 10%.[99]

Tunnel construction may be associated with respiratory disease risk. In a study of lung function of tunnel workers using shotcrete techniques under compressed air, Kessel et al. found a statistically significant increase in airways resistance and a significant decrement in some flow-volume parameters after one workshift.[40] They also found a significant decrease in mean expiratory flow (MEF_{50} and MEF_{25}) after 2 years of exposure. They concluded that small airways damage may occur in these operations.

Assessing potential respiratory effects of exposure to paint in the construction trades, Schwartz and Baker concluded that painters may be at risk of developing airflow obstruction.[80] Evidence of airflow obstruction was significantly related to duration of exposure, and smoking painters demonstrated evidence of obstructive changes earlier than nonsmoking painters. Painters exhibited a significant excess of symptoms (cough, wheezing, dyspnea) and, in various analyses on subgroups, a significant decrement of percent predicted FEV_1 and FEV_1/FVC.

White and Baker examined the prevalence of respiratory illness among male construction painters using a cross-sectional design.[100] Prevalence of COPD was related to duration of employment. An interactive effect was reported between smoking and duration of employment as a painter. An increasing decrement of FEV_1 equal to 11 mL was observed for each year worked, although most painters experiencing a decrement were smokers.

Kilburn and Warsaw documented COPD among 226 male construction arc welders who had not worked in shipyards and had no radiologic evidence of asbestosis or pleural abnormality.[43] After controlling for smoking, logistic regression analysis predicted that 40 years of exposure to arc welding gases and fumes reduced FVC to 95.2%, FEV_1 to 92.2%, midflow to 79.2%, and FEF_{75-85} to 81.7% of predicted.

Heederik et al. found a significantly increased prevalence of chronic nonspecific lung disease symptoms among construction workers, woodworkers, and painters.[33] In further work, Heederik et al. found a significantly increased incidence density ratio (IDR = 2.62) for chronic nonspecific lung disease among construction workers after adjusting for smoking and age.[32] Specific exposures associated with excess risk of chronic nonspecific lung disease included heavy metals, mineral dust, and adhesives.[31]

Bourbeau et al. documented a significant decrease in FEV_1 and FVC ($p < 0.05$) and increased prevalence of dyspnea among construction insulators with isolated pleural plaques independent of pulmonary fibrosis evident by radiography, after controlling for smoking, age, height, and parenchymal abnormality evident by radiographic techniques.[6] Kilburn and Warshaw documented reductions in FEV_1 and FEV_1/FVC in construction and shipyard workers with isolated diaphragmatic pleural plaques.[41]

OCCUPATIONAL ASTHMA

Chan-Yeung reviewed agents and trades at risk for occupational asthma, including construction.[10] Possible causal exposures include wood dust and welding flux.[10] Welders are at increased risk of occupational asthma as a result of exposure to ammonium chloride fume.[72] Kilburn and Warshaw found that 11% of male arc welders who had worked at construction sites reported a history of asthma.[44]

Inhalation Injury, Irritation, and Fevers

Painters may experience irritation of the respiratory system following exposure to acetone, amyl acetate, methyl ethyl ketone (2-butanone), and n-Butyl lactate used as components or solvents in paints, varnishes, or lacquers.[72] Cement workers also may be at risk of respiratory irritation from components of cement, including amyl acetate and methyl ethyl ketone (2-butanone).[72]

Welders are exposed to several respiratory irritants, including ammonium chloride and boron trifluoride in soldering flux. Metal fume fever has been reported with exposure to nickel, chromates, copper fumes, beryllium, cadmium, and other metal fumes that may be present during welding.[57,64] Symptoms include upper respiratory tract irritation, metallic taste, nausea, and fever.

Respiratory Infection

Construction workers involved in excavation in tropical or subtropical areas may be at risk for nocardiosis, especially if they have another risk factor for the disease, such as lymphoma, deficient cell-mediated immunity, or immunosuppressive therapy. Pulmonary infection follows inhalation of fragmented aerobic mycelia, and dissemination may occur to the brain, kidney, skin, and central nervous system. Possible serious complications of the disease require treatment.[21]

Road and bridge work and construction activities involving clearing of bird and bat roosts in river valleys in the eastern and central U.S. can result in histoplasmosis, a pneumonitis caused by respiratory infection occurring after inhalation of airborne fungal spores. The disease may be acute, inactive, or chronic, and can result in disability and death if untreated.[4,26,73,84]

Elevated tuberculosis risk is found among silicotics.[98] Legionnaires' disease has occasionally been reported in construction activities involving excavation or in the vicinity of cooling towers.[58]

CHARACTERIZATION OR CONTROL OF EXPOSURE

Most exposure limits have been developed to assure safety under conditions of relatively uniform exposure for a 35–40 year working lifetime. In most industries, respiratory hazards are controlled by limiting long-term exposure to agents known to produce respiratory disease. However, respiratory diseases arising from exposure to toxic substances may result from a single peak or short-term exposure. Construction workers may be exposed to extremely high concentrations for brief periods and then to very low concentrations, perhaps averaging over the long-term to levels normally considered safe. Both situations present unique problems for exposure characterization at construction sites.

Peak or short-term exposures may occur only when certain tradesmen are performing their functions. For example, exposures to asphalt fumes may occur only when the roofing or paving subcontractors are on site.[17] Other exposures may occur unexpectedly, such as when bridge maintenance workers experienced an acute histoplasmosis infection from a brief exposure to bat guano,[84] or when several bulldozer operators cleared a four-acre site that had previously served as a roost for blackbirds and starlings.[73] Predictable and scheduled activities such as painting, welding, roofing, paving, installing insulation, and carpentry could be monitored to control exposure to agents known to be associated with those trades.[16,80] However, the unexpected presence of toxic or biologic hazards at the work site presents difficult challenges for effective exposure documentation and risk assessment. For demolition workers, where short-term exposures can be extremely high, regulatory agencies have viewed transient exposures to a mixture of toxic substances as "insufficient for citation and legal action."[37] Short-term/high-intensity exposures are common in construction operations, and regulators may be misguided in dismissing them under the assumption that health effects result only from long-term exposure. Acute loss of pulmonary function has been documented over as brief an exposure period as 26 days.[37] One large construction project, the building of the bypass tunnel at Hawks Nest, West Virginia, left hundreds dead from acute silicosis.[12]

Special Problems in Epidemiologic Studies of Construction Workers

Many respiratory diseases become manifest only after a long latency following the initial exposure. The extent to which disease risk varies with intensity or duration of exposure is often unknown, with epidemiologic investigations relying on associating disease outcomes with estimates of cumulative exposure. In situations where workers change jobs, employers, and work sites frequently, as in construction, it is difficult to assess and track exposure histories. In addition, since construction presents a complex weave of exposures, attributing a health response to any one agent is often not feasible, particularly with health effects such as lung cancer and chronic bronchitis, which are not uniquely occupational. The transient and serial nature of exposures at construction sites, as well as the diversity of construction-related trades and activities that may coexist at a particular work site, contribute to the complexity of the exposure. Consequently, most occupational health studies of construction workers tend to focus on occupation and tenure rather than attempting quantitative exposure assessment.

The mobility of the construction workforce poses special problems for epidemiologic research. Trade unions provide a convenient way to identify and access potential subjects, but only 20% of known construction workers are unionized,[*,93] and other workers may work off-the-record for independent construction contractors. Thus, identification of a representative cohort in this industry is also problematic.

Construction workers are exposed to hazardous substances, chemicals, and mixtures that may produce or exacerbate respiratory disease processes. They also may be exposed to the hazards of other construction trades due to concomitant exposure in shared work sites. Risks from concurrent exposures may act independently or synergistically, resulting in an additive or multiplicative effect.Also, special problems in studying the relationship between lung cancer and occupational exposure include the rapidly fatal nature of most lung cancer. Rapid mortality frequently means that interviews to identify occupational exposures or potential confounders must be conducted with surrogate respondents. Use of proxy respondents increases the likelihood of exposure misclassification, especially among the construction workforce, where families are unlikely to be aware of transient exposures at serial work sites.Finally, the study of longitudinal changes in lung function requires special statistical methods to account for correlation between repeated measures on a single individual.[45,47,97]

CONCLUSION

Construction workers are exposed to a variety of potentially hazardous agents. Exposures may be intermittent, with short-term excessive peak exposures coupled with intervals of low or no exposure. Construction work sites are usually complex

---

* Editor's note: Estimates of the percentage of the industry that is unionized vary according to the source. If an estimate is based on Standard Industrial Classification codes, the percentage is lower than if Standard Occupational Classification codes are used. SIC coding includes all types of employees, such as management, clerical, sales, and design. SOC, which is defined by trade, excludes white collar workers. The source for this chapter uses SIC codes.

environments where exposures to mixtures of agents under a variety of outdoor, indoor, and confined space settings are common. Inhalation exposure to construction-generated dusts and particles, including wood dust, welding fumes, silica, and insulation materials, presents an increased risk for morbidity and mortality from lung diseases such as lung cancer, mesothelioma, pneumoconiosis, and chronic obstructive lung disease. Other substances used in construction, such as formaldehyde, resin adhesives, sealants, and solvents, present chemical toxicity hazards or may produce sensitization and occupational asthma. Diverse materials or contaminants may be encountered during demolition or renovation at construction sites, producing unpredictable and variable mixes of workplace exposures. Standard industrial hygiene techniques are often inadequate to provide comprehensive exposure characterization under these conditions. The difficulty in devising meaningful exposure sampling strategies for construction sites may explain the paucity of OSHA compliance data in the construction industries.

The nature of the construction workforce and the industry pose special challenges to investigators. Epidemiologic research should be pursued to quantify disease associations with construction workplace exposures. Similarly, research to improve exposure characterization and risk assessment is needed, particularly as it applies to short-term, intermittent, high-level exposures to complex mixtures.

Progress in prevention of respiratory disease in construction workers can be achieved through hazard recognition and exposure control, combined with effective environmental monitoring and disease surveillance. Many hazardous exposures found in the construction industry have been studied in other work settings. Effective engineering controls and work practices should be adapted from those settings for construction work sites.

Evidence from epidemiologic studies shows that construction workers have an increased risk of developing occupational respiratory disease. Notable is the increased risk of lung cancer observed in most construction trades. Some of this disease is associated with asbestos exposure. Other potential causal exposures include diesel exhaust fumes and silica dust prevalent on road, bridge, and mine construction sites; exposure to polycyclic aromatic hydrocarbons from asphalt fumes; exposure to metal fumes during welding operations; and exposure to many other agents that may act independently or synergistically.

Disease risk among construction workers can be reduced through hazard surveillance coupled with effective exposure controls. Specific exposures and work conditions that lead to disease need to be identified. Communication of known risks to employers, employees, and state and local officials can lead to effective preventive interventions. Engineering control technologies available for standard construction operations such as drilling, cutting, abrasive blasting, and welding should be used. Employee training should promote work practices that minimize exposure. Finally, an exposure monitoring program should be established to monitor compliance and assure maintenance of a safe and healthful work environment at construction sites.

ACKNOWLEDGMENT

The authors would like to thank Dr. Jay H. Kim and Mr. Steve Game for providing mortality statistics and prevalence estimates from the HIS data, and Mr. Kenneth Linch, Ms. Janet Roman, and Mr. Joseph Costello for their technical contributions, providing insights into the construction industry, and accessing computer-stored compliance data and literature on construction-related disease.

REFERENCES

1 American Conference of Governmental Industrial Hygienists: 1994-1995 Threshold Limit Values for Chemical Substances and Physical Agents and Biological Exposure Indices. ACGIH, Cincinnati, 1994.

2. Baker EL, Dagg T, Greene RE: Respiratory illness in the construction trades. I.The significance of asbestos-associated pleural disease among sheet metal workers. J Occup Med 27:483–489, 1985.

3. Begin R, Gauthier JJ, Desmeules M, Ostiguy G: Work-related mesothelioma in Quebec, 1967–1990. Am J Ind Med 22:531–542, 1992.

4. Bertolini R: Histoplasmosis: A Summary of the Occupational Health Concern. Canadian Centre for Occupational Health and Safety, Hamilton, Ontario, 1988, report P88-8E.

5. Blot WJ, Davies JE, Brown LM, et al: Occupation and the high risk of lung cancer in northeast Florida. Cancer 50:364–371, 1982.

6. Bourbeau J, Ernst P, Chrome J, et al: The relationship between respiratory impairment and asbestos-related pleural abnormality in an active work force. Am Rev Respir Dis 142:837–842, 1990.

7. Brown LM, Mason TJ, Pickle LW, et al: Occupational risk factors for laryngeal cancer on the Texas Gulf Coast. Cancer Res 48:1960–1964, 1988.

8. Buiatti E, Kriebel D, Geddes M, et al: A case control study of lung cancer in Florence, Italy. I. Occupational risk factors. J Epidemiol Community Health 39:244–250, 1985.

9. Burns C, Ottoboni F, Mitchell HW: Health hazards and heavy construction. Ind Hyg J July-August:273–281, 1962.

10. Chan-Yeung M: Occupational asthma. Chest 98:148S–161S, 1990.

11. Chellini E, Fornaciai G, Merler E, et al: Pleural malignant mesothelioma in Tuscany, Italy (1970–1988): II. Identification of occupational exposure to asbestos. Am J Ind Med 21:577–585, 1992.

12. Cherniack M: The Hawk's Nest Incident—America's Worst Industrial Disaster. New Haven, CT, Yale University Press, 1986.

13. Chinn DJ, Stevenson IC, Cotes JE: Longitudinal respiratory survey of shipyard workers: Effects of trade and atopic status. Br J Ind Med 47:83–90, 1990.

14. Coggon D, Pannett B, Osmond C, Acheson ED: A survey of cancer and occupation in young and middle aged men. I.Cancers of the respiratory tract. Br J Ind Med 43:332–338, 1986.

15. Comba P, Battista G, Belli S, et al: A case-control study of cancer of the nose and paranasal sinuses and occupational exposures. Am J Ind Med 22:511–520, 1992.

16. Darby FW, Willis AF, Winchester RV: Occupational health hazards from road construction and sealing work. Ann Occup Hyg 30:445–454, 1986.

17. Emmett EA: Cutaneous and ocular hazards of roofers. Occup Med State Art Rev 1:307–322, 1986.

18. Engholm G, von Schmalensee G: Bronchitis and exposure to man-made mineral fibres in non-smoking construction workers. Eur J Respir Dis 63(suppl 118):73–78, 1982.

19. Environmental Protection Agency: Guidance for controlling asbestos-containing materials in buildings. Washington, DC, Environmental Protection Agency, 1985, EPA publication 560/5-85-024.

20. Feldman JP, Gerber LM: Sentinel health events (occupational): Analysis of death certificates among residents of Nassau County, NY between 1980-82 for occupationally related causes of death. Am J Public Health 80:158–161, 1990.

21. Filice GA: Nocardiosis. In Sarosi GA, Davies SG (eds): Fungal Diseases of the Lung. Orlando, Grune & Stratton, 1986, pp 231–250.

22. Finkelstein MM: Analysis of mortality patterns and workers' compensation awards among asbestos insulation workers in Ontario. Am J Ind Med 16:523–528, 1989.

23. Fischbein A, Luo JCJ, Rosenfeld S, et al: Respiratory findings among ironworkers: Results from a clinical survey in the New York metropolitan area and identification of health hazards from asbestos in place at work. Br J Ind Med 48:404–411, 1991.

24. Fischbein A, Rohl AN, Langer AM, Selikoff IJ: Drywall construction and asbestos exposure. Am Ind Hyg Assoc J 40:402–407, 1979.

25. Fitzgerald EF, Stark AD, Vianna N, Hwang SA: Exposure to asbestiform minerals and radiographic chest abnormalities in a talc mining region of upstate New York. Arch Environ Health 46:151–154, 1991.

26. George RB, Penn RL: Histoplasmosis. In Sarosi GA, Davies SF (eds): Fungal Diseases of the Lung. Orlando, Grune & Stratton, 1986, pp 69–85.

27. Hall NEL, Rosenman KD: Cancer by industry: Analysis of a population-based cancer registry with an emphasis on blue-collar workers. Am J Ind Med 19:145–159, 1991.

28. Hansen ES: Mortality of mastic asphalt workers. Scand J Work Environ Health 17:20–24, 1991.

29. Harrington JM, Blot WJ, Hoover RN, et al: Lung cancer in coastal Georgia: A death certificate analysis of occupation [brief communication]. J Natl Cancer Inst 60:295–298, 1978.

30. Hedenstierna G, Alexandersson R, Kolmodin-Hedman B, et al: Pleural plaques and lung function in construction workers exposed to asbestos. Eur J Respir Dis 62:111–122, 1981.

31. Heederik D, Kromhout H, Burema J, et al: Occupational exposure and 25-year incidence rate of non-specific lung disease: The Zutphen Study. Int J Epidemiol 19:945–952, 1990.

32. Heederik D, Kromhout H, Kromhout D, et al: Relations between occupation, smoking, lung function, and incidence and mortality of chronic non-specific lung disease: The Zutphen Study. Br J Ind Med 49:299–308, 1992.

33. Heederik D, Pouwels H, Kromhout H, Kromhout D: Chronic non-specific lung disease and occupational exposures estimated by means of a job exposure matrix: The Zutphen Study. Int J Epidemiol 18:382–389, 1989.

34. Hernberg S, Collan Y, Degerth R, et al: Nasal cancer and occupational exposure: Preliminary report of a joint Nordic case-referent study. Scand J Work Environ Health 9:208–213, 1983.

35. Hodgson MJ, Parkinson DK, Sabo S, et al: Asbestosis among electricians. J Occup Med 30:638–640, 1988.

36. Imbus HR, Dyson WL: A review of nasal cancer in furniture manufacturing and woodworking in North Carolina, the United States, and other countries. J Occup Med 29:734–740, 1987.

37. Kam JK: Demolition worker hazard: The effect of short-term, low-level combined exposures. J Environ Health 52:162–163, 1989.

38. Kaminski R, Geissert KS, Dacey E: Mortality analysis of plumbers and pipefitters. Cincinnati, NIOSH, 1979

39. Kennedy SM, Vedal S, Muller N, et al: Lung function and chest radiograph abnormalities among construction insulators. Am J Ind Med 20:673–684, 1991.

40. Kessel R, Redl M, Mauermayer R, Praml GJ: Changes in lung function after working with the shotcrete lining method under compressed air conditions. Br J Ind Med 46:128–132, 1989.

41. Kilburn KH, Warshaw RH: Abnormal pulmonary function associated with diaphragmatic pleural plaques due to exposure to asbestos. Br J Ind Med 47:611–614, 1990.

42. Kilburn KH, Warshaw RH: Asbestos disease in construction, refinery, and shipyard workers. Ann N Y Acad Sci 643:301–312, 1991.

43. Kilburn KH, Warshaw RH: Pulmonary functional impairment from years of arc welding. Am J Ind Med 87:62–69, 1989.

44. Kilburn KH, Warshaw RH: Pulmonary functional impairment from years of arc welding. In Proceedings of the VIIth International Pneumoconiosis Conference, Part II. Pittsburgh, Pennsylvania, August 23–26, 1988, NIOSH publication 90-108, Part II, 1990, pp 1264–1268.

45. Laird NM, Ware JH: Random-effects models for longitudinal data. Biometrics 38:963–974, 1982.

46. Lerchen ML, Wiggins CL, Samet JM: Lung cancer and occupation in New Mexico. J Natl Cancer Inst 79:639–645, 1987.

47. Liang KY, Zeger SL: Longitudinal data analysis using generalized linear models. Biometrika 73:13–22, 1986.

48. Luce D, Leclerc A, Morcet JF, et al: Occupational risk factors for sinonasal cancer: A case-control study in France. Am J Ind Med 21: 163–175, 1992.

49. Lynge E, Thygesen L: Occupational cancer in Denmark. Cancer incidence in the 1970 Census population. Scand J Work Environ Health 16(suppl 2):1–35, 1990.

50. Matanoski G: Mortality of workers in the painting trades. Proceedings of the Fourth NCI/EPA/NIOSH Collaborative Workshop: Progress on Joint Environmental and Occupational Cancer Studies, April 22–23, 1986, Rockville, MD, NIH publication 88-2960, 1988, pp 137–143.

51. Menck HR, Henderson BE: Occupational differences in rates of lung cancer. J Occup Med 18:797–801, 1976.

52. Merletti F, Boffetta P, Ferro G, et al: Occupation and cancer of the oral cavity or oropharynx in Turin, Italy. Scand J Work Environ Health 17:248–54, 1991.

53. Michaels D, Zoloth S, Lacher M, et al: Asbestos disease in sheet metal workers: II.Radiologic signs of asbestosis among active workers. Am J Ind Med 12:595–603, 1987.

54. Milham S: Mortality Experience of the AFL-CIO United Brotherhood of Carpenters and Joiners of America, 1969-1970 and 1972–1973. Washington, DC, NIOSH, 1978, NIOSH publication 78-152.

55. Milne KL, Sandler DP, Everson RB, Brown SM: Lung cancer and occupation in Alameda County: A death certificate case-control study. Am J Ind Med 4:565–575, 1983.

56. Mohtashamipur E, Norpoth K, Luhmann F: Cancer epidemiology of woodworking. J Cancer Res Clin Oncol 115:503–515, 1989.

57. Moreton J: Fume hazards in welding, brazing and soldering. Metal Construction and British Welding Journal 9:33–34, 1977.

58. Morton S, Bartlett CLR, Bibby LF, et al: Outbreak of legionnaires' disease from a cooling water system in a power station. Br J Ind Med 43:630–635, 1986.
59. Mowe G, Andersen A, Osvoll P: Trends in mesothelioma incidence in Norway. Ann N Y Acad Sci 643:449–453, 1991.
60. Muscat JE, Wynder EL: Cigarette smoking, asbestos exposure, and malignant mesothelioma. Cancer Res 51:2263–2267, 1991.
61. Nakagawa H, Yamada Y, Okumura Y, et al: Studies of Silicosis among Migrant Workers (Report I). The Frequent Occurrence and Relevant Factors of Silicosis. Cincinnati, NIOSH, 1990, pp 1387–1394, NIOSH publication 90-108 Part II.
62. National Institute for Occupational Safety and Health: ALERT—Request for Assistance in Preventing Silicosis and Deaths From Sandblasting. Cincinnati, NIOSH, 1992, NIOSH publication 92-102.
63. National Institute for Occupational Safety and Health: ALERT—Request for Assistance in Preventing Silicosis and Deaths in Rock Drillers. Cincinnati, NIOSH, 1992, NIOSH publication 92-107.
64. National Institute for Occupational Safety and Health: NIOSH Testimony on Occupational Exposure to Cadmium by R. W. Niemeier, May 7, 1990. Cincinnati, NIOSH, 1990.
65. National Institute for Occupational Safety and Health: Occupational Characteristics of White Cancer Victims in Massachusetts, 1971-1973. Cincinnati, NIOSH, 1984, NIOSH publication 84-109.
66. National Institute for Occupational Safety and Health: Operative Plasterers' and Cement Masons' International Association. Cincinnati, NIOSH, 1986, NIOSH publication HETA81-025-1668.
67. National Institute for Occupational Safety and Health: Work Related Lung Disease Surveillance Report 1994. Morgantown, WV, NIOSH, 1994, NIOSH publication 94-120.
68. Neuberger M, Kundi M: Occupational dust exposure and cancer mortality: Results of a prospective cohort study. In Simonato L, Fletcher AC, Saracci R, Thomas TL (eds): Occupational Exposure to Silica and Cancer Risk. IARC Sci Publ 97:65–73, 1990.
69. Ng TP: A case-referent study of cancer of the nasal cavity and sinuses in Hong Kong. Int J Epidemiol, 15:171–175, 1986.
70. Ng TP: Occupational mortality in Hong Kong, 1979-1983. Int J Epidemiol 17:105–110, 1988.
71. Ng TP, Yeung KH, O'Kelly FJ: Silica hazard of caisson construction in Hong Kong. J Soc Occ Med 37:62–65, 1987.
72. Occupational Safety and Health Administration: 29 CFR Par 1910. Air Contaminants: Proposed Rule. Fed Reg 57:26002–26601, 1992.
73. Powell KE, Hammerman KJ, Dahl BA, Tosh FE: Acute reinfection pulmonary histoplasmosis. Am Rev Respir Dis 107:374–378, 1973.
74. Pukkala E, Teppo L, Hakulinen T, Rimpela M: Occupation and smoking as risk determinants of lung cancer. Int J Epidemiol 12:290–296, 1983.
75. Rafnsson V, Johannesdottir SG: Mortality among masons in Iceland. Br J Ind Med 43:522–525, 1986.
76. Riala, R: Dust and quartz exposure of Finnish construction site cleaners. Ann Occup Hyg 32:215–220, 1988.
77. Robinson C, Stern F, Halperin W, et al: Assessment of mortality in the construction industry in the United States 1984–1986, 1993 (unpublished).
78. Ronco G, Ciccone G, Mirabelli D, et al: Occupation and lung cancer in two industrialized areas of Northern Italy. Int J Cancer 41:354–358, 1988.
79. Roush GC, Meigs JW, Kelly J, et al: Sinonasal cancer and occupation: A case-control study. Am J Epidemiol 111:183–193, 1980.
80. Schwartz DA, Baker EL: Respiratory illness in the construction industry-airflow obstruction among painters. Chest 93:134–137, 1988.
81. Selikoff IJ, Lilis R: Radiologic abnormalities among sheet-metal workers in the construction industry in the United States and Canada: Relationship to asbestos exposure. Arch Environ Health 46:30–36, 1991.
82. Selikoff IJ, Seidman H: Asbestos-associated deaths among insulation workers in the United States and Canada, 1967-1987. Ann N Y Acad Sci 643:1–14, 1991.
83. Simonato L, Fletcher AC, Andersen A, et al: A historical prospective study of European stainless steel, mild steel, and shipyard welders. Br J Ind Med 48:145–154, 1991.
84. Sorley DL, Levin ML, Warren JW, et al: Bat-associated histoplasmosis in Maryland bridge workers. Am J Med 67:623–626, 1979.
85. Sprince NL, Oliver LC, McLoud TC: Asbestos-related disease in plumbers and pipefitters employed in building construction. J Occup Med 27:771–775, 1985.
86. Stayner L, Smith R, Thun M, et al: A dose-response analysis and quantitative assessment of lung cancer risk and occupational cadmium exposure. Ann Epidemiol 2:177–194, 1992.

87. Steenland K, Beaumont J, Elliot L: Lung cancer in mild steel welders. Am J Epidemiol 133:220–229, 1991.

88. Tagnon I, Blot WJ, Stroube RB, et al: Mesothelioma associated with the shipbuilding industry in coastal Virginia. Cancer Res 40:3875–3879, 1980.

89. U.S. Bureau of the Census, Statistical Abstract of the United States: 1992. 112th ed. Washington, DC, 1992.

90. U.S. Department of Health and Human Services, National Center for Health Statistics: Public Use Data Tape Documentation: Part 1-Tape Formats, National Health Interview Survey, PB90-155482, 1988.

91. U.S. Department of Health and Human Services, National Center for Health Statistics: Public Use Data Documentation: Multiple Cause of Death for ICD-9 1987 Data, Hyattsville, MD, Govt. Printing Office, 1989.

92. U.S. Department of Health, Education, and Welfare: Occupational Diseases: A Guide to their Recognition. Cincinnati, NIOSH, 1977, NIOSH publication 77-181.

93. U.S. Department of Labor: Employment and Earnings 40(1). Washington, DC, Bureau of Labor Statistics, 1993.

94. U.S. Department of Labor: Occupational Injuries and Illnesses in the United States by Industry, 1991. Washington,DC, Bureau of Labor Statistics, 1993, bulletin 2424.

95. Vaughan TL: Occupation and squamous cell cancers of the pharynx and sinonasal cavity. Am J Ind Med 16:493–510, 1989.

96. Verma DK, Middleton CG: Occupational exposure to asbestos in the drywall taping process. Am Ind Hyg Assoc J 41:264–269, 1980.

97. Ware JH: Analysis of longitudinal data: Choosing and interpreting regression models. Eur Respir J 6:325–327, 1993.

98. Weeks JL, Levy BS, Wagner GR (eds): Preventing Occupational Disease and Injury. Washington, DC, American Public Health Association, 1991.

99. Welch LS, Michaels D, Zoloth S: Asbestos-related disease among sheet-metal workers. Preliminary results of the National Sheet Metal Worker Asbestos Disease Screening Program. Ann N Y Acad Sci 643:287–295, 1991.

100. White MC, Baker EL: Measurements of respiratory illness among construction painters. Br J Ind Med 45:523–531, 1988.

101. Zoloth S, Michaels D: Asbestos disease in sheet metal workers: The results of a proportional mortality analysis. Am J Ind Med 7:315–321, 1985.

REINHOLD RÜHL, DrRerNat
NORBERT KLUGER, DiplGeogr

HAZARDOUS SUBSTANCES IN CONSTRUCTION WORK

From the Hazardous Substances
Information System for the
Construction Sector (GISBAU)

Reprint requests to:
Dr. R. Rühl
Bau-Berufsgenossenschaft
Frankfurt
Postfach 600112
60331 Frankfurt am Main
Germany

In the modern construction industry, chemicals such as paints, adhesives, flooring sealings, and wood preservatives, are used increasingly often. When working in chemically polluted areas, construction workers are at risk for the adverse health effects associated with chemicals. However, although chemicals can lead to health hazards, the hazards can be controlled.

The Injuries Insurance Institutions of the construction industry in Germany has established a program to determine protective measures that are needed when handling hazardous materials and to inform workers about them.

Construction workers often underestimate the dangers of hazardous materials in the workplace, because many of the same materials are used at home. This chapter discusses problematic ingredients of chemicals used in the construction industry and hazardous materials used in different branches of construction. Asbestos, crystalline silica, and lead compounds used in construction are discussed in chapters 6 and 8.

PROBLEMATIC INGREDIENTS OF CHEMICALS USED IN CONSTRUCTION

Knowledge of the hazards resulting from chemicals used in construction is based on knowledge of the hazards caused by their ingredients. The classifications of the following materials are normally based on the regulations of the European Union and/or the German list for maximum permitted exposures at the workplace (Maximale Arbeitsplatz-Konzentration, or MAK); they are

TABLE 1.   Areas of Use of Transdermal and Sensitizing Materials in Construction

Substance	Transdermal (T) or Sensitizing (S)	Areas of Use
Benzene	T	Gasoline
Carbon tetrachloride	S	Solvent
Diphenylmethane-4,4'diisocyanate	S	Polyurethane
2-Ethoxyethanol	T	Solvent
Ethylbenzene	T	Solvent
Formaldehyde	S	Cleaning, disinfection
Hexamethylene diisocyanate	S	Polyurethane
Hydrazine	T,S	Water treatment
Isophorone diisocyanate	S	Polyurethane
Methanol	T	Solvent
2-Methoxyethanol	T	Solvent
Methyl methacrylate	S	Coating
Nickel	S	Welding electrode
Oil of turpentine	S	Solvent
Phenol	T	Solvent
Tin compounds	T	Wood protection
Toluene diisocyanate	S	Polyurethane
Wood dust	S	Joinery
Xylene	T	Solvent

mostly similar to the classifications in the U.S.[1,8,28] For some characteristics, such as neurotoxicity, official classifications do not yet exist. In these cases, literature is cited in which the values are generally accepted.

Materials with Transdermal and Skin-Sensitizing Effects

Materials can be absorbed through the skin and damage health. Table 1 shows the most important transdermal and sensitizing materials used in construction. Although some gloves can protect the skin from direct contact with many hazardous materials, at least for a certain period, transdermal materials can be absorbed even if gloves are worn. Adherence to the limits for air that is inhaled does not provide any protection from the dangers resulting from absorption through the skin. Therefore, in Germany, the level provoking a reaction (the trigger level) is considered to be exceeded if the possibility of skin contact with a transdermal material exists. Exceeding a trigger level sets comprehensive steps into effect, i.e., an occupational medical examination and the restriction of occupation for women of childbearing age and for workers younger than 16.

Sensitizing materials can cause allergic symptoms of different severity and duration depending on the individual. Adherence to the limits of concentrations in the air does not give information about the dangers of allergic reactions. Skin diseases are a major result of the use of hazardous materials. If an allergy to a certain material exists, traces of that material are sufficient to provoke an allergic reaction. These slight amounts can be present in a product as an impurity of an ingredient without the manufacturer's knowledge. This is more often the case if a manufacturer obtains the raw materials from a third party.

TABLE 2. Carcinogens Relevant to Construction

	Uses or Where Encountered
C1: Established human carcinogens	
Beechwood dust	Joinery, circular saw on building sites
Benzene	Gasoline
Nickel compounds	Welding electrode
Oak wood dust	Joinery, circular saw on building sites
Tar, pitch	Road works
Zinc chromates	Old coatings
C2: Probable human carcinogens	
Benzo(a)pyrene	Road works, diesel engine emission, chimney sweeping
Cadmium compounds	Old coatings
Chromium(VI)-compounds	Wood protection
Diesel engine emissions	Diesel engines
Hydrazine	Water treatment
C3: Suspected human carcinogens	
Dichloromethane	Stripper, solvent
Diphenylmethane-4'4 diisocyanate	Polyurethane
Formaldehyde	Conservation of dispersion products
Lead chromate	Old coatings
Wood dust (besides beech wood and oak wood dust)	Joinery, circular saw on building sites

The most common skin disease in Germany, allergic cement eczema, is caused by the presence of soluble chromium (IV) compounds in cement and occurs after years of exposure to cement.

Carcinogenic Materials

The carcinogenic effects of materials are a permanent topic of controversy. The arguments are often put forward emotionally, as information on these carcinogenic effects becomes available. A material is officially classified as a carcinogen only after years of scientific debate.

Luckily, the suspicion of carcinogenic effects is not always proved to be true. Nonetheless, materials that are "only" suspected of being carcinogens must be treated with the utmost care. In a scheme similar to schemes adopted by the International Agency for Research on Cancer and the U.S. Environmental Protection Agency, the European Union divides carcinogenic materials into three groups:[4,5,30]

C1: Established human carcinogen

C2: Probable human carcinogen

C3: Suspected carcinogen

Examples of these types of carcinogens are listed in Table 2. Other carcinogenic materials also may be encountered as contaminants on work sites. Carcinogens should be used in construction only when their application is deemed essential. Whenever possible, less dangerous products should be substituted for suspected carcinogenic materials.

Table 2 also shows how the carcinogens are used in the construction industry. While the hazards of using C1 and C2 materials are widely known, sufficient attention is not paid to C3 materials. In Germany, the law requires that the health of workers using C3 materials be closely supervised to keep the effects of exposures to a minimum. The European Union requires suspected carcinogens to be classified as

R40: having "possible risks of irreversible effects." Dichloromethane, formaldehyde, and lead chromate are classified as R40. Their handling must be far more limited than the handling of materials that are not suspected carcinogens.

Embryotoxic Chemicals

Chemicals with embryotoxic characteristics have been increasingly under discussion since toluene, one of the most common solvents, has become regarded as probably embryotoxic (Table 3). In construction, the best-known embryotoxic materials, lead and its compounds, are mainly found in residential and steel structure renovation work (see chapter 8).

The European Union divides embryotoxic chemicals into two main classifications: "R_F" for influence on fertility and "R_E" for teratogenic effects. These classifications are each divided into three subclassifications. Groups having an influence on fertility are:

R_F1: Established effects on fertility
R_F2: Probable effects on fertility
R_F3: Suspected effects on fertility

Substances having teratogenic effects are classified as follows:

R_E1: Established risk of damage to the developing embryo or fetus
R_E2: Probable effects to the developing embryo or fetus
R_E3: Suspected effects to the developing embryo

The identification of embryotoxic materials is made more difficult by the use of several names for the same chemical: 2-ethoxyethanol is also called ethylene glycol; 2-ethoxyethyl acetate is also called ethylglycol acetate.

Embryotoxic materials should be eliminated from the workplace. If they cannot be eliminated, exposure should be reduced as much as possible. Pregnant women should not have anything to do with embryotoxic materials. The danger for the unborn child is extremely high particularly during the first weeks of pregnancy. During this period, the employer and, possibly, the pregnant woman often know nothing about the pregnancy. The well-publicized damage from thalidomide was caused by its administration between the 26th and 28th day of pregnancy. For this reason, the limitation of this type of work is applied to all women of childbearing age in Germany (under the German Law for Protection of Expectant and Nursing Mothers).

Mutagenic Materials

Mutagenic materials cause damage to the male and female germ cells and thus cause genetic diseases in the direct descendants or subsequent generations. The European Union classifies mutagenic materials in three groups:

TABLE 3. Construction Materials Classified Embryotoxic by the European Union

Material	Source
Lead compounds	Old coatings
2-Ethoxyethanol	Solvent
2-Ethoxyethylacetate	Solvent
2-Methoxyethanol	Solvent
2-Methoxypropylacetate	Solvent
Toluene	Solvent

TABLE 4.	Construction Materials Classified Mutagenic by the German Federal Health Authority

Material	Source
Benzo(a)pyrene (Group M2)	Tar, pitch, diesel engine emission, chimney sweeping
Benzene (Group M2)	Gasoline
Ethanol (Group M2)	Solvent
Potassium dichromate (Group M2)	Wood protection
Toluene (Group M3)	Solvent
Trichlorethylene (Group M2)	Solvent

M1: Established human mutagen
M2: Probable human mutagen
M3: Suspected mutagen
However, nothing is listed or is likely to be listed under M1 in the foreseeable future. One reason is that the causes of most genetic diseases are not yet known. It is difficult to prove a connection between exposure to a certain chemical and the presence of a genetic disease.

Based on a survey of the literature, the Federal Health Authority in Germany in 1987 allocated 182 substances, some of which are relevant to construction, to groups M2 and M3 (Table 4).[3,16]

Neurotoxic Substances

Neurotoxic substances can, at least in high concentrations, damage the nervous system. The effects of ethanol, probably the best-known neurotoxin, are clear to anybody who has imbibed too much alcohol. Because of the innumerable neurotoxic effects, which often act against one another, specific symptoms are the exception. For this reason, there are often great problems in relating a neurotoxic disease to a particular substance. Table 5 lists neurotoxic substances relevant to the construction industry and their uses.[20] N-hexane is an ingredient in the low-boiling test benzenes, now normally in concentrations below 5%. Besides the substances named in Table 5, solvent mixtures are generally believed to cause neurotoxic diseases.

PROBLEMS WITH SPECIFIC SUBSTANCES

Solvents

INHALATION OR SKIN CONTACT

Work on the Hazardous Materials Information System for the Construction Trades Association of the Construction Industry, GISBAU,* found considerable shortfalls in information about the use of filters for respiratory protection and glove materials.[6,17,18] The shortfalls mean that protection measures applied for some chemicals used in construction are ineffective.

RESPIRATORY PROTECTION AND SOLVENT MIXTURES

Products with a boiling point below 65°C are often used in the construction industry. Such materials can be controlled only with great difficulty in a limited way

---

*GISBAU stands for Gefahrstoff-Informationssystem der Berufsgenossenschaften der Bauwirtschaft (Hazardous Substances Information System for the Construction Sector).

TABLE 5.   Selected Neurotoxic Substances and Their Uses in Construction

Material	Source
Benzene	Gasoline
Ethanol	Solvent
n-Hexane	Solvent
Styrene	Solvent
Toluene	Solvent
Xylene	Solvent

with special breathing filters. If other organic substances are also present, no type of gas filter exists that can block the materials with a low boiling point. The only protection would be a respiratory appliance independent of the surrounding air. However, in the construction industry, pure substances are used only rarely; mixtures of several substances normally are used. The materials with a low boiling point, dichloromethane (boiling point 40°C), acetone (56°C), methylacetate (57°C), and methanol (65°C) are contained in many chemicals used in construction. Methanol, methylacetate, and acetone are used in primers and adhesives; dichloromethane and methanol are used in strippers. The low-boiler problem is an important argument for the use of less dangerous products with a lower solvent content.

GLOVE USE

Glove manufacturers often give insufficient information about their products, which are often the only form of protection from aggressive chemicals. The materials normally mentioned in the safety data sheet by the manufacturers often fail to provide protection for the duration of a work shift (Table 6). The usual practice of wearing the same gloves for several days is ill-advised in any case.

No glove offers protection from the chemical dichloromethane, contained in strippers, for longer than 2 hours. For many other solvent mixtures, there are no gloves that protect for a whole shift. This applies to mixtures that simultaneously contain acetone and toluene or methanol and xylene. Products containing such solvent mixtures can be used only if the people concerned are using technical protection measures. If possible, less dangerous materials should be used.[34]

TABLE 6.   Cross-Classification of Some Solvents and Protective Glove Material[34]

Solvent	Glove Material		
	NBR (Acrylnitrile-butadien rubber)	FKM (Fluorosilicone-polymers)	IIR (Isobutyl-iso-prene rubber)
Benzylalcohol	—	X	X
Cyclohexanol	X	X	X
Butylacetate	(X)	—	(X)
Ethyleneglycoldibutylether	X	—	—
Aliphatic hydrocarbons	X	X	—
Solvent naphtha	—	X	—
Xylole	—	X	—

Note: X designates suitable; (X), suitable with restrictions; —, not suitable.

Primers and Adhesives

Problems are caused especially by primers and adhesives containing solvents for flooring work.[13] The health risks caused by these products are mostly caused by the solvents. The most important ones in use are alcohols (methanol, ethyl alcohol, isopropyl alcohol), aromatic hydrocarbons (xylene, toluene), and special benzenes (low content of aromatic hydrocarbons and n-hexane).

The most problematic substances are solvent mixtures. Although the hazards caused by individual solvents are studied often, the health effects of solvent mixtures cannot be evaluated at present. The hazards caused by individual solvents can accumulate and even multiply themselves.

Based on measurements carried out at work sites, it appears that the limits for primers and flooring adhesives containing solvents are nearly always exceeded. Protection measures must be introduced to reduce the concentrations of hazardous substances. Only in a few cases is a sufficient reduction of pollutant concentrations possible by opening doors and windows. Normally, explosion-protected ventilators with flexible pipes should be used.

If the solvent concentration in the inhaled air cannot be reduced sufficiently, workers must wear respiratory protection. Solvents with low boiling points lead to the problems mentioned below. Therefore, if the limits are exceeded, air-supplied respiratory appliances must be worn.

Products with high solvent content are needed in construction only rarely. For this reason, the Technical Regulation for Hazardous Materials 610 has been developed in Germany.[24] It defines solvents as volatile organic substances and their mixtures, with a boiling point below 200°C, which are liquid in normal conditions (20°C and 1013 hecto Pascal) and dissolve or dilute other materials.[32]

There is a sufficiently wide choice of water-based primers and flooring adhesives that are low in solvent content or solvent-free.

To facilitate the choice of suitable substitutes for flooring or parquet workers and to provide information on the health hazards of these products, in Germany, GISBAU has developed GISCODE in cooperation with adhesive manufacturers. GISCODE divides all the important primers and adhesives for flooring work into 21 product groups. The groups describe products with similar health hazards and carry code names (for instance, D1 for solvent-free dispersion adhesives or primers). GISBAU has drawn up information on the 21 GISCODE groups tailored to employers, works councils, technical supervisors, occupational physicians, and workers. The advantage provided by GISCODE is that the user need only have access to these 21 items of product information. An evaluation of the hazard potential of a product is made possible by GISCODE.

The German manufacturers of primers and adhesives for flooring work have introduced GISCODE in containers, safety data sheets, technical leaflets, and price lists and inform their customers correspondingly. Other European organizations, such as Stichting Arbouw, the Dutch organization for worker protection, may adopt the GISCODE system.[5] Within the framework of a standardization and equal choices in the European Union, this adoption would be desirable.

Wood Dust, Plastic Woods, and Sealing Agents

Flooring workers are at danger from the dust arising from sanding wooden flooring. The European Union classifies oak and beech dust as carcinogenic. It can cause malignant tumors in the nose (adenocarcinoma). Measurements of total dust taken at workplaces show that the limits are continually exceeded by 2 mg/m³ during sanding of wooden floors.[23]

Flooring workers encounter their highest solvent levels when working with plastic wood solvents and sealing wooden floors. To seal the joints in parquet or wooden flooring, normally the dust caused during sanding is mixed with a plastic wood solvent. Until the present, the usual plastic wood solvents have contained up to 90% solvent. The most widely used are ester (n-butyl acetate, isobutyl acetate, propylene glycol mono methyl ethene), ketones (acetone), and test benzenes. Measurements taken when working with these plastic wood solvents of high solvent content show that the limits for these solvents at the workplace are exceeded in three fourths of the cases. Therefore, improved ventilation, respiratory protection, or less hazardous products, such as water-dilutable plastic woods, should be used. The water-dilutable plastic woods contain glycol derivatives, alcohols, and n-methyl-2-pyrrolidine. They are not yet widely accepted because of the long airing period necessary. However, solvent-free plastic woods have recently become available. They are ready-mixed or are based on a powder that, when mixed with water, can be used as joint sealing. If substitutes cannot be used, protective measures must be taken.

Problems similar to those arising from handling solvent-containing primers and adhesives are experienced when sealing floors. GISBAU's Technical Regulation for Hazardous Materials No 617 addresses this issue[27] and defines solvents as volatile organic substances with a vapor pressure of more than 1 mm Hg at 20°C. Potential substitutes are water seals and other materials used for treating the surface of wooden floorings that contain less than 25% solvent or are solvent-free. Climatic reasons (such as too-high humidity) may not be used as an excuse for not using water seals in these cases. A room climate suitable for work can be created using ventilation and heating.

So many different definitions are used for solvents that it is impossible to find a standard definition that would be accepted throughout Europe. The European Union is expected to agree on a definition of volatile organic compounds in the future.

Wood Protectants

Chemicals are used to protect wood from fungi and insects. Thus, the main characteristics of chemical wood protectants are their biocidal effects.

Wood Protection Salts

A distinction should be made between water-soluble and oily wood protectants. The water-soluble wood protectants include, most importantly, different salt compounds such as anorganic boron compounds, fluorosilicates, hydrogen fluorides, chromium-copper-boron compounds, and organic bi-(n-cyclohexyldiacenium-dioxy)-copper(copper-HDO) compounds.

All fixing water-soluble wood protectants contained chromates (chromium(VI) compounds) until a few years ago.[7] The chromate content is problematic for workers and environmental protection. Chromium(VI) compounds (in the form of dusts or aerosols) are classified as carcinogenic. Therefore, German manufacturers have decided to provide wood protectants containing chromium only in paste or liquid form. This has greatly reduced their danger to health. Besides the risk of cancer, other acute dangers are connected with the use of wood protectors containing chromium. Because of the low pH value of the solvents, the products have a caustic effect and lead to wounds that heal slowly. Moreover, chromium(IV) compounds can cause skin allergies.

In 1992, the first chromate-free fixing wood protectant was awarded an environmental symbol in Germany. It contains copper-HDO as fixing agent and active agent and also contains boron compounds.

OILY WOOD PROTECTANTS

Among the oily wood protectants, the preparations containing solvents have a particularly high-test benzene content. Their efficacy against fungi and insects is based on organically active substances. Although pentachlorophenol and lindane were previously used as active agents, these substances have been replaced because of their known health effects. For the most part, synthetic pyrethroids (Permatrin, Deltametrin, Cypermatrin), azoles (Tebukonazol, Propikonazol), and dichlofluanide are now used.

Besides wood protectants containing solvents, pure coal tar oil distillates are among the oily preparations. They may be used only for woods outdoors and cannot be recommended for use indoors, not the least reason being their strong odor. Skin contact with preparations containing coal tar oil can lead to cancer. The coal tar oils have limited uses depending on their benzoapyrene content.

The hazards that can be caused by oily wood protectants are paramount. The operating substances in these preparations are normally in concentrations of 2–3%. But, depending on whether other ingredients such as binding agents and pigments are included, their solvent content can be 60–90%. Unfortunately, there is neither a limit nor an analysis method for most active agents in wood protectants containing solvents. Therefore, quantification of these problems is currently impossible.

To protect wood from damaging effects, one does not immediately need to resort to chemical "hammers." A hot-air procedure is suitable for killing pests: the complete roof truss is heated to 80°C to destroy any insects causing damage. Chemical preparations now on the market have a greatly reduced solvent content. In addition, water-soluble products that can be used for these purposes are expected to be introduced.

Insulation

Insulation ranges from thermal insulation to sound insulation to fire protection and damp sealing indoors. From the viewpoint of worker protection, a whole line of products can be inhaled at the workplace in the form of fiber particles (dusts) or as gases or vapors. Examples are mineral-wool insulation and ceramic-fiber products, which contain fibers able to enter the lungs: the bitumen vapors containing benzoapyrene that are released during the hot processing of bitumen, or the release of isocyanates in the use of polyurethane foams (see chapter 6).

MAN-MADE MINERAL FIBERS

Man-made mineral fibers in the construction industry are classified in groups of mineral-wool insulation and ceramic-fiber products, whereby the mineral-wool insulation is the far more common and more important group. Mineral-wool insulation is in the form of tiles or in rolls, either raw or lined with aluminum foil. Mineral-wool is used for insulation of heat in civil engineering, mechanical insulation, and ship insulation.

The mineral fibers are usually bonded in the products by means of an artificial resin of phenol-urea-formaldehyde basis (bakelite) and also contain small amounts of oils (mostly mineral oil) to bind the dust. After evaporation, the products are practically free of formaldehyde. A main danger of using mineral-wool insulation and ceramic fiber products is that some fibers that collect in the air at the workplace can be inhaled. Since 1980, man-made mineral fibers with a diameter smaller than 1 μm have been classified in Germany as a suspected human carcinogen.

Man-made mineral fibers with a diameter smaller than 3 μm have been limited to 500,000 fiber/m³ or to 1,000,000 fiber/m³ for building sites where light microscopic evaluation is done. Working areas at which high dust concentrations occur are excepted from this regulation—i.e., where there is spraying of insulation materials or demolition of thermally affected insulation materials. After evaluating a large number of measurements taken at building sites and simulation measurements (full-scale tests), it should be possible, by adhering to corresponding criteria, to stay below the limits in all work procedures involving mineral-wool insulation materials.[36]

In handling ceramic-fiber products, the measurements available show that exceeding the limit cannot be avoided when adding new blankets between fiber modules in facilities already in operation, or when dismantling thermally damaged additions. In these cases, corresponding measures are essential, such as installation of exhaust or the wearing of personal protection equipment.

BITUMEN PRODUCTS

Bitumen is used in insulation as a sealing and waterproofing component. There are bitumen products in the form of strips of sealing that are welded to a background, as emulsions or cold paints containing solvents, as adhesives to pour on or surface with, or as surrounding parts made of mineral-porous sealing components such as vermiculite or perlite.

Bitumen has always been suspected of being a potential carcinogen.[12] The origin of this classification was the content of polycyclic aromatic hydrocarbons (main component benzoapyrene) that occurred in products about 10 years ago because of impurities or dilution with tar. Bitumen products now contain only the slightest traces of polycyclic aromatic hydrocarbons; improved procedures mean that dilution with tar and similar compounds is no longer done.

The use of bitumen products or other products containing solvents can involve the same hazards. Therefore, corresponding safety measures are not specific to products but to the general standard for the use of products containing solvents. Safety measures are necessary every time hot bitumen is used; eyes, skin, and the respiratory tract can be irritated, and the eyes and skin can be injured.

Many field measurements have been done of polycylcic aromatic carbon emissions during the sealing of flat roofs with strips of bitumen, for cold processing and for hot processing up to 250°C. Evaluations of the measurements have resulted in the setting of limits that were below 50 ng/m³ and therefore in the detectable range. The air concentrations of benzoapyrene were 50 times below the limit of 2 μg/m³.

Products for Structural Engineering

SEPARATING AGENTS

Separating agents are special building aids that make a reliable separation of shuttering from partially or totally dried concrete. The bases of separating agents are mineral oils, synthetic oils, gasolines, glycols, alcohols, and aromatic and halogenated hydrocarbons. Active agents used include paraffins, earth and vegetable waxes, metallic soaps, natural and synthetic fatty acids, synthetic fatty acid esters, and saponifiable resins. All shuttering materials can contain other additives such as rust protection, antioxidants, antipore agents, preservatives, water displacement agents, emulsifiers, and wetting agents.

Separating agents can have various health effects. The low-boiling hydrocarbons can cause damage to the skin after only short contact because of the separation of natural fats. Some materials are capable of penetrating the skin barrier and are absorbed by the body, thus damaging different inner organs. Oil vapors and oil mists can cause irritation of the respiratory tract and health hazards when absorbed through the respiratory tract. Since separating agents are also flammable, explosive mixtures can occur when spraying, misting, or vaporizing with these substances. To avoid eye irritation, respiratory protection or protective goggles should be worn if a danger of splashing exists.

The procedure used for handling separating agents can cause health hazards. Because applying these agents manually with a rag, sponge, spatula, brush, or roller increases the danger of skin contact, these methods should be avoided. If they are necessary, the hands should be protected. Generally, separating agents are now applied with spray guns, meaning that they are sprayed so finely that respiratory protection against aerosols should be worn. A fully mechanical apparatus—in which all stages of work, including cleaning and application of the separating agent, are done by machine—should be used whenever possible.

CEMENT AND PRODUCTS CONTAINING CEMENT

One of the most common diseases among construction workers is builders' itch, a skin disease caused by the chromate content of cement.[2,9] However, only about 20 ppm of soluble chromate in the form of chromium(VI) compounds are contained in cement. Through the continual contact with cement, chromium(VI) ions penetrate the skin and enter the body and lead to a sensitization in the worker. The sensitization depends on the concentration of the chromate ions in the cement and the duration of handling of cement. The use of gloves does not prevent the problem. Only the reduction of the chromium content in the cement is an effective prevention. In cement works in Rostock, Germany, a substantial reduction of skin disease was observed after the introduction of Portland cements with low alkali and chromium content.

The chromium content of cement varies greatly but is irrelevant to cement's effectiveness. In German cements, the chromium content is between 20–100 ppm, about 20% of which is soluble. The chromate content of cements can be reduced by reducing the soluble chromium(VI) ion to the chromium(III) ion by adding iron(II) sulphate. (The reduction only takes place when cement and iron(II) sulphate are mixed with water.) Iron sulphate can be added to cement during grinding. Problems in storage only occur if the cement becomes damp; in such cases, resulting oxidation produces triple-value iron, which does not change the chromium(VI).

Swedish and Danish companies have shown that these problems can be technically solved. They have been providing storable cement with iron(II) sulphate for years. In Denmark, a law stipulates the addition of iron(II) sulphate to reduce the chromate content in cement.[31] Corresponding regulations apply in Finland, Norway, and Sweden.[14,15,21]

In Germany, the use of low-chromate cements and low-chromate cement products also has come under regulation. In a technical regulation for hazardous materials, which is valid in Germany, the use of cement and cement products with a chromate content of less than 2 ppm is recommended.[26]

HAZARDOUS EXPOSURE RISKS ASSOCIATED WITH SPECIFIC TASKS

Work in Contaminated Areas

Contaminated areas are polluted by hazardous materials. Work in such areas can occur during construction work on land, in polluted buildings, and during decontamination after accidents in chemical facilities. In construction, hazardous materials may be encountered by chance, which makes it difficult to protect workers' health. Contamination of the ground often is discovered unexpectedly during earth moving. In such cases, the protection of the worker depends on rapid decision making.

The first evaluation and estimation of the dangers can only be carried out by experts. To develop a strategy for worker protection, the experts need quick access to information on the potential spectrum of hazardous materials present in similar situations. Although a wish is often expressed for a list of materials and equipment needed to protect workers in contaminated areas, this wish essentially cannot be fulfilled.

Before conveying information on workers' protection for these areas, three questions must be asked. First, which hazardous materials are to be expected on site. Second, what detailed information is available on components or ingredients in the hazardous substances. Third, which concentrations of pollutants can be expected on site and in the air to be inhaled by the worker. Another approach is to assume the contaminated area is highly toxic and provide full protection such as an air supply and a full-body suit.

If comprehensive information is available on all points, a plan can be formulated for worker protection and the decisions on technical and personal protection measures made. When answering these questions, although it is not possible to use prefashioned or rubber-stamp solutions, experience and knowledge arising from work in similar cases can help if it is readily available. Often, however, the information may not be in a central repository. Protection authorities are rarely informed about work with hazardous materials in contaminated areas. To resolve this dilemma, in Germany, the *Guidelines for Work in Contaminated Areas* (ZH 1/183)[33] requires registration of such cases to help develop a registry of such data and information.

A list of typical problem substances in each particular branch of industry can be of help in the planning of protection measures for workers.[11] For example, when decontaminating former gasoline stations, one could count on the existence of mostly similar substances, even if it is in different concentrations.

Until now, special preventive occupational medicine and concomitant examinations for the workers in contaminated areas have been a rarity. Standard protocols for such examinations and medical supervision are needed (see chapter 13).

Based on past experience, *Guidelines for the Medical Care of Workers in Contaminated Areas* has been developed in Germany.[19] Using these guidelines, exposure data and medical results are being collected and summarized to make the knowledge gained available for future decontamination projects.

Concrete Renovation

Damage to concrete appears as cracks, sanding of the surface, and flaking. When damage is discovered on concrete parts, different concrete renovation systems come into use. Although there are problems with several products—i.e., plastic-coated cement products and dispersions containing solvents and water—health risks are most often found in work using products that contain epoxy resin. Because of their good mechanical and chemical characteristics, epoxy resin products are used in many ways in building and concrete renovations. They are composed of at least one resin and one hardener, and filling components are often added. The filling component consists of amines or aminadducts. The resin component is made of bisphenol A or other monovalent or multivalent alcohols and epichlorohydrin. According to the characteristics required in the end product, softeners and auxiliary agents such as glycidic ether, epoxidized oils, polyester, polyurethane, and phtalates are added. Filling agents such as aluminum oxide, ferrous oxide, glass fiber, mica, and talcum modify the mechanical and electrical characteristics. All components are stirred hard before use, until a homogeneous mass is produced. The addition of hardeners (amines, amides) to the unhardened epoxy resin causes a reaction that combines the components with one another and leads to the curing.

The main health hazards caused by epoxy resins are allergic skin diseases. The substance causing the allergy is identified by means of epicutaneous tests. Epoxy resins with a low molecular weight, including many of the glycidic ethers, are especially problematic. Resins with high molecular weight and hardeners also cause problems.

A Finnish study has shown that the allergy is usually localized on the hands and forearms, but a reaction may occur on the face alone or on both the face and hands or forearms.[10] As a whole, according to this study, skin diseases caused by epoxy resins are the third largest group of occupational illness. In Finland, after the introduction of a program requiring the training of workers in handling epoxy resins, skin diseases caused by them were reduced from 12% to 8% of all occupational diseases.

Since there are no measuring methods or limits for measuring the resins or most of the hardeners, both the implementation of measurements at the workplace and the evaluation of the health risk caused by these components are often difficult. In many cases, only an evaluation of the solvents is possible. This, however, does not show any deviation from the measurements at the workplace carried out for other products with corresponding solvent content. The solvents in epoxy resin products are most often ethylene glycol, ethanol, cyclohexanol, isobuytl alcohol, acetone, methyl ethyl ketone, methyl isobutyl ketone, benzyl alcohol, xylene, and toluene.

If, during concrete renovation, coating must be applied at low temperatures (< 5°C) or if a coating must quickly regain its resilience, methylmethacrylate systems are often applied. When using methylmethacrylate, some special problems are encountered because it has a low odor limit. This can cause difficulties with people living near the building site and, as a result, the authorities.

Numerous measurements also show that, in coating work with methylmethacrylate systems, the limit is exceeded by up to three times the amount permitted. Tests as carried out in Scandinavia with a flexible suction system to suck off whole surfaces have not been successful.[35] On the basis of these results, the use of airstream helmets is recommended when working with methylmethacrylate systems.

Flooring Work

Health hazards caused by materials occur during almost all stages of flooring and parquet work. Starting with the sanding of the stone flooring, fine quartz dust can pervade the air inhaled by the worker and cause silicosis after longer exposures (see chapter 6).

Tiling

Work-related health problems for tilers involving hazardous materials involve the hands and the respiratory tract. As noted above, the chromate content of cement leads to allergic eczemas. Because many tile adhesives and, more importantly, materials for filling in joints are cement-based, chromate eczemas are often observed in tilers. Although the number of chromate eczemas in bricklayers or concrete workers is about 0.5%, about 2% of all tilers suffer from chromate eczema. The continual skin contact with the suspended cement-based joint fillers is especially problematic. Since part of the chromate dissolves in the water and the tiler normally works without gloves and has direct skin contact with the suspended joint filler, the danger is high. A reduction of cases of chromate eczema or an improvement in existing eczemas would be possible with the use of low-chromate products. These tile adhesives, spatula materials, and joint fillers have a chromate content of less than 2 ppm.

Further skin diseases occur when handling tiling adhesives containing epoxy. Epoxy resins can cause allergic eczemas. An additional problem observed in tilers is an allergic reaction to rubber ingredients, caused by wearing rubber gloves that are needed when working with epoxy resins.

The respiratory tracts of tilers are most at danger through dust, such as that arising from cement mortar. Irritation of the respiratory tract is also caused when working with permanently viscous joint fillers. Some sealing agents based on silicone rubber release acetic acid during polymerization, which can lead to irritation of the respiratory tract in sensitive patients. With the use of sealing agents that contain polysulphides, there are often complaints about unpleasant odors, which seem to be caused by the slightest levels of released mercaptans (organic sulphur compounds).

Removal of Old Coatings

During renovation, old coatings may need to be removed from wood, steel, concrete, or other materials. Strippers containing chlorinated hydrocarbon are a major problem in the protection of workers and the environment because of their high chloride content. Although there are many alternatives to primers containing chlorinated hydrocarbon, about 80% of all stripping work in Germany is carried out with products containing dichloromethane. The dangers of dichloromethane have led to stricter regulations and some prohibitions in the past few years in Germany; some cities forbid the use of strippers with a dichloromethane base.

Dichloromethane is problematic for worker protection not only because it has such a low boiling point; it also evaporates quickly, so that high pollutant concentrations occur in the air at the workplace during processing, as has been demonstrated in trials.[13] When work is carried out with primers containing chlorinated hydrocarbon, the limits of the German list for maximum permitted exposures at the workplace are always exceeded.

Since the autumn of 1990, dichloromethane has been classified on the German listing of maximum permitted exposures at the workplace as a suspected carcinogen (B substance) and must be identified throughout the European Union with the phrase "irreversible damage possible" (R 40). Moreover, the systemic effects may include damage to the central nervous system. In high concentrations, dichloromethane has an effect similar to that of anesthesia and leads to fatigue, an inability to concentrate, and even loss of consciousness and death.

If the concentrations in the air cannot be reduced by technical protection measures, an air-supplied respiratory system must be used. No type of gas filter exists that offers sufficient protection. Such air-supplied respiratory apparatus may be used only by people who have previously undergone a medical examination.

Just as there are no suitable respiratory protection filters to protect against primers containing chlorinated hydrocarbon, neither are there gloves that protect against dichloromethane for longer than 2 hours. This is important in light of the fact that this substance easily enters the body through the skin.

A wide range of strippers on the market do not contain dichloromethane and have a correspondingly lower hazard potential. Mixtures of diglycolic ethers, dibase esters, test benzenes, and n-methylpryrrolidon are mostly used as solvents. In addition, it is often possible to use jet blasting apparatus. Different surfacing, the size of the surface to be cleaned, the type of product to be removed, and other factors do not permit generalizations on which process to use in which case. Mechanical removal, work with a hot air blower, and primers without chlorinated hydrocarbon are nearly always a reasonable alternative. A special Technical Regulation for Hazardous Materials addresses these issues.[13,25]

Painting and Varnishing

Both indoor and outdoor coating work nearly always consists of painting and varnishing and can be done in various ways, such as brushing, spraying, and rolling.[29] In addition to varnishes (i.e., alkyde resin varnishes) and paints, undercoatings come into use where a multilayer coating is necessary. The coating materials can be roughly divided into three groups: oil paints, dispersion oil paints, and dispersion paints.

Varnishes are often used in new extension building and in redecorating and repair work. Varnishes contain many different materials, such as binding agents (i.e., alkyde resin and polymerizate resin), pigments (mostly metal oxides such as titanium oxide or ferrous oxide), filling agents (i.e., lime, calcite, and kaoline), and solvents. The solvents in building varnishes are usually hydrocarbon mixtures (test benzenes) with differing aromatic hydrocarbon contents (xylene, ethylbenzene).

Building varnishes such as alkyde resin varnishes and wood varnishes may have a solvent content of up to 40%; in undercoats, up to 80%. High-solid varnishes contain the same quality ingredients as building varnishes with a high solvent content. Because the high-solid varnishes' content is less than 25%, the binding agent content is much higher. However, only a few high-solid varnishes are on the market for construction.

Dispersion gloss paints are coating materials based on a watery synthetic dispersion such as acrylic resin or styrenated acrylate, which provide coatings similar to varnishing. The pigment content in dispersion paints is low. They have a solvent content of below 10% and are water-soluble.

Dispersion gloss paints contain different glycolic ethers as solvents, such as ethyl diglycol, butyl diglycol, 2-butoxyethanol, propylene glycol or ethylene glycol. Some of these glycolic ethers have limits for use in Germany.

Dispersion paints are manufactured on an acrylate basis, which, in contrast to the dispersion gloss paints, has a high pigment and filling agent content. Dispersion gloss paints must not be confused with dispersion paints that are used for large surfaces such as ceilings and inside walls, for instance, for painting wood-chip wallpapers when a gloss effect is not desired or necessary. In contrast to the gloss paints, dispersion paints contain only slight amounts of volatile organic compounds. Their solvent content is 1–3%. Solvents can be glycolic ethers or, as in building paints with solvents, test benzenes.

Health hazards occur during the use of paints and varnishes containing solvents, mostly by inhaling solvent vapors or aerosols and the absorption through the skin (especially xylene and ethyl benzene are transdermal).

Hydrocarbon mixtures (test gasolines) are often used in building paints and varnishes containing solvents. In Germany, these mixtures are evaluated on the basis of the limits for aromatic hydrocarbon and n-hexane content in the air at the workplace.[22]

REFERENCES

1. American Conference of Governmental Industrial Hygienists: Guide to Occupational Exposure Values. ACHIH, 1992.
2. Avnstorp C: Risk factors for cement eczema. Contact Dermatitis 25:81–88, 1991.
3. Basler A, van der Hude W: Mutagenic substances. Bundesgesundheitsamt. Max-von-Pettenkofer-Institut, bga-Schriften vol. 3/87, MMV Medizin Verlag, München. 1987.
4. Bolt HM, Gelbke HP, Greim H, et al: Substances suspected of having a carcinogenic potential, problems and possibilties of solution. ASP 6:139–144, 1988.
5. Carnevale F, Montesano R, Partensky C, Tomatis L: Comparison of regulations on occupational carcinogens in several industrialized countries. Am J Ind Med 12:453–473, 1987.
6. van Duivenbooden JC: International Cooperation between ARBOUW and GISBAU, II. International Colloquium on Industrial Medicine in the Building Trades, Baden-Baden, Germany, October 1992.
7. Institut für Bautechnik (IfBt): IfBt-Inventory listing for products of wood protectants, Erich Schmidt Verlag GmbH & Co., Berlin, Germany, 1994.
8. International Labour Office (ILO): Occupational exposure limits for airborne toxic substances: Values of selected countries. 3rd ed. Occupational Safety and Health Series, Geneva, No. 37, 1991.
9. Jansen K, Rühl R: Low-chromate cements—Application and potential, II. International Colloquium on Industrial Medicine in the Building Trades, Baden-Baden, Germany, October 1992.
10. Jolaniki R, Kanverva L, Estlander T, et al: Occupational dermatoses from epoxy resin compounds. Contact Dermatitis 172–183, 1990.
11. Kinner U, Kötter L, Niklauß M: Inventory listing typical soil-contaminations of instustrial branches: A first assesment of the risk potential of contamination on closed-down factory sites. Umweltforschungsplan des Bundesministers für Umwelt, Naturschutz und Reaktorsicherheit, Forschungsbericht 107 03 001; Umweltbundesamt, Texte 31/86, 1986.
12. Knecht U, Woitowitz H-J: Risk of cancer from the use of tar bitumen in road works. Br J Ind Med 46:24–30, 1989.
13. Ludwig S, Rheker R: New developments in the field of low toxicity construction materials: Adhesives, bonding and stripping agents, II. International Colloquium on Industrial Medicine in the Building Trades, Baden-Baden, Germany, October 1992.
14. Order about content of chromate in construction- and bricklayer-cement, Helsinki, Finnish Goverment, 1986.
15. Regulations about watersoluble chromate in cement. Fastsatt av Direktoratet for arbeidstifsynet, Oslo, October 23, 1987.
16. Rüdiger H W: Mutagenic effects of substances: Facts and conclusion. ASP 6:277–282, 1990.
17. Rühl R: GISBAU-Hazardous Substances Information System for the Construction Sector. Work & Health Conference, Copenhagen, February 1993.
18. Rühl R: GISBAU-Hazardous Substances Information System for the Contruction Sector. International Section of the I.S.S.A. for the Prevention of Occupational Risks in the construction Industry, XIII. International Colloquium, Brüssel, September 1991.
19. Rumler R, König K, Georgs L: Guideline for the medical care of workers in contaminated areas. Tiefbau-Berufsgenossenschaft, Am Knie 6-81237 Munich, Germany, 1992.
20. Spencer P, Schaumburg H: Organic solvent neurotoxicity, facts and research needs. Scand J Work Environ Health 11(suppl 1): 53–60, 1985.
21. Staatl. Schwedische Chemikalieninspektion: Kemikalieinspektionens föreskrifter om kromicement. Schwedisches Reichsgesetzblatt, March 15, 1989.
22. Technical Regulation for Hazardous Materials 404: Evaluation of hydrocarbon vapors in the air at the place of work. BArbBl 9:40–41, 1992.
23. Technical Regulation for Hazardous Materials 553: Wood dust. BArbBl 9:45–53, 1992.
24. Technical Regulation for Hazardous Materials 610: Substitutes and substitute procedures for primers and flooring adhesives with high solvent content. BArbBl 10:123–130, 1994.
25. Technical Regulation for Hazardous Materials 612: Substitutes, substitute procedures and limits of use for dichloromethane used in strippers. BArbBl 4:54–62, 1993.
26. Technical Regulation for Hazardous Materials 613: Substitutes, substitute procedures and limits of use for chromate-content cement and chromate-content cement preparations. BArbBl 4:63–64, 1993.

27. Technical Regulation for Hazardous Materials 617: Substitutes and substitute procedures for surface treatment products for parquet and other wooden floorings. BArbBl 9:61–63, 1993.

28. Technical Regulation for Hazardous Materials 900: Maxium concentrations at the workplace and biological exposure indices of the Commission for Evalution of Hazardous Material of the German Research Association (DFG). BArbBl 12:40, 1992.

29. Teich E, Gerner HW, Rastetter M: Painters' exposure to solvents—Simulation tests; II. International Colloquium on Industrial Medicine in the Building Trades, International Colloquium on Industrial Medicine in the Building Trades, Baden-Baden, Germany, October 1992.

30. Vainio H, Wilbourn J: Identification of carcinogens within the IARC monograph program. Scand J Work Environ Health 18(suppl 1): 64–73, 1992.

31. Watersoluble chromate in cement, Veröffentlichung der dänischen Gewerbeaufsichtsverwaltung: Arbejdstilsynets bekendtgorelse, 28.11.1983; 661.

32. Vorschriften des Bundesminister für Umwelt, Jugend und Familie over prohibitions and restrictions of organic solvents. Bundesgesetzblatt für die Republik Österreich, 11. September 1991: 2125–2127.

33. Zentralstelle für Unfallverhütung und Arbeitsmedizin des Hauptverbandes der gewerblichen Berufsgenossenschaften e.V.: Guidelines for work in contaminated areas, vol. ZH 1/183, Alte Heerstraße 111 - 53757 St. Augustin, Germany, August 1992.

34. Geerißen H: GloSaDa—A computer based information system for optimal choice of gloves against hazardous materials; Die BG; 10/92; 616–20, 1992.

35. Fa. ULFCAR Danemark, private communication, 1993.

36. Zentralstelle für Unfallverhütung und Arbeitsmedizin des Hauptverbandes der gewerblichen Berufsgenossenschaften e.V.: Safety and health regulations for use of man-made mineral fibres. vol. ZH 1/294, Alte Heerstraße 111 - 53757 St. Augustin, Germany, August 1992.

ANA MARIA OSORIO, MD, MPH
JAMES MELIUS, MD, DRPH

LEAD POISONING IN CONSTRUCTION

From the Division of
  Environmental and Occupational
  Disease Control
California Department of Health
  Services
Emeryville, California (AMO)
  and
Division of Occupational Health
  and Environmental Epidemiology
New York State Department of
  Health
Albany, New York (JM)

Reprint requests to:
Ana Maria Osorio, MD, MPH
Division of Occupational Disease
  Control
California Department of Health
  Services
Suite 600
5801 Christie Avenue
Emeryville, CA 94608

A REGULATORY SHORTFALL

In the United States, Occupational Safety and Health Administration (OSHA) standards for occupational lead exposure have been in effect since 1971 for the construction and general industries. In 1978, OSHA revised the general industry lead standard to provide better protection and included biologic monitoring of lead-exposed workers and a lowered permissible air lead concentration.[15] The revised occupational lead standard excluded construction, reportedly because of insufficient information regarding lead use in the industry.

In 1990, the National Institute for Occupational Safety and Health (NIOSH) set a national goal to eliminate worker exposures resulting in blood-lead concentrations in excess of 25 micrograms of lead per deciliter of whole blood by the year 2000.[6] Two years later, Congress passed Title X of the Housing and Community Development Act of 1992, which required OSHA to issue an interim final lead standard for the construction industry. In June 1993, the OSHA interim final rule for the protection of construction workers exposed to lead took effect.[14] Aside from the inclusion of biologic monitoring, the most notable change in the interim OSHA standard involved the lowering of the air-lead permissible exposure limit from 200 µg to 50 µg lead per cubic meter of air as an 8-hour time-weighted average; the lower limit is consistent with the air level of the general industry standard. Title X also required the U.S. Environmental Protection Agency to develop training and accreditation standards for lead abatement and standards for lead abatement work practices by April 1994.

OCCUPATIONAL MEDICINE: State of the Art Reviews—
Vol. 10, No. 2, April 1995. Philadelphia, Hanley & Belfus, Inc.

353

THE EXTENT OF THE PROBLEM

Workers at Risk

OSHA estimates that nearly 1 million U.S. construction workers are exposed to lead on the job (Table 1).[14] Most (78%) of these workers are involved in commercial or residential remodeling and potentially are exposed to lead-based paint. That proportion should increase as a result of 1991 Centers for Disease Control guidelines for the prevention of childhood lead poisoning. Increased lead testing of small children specified under the guidelines is expected to result in increased residential lead abatement activity and, thus, more potential risk of exposure to lead among workers and members of workers' households.[5] The high-risk work associated with lead exposure includes tasks that disturb or alter surfaces with lead-based coatings or paint: abrasive blasting, welding, cutting, and torch burning. Without appropriate control measures, these tasks may lead to the inhalation of lead dust or fumes, the unintentional ingestion of lead dust, and possible family contact exposures.

TABLE 1. Estimated Number of U.S. Construction Workers Exposed Annually to Lead

Type of Construction	Number of Workers (% of Total)	Source of Lead
Commercial/institutional remodeling	546,798 (58.4)	Lead paint
Residential remodeling	178,544 (19.1)	Lead paint
Highway/railroad bridge repainting and rehabilitation	48,377 (5.2)	Lead paint
Water lines repair and removal	41,042 (4.4)	Lead pipes and solder
Housing in-place management	35,244 (3.8)	Lead paint
Reinsulation over mineral wool	18,333 (2.0)	Wool with lead contaminants
Lead joint work on cast-iron soil pipe	15,337 (1.6)	Lead joint material
Housing lead abatement	12,238 (1.3)	Lead paint
Elevator cable splicing/babbitting	9,500 (1.0)	Lead splicing material
Commercial/industrial demolition	7,440 (0.8)	Lead paint
Transmission/communication tower	7,333 (0.8)	Lead paint maintenance
Water tank repainting	5,113 (0.5)	Lead paint
Industrial facility maintenance and renovation (indoor/outdoor)	5,094 (0.5)	Lead paint
Petroleum tank repainting	4,364 (0.5)	Lead paint
Installation of certain roofing	576 (0.1)	Lead steel roof and solder
Industrial process equipment manufacturing/repair	409 (< 0.1)	Lead bricks, mortar, sheets
Industrial vacuuming	392 (< 0.1)	Lead dust
Underground storage tank demolition	288 (< 0.1)	Lead pain
Stained glass window removal	208 (< 0.1)	Lead support rods
Installation of radiation shielding	40 (< 0.1)	Lead building material
Estimated total	936,670	

From Occupational Safety and Health Administration (OSHA), Department of Labor: Lead Exposure in Construction, 29 CFR Part 1926, Interim.Final Rule, Federal Register 58(84):26590–26649, 1993.

TABLE 2.   Number of Construction Workers Reported to New York State Heavy Metals Registry, 1991–93

| Year | Type of Construction | |
	Residential	Bridge/Steel Structures
1991	74	144
1992	96	289
1993	75	663

Note: Individuals with blood-lead levels greater than 25 µg/dL must be reported to the registry.
Data from the New York State Department of Health.

Identification of High-Risk Work Activities

In 1991, OSHA and NIOSH jointly issued recommendations intended to prevent lead exposure in construction. The document recommended using engineering controls, appropriate work practices, personal protective equipment (including respirators), and evaluation of the effectiveness of these measures by air and blood-lead monitoring.[16] In 1992, NIOSH published an alert for preventing lead poisoning in construction workers.[13] This publication identified high-risk activities associated with lead dust and fumes among bridge and structural steel workers: abrasive blasting, sanding, burning, cutting or welding on steel structures coated with lead paint, and the use of containment enclosures at these sites that could result in higher lead concentrations. To illustrate this problem, 42 construction workers at eight bridge projects were described with respect to the severity of their blood-lead levels. The workers' blood-lead levels ranged from 51-160 µg/dL whole blood; 26 (62%) of these blood-lead elevations involved work in a containment structure.

Lead Registries

NEW YORK STATE

Since 1981, the New York Heavy Metal Registry has required reporting for blood-lead levels ≥ 40 µg/dL from all hospitals, laboratories, and physicians in the state. The reporting level was changed to 25 µg/dL in 1986.[22] Data from this registry from 1991–1993 indicate a large increase in the number of construction workers reported with blood-lead levels greater than 25 µg/dL, especially in bridge workers (Table 2).

CALIFORNIA

Based on 1986 state employment figures, there are approximately a half million construction workers in California.[2] A survey of 161 construction firms in California indicated that none of the employers had conducted biologic monitoring for lead. This is in contrast to biologic monitoring administered to 95% of battery plant workers and 33% of nonferrous smelter employees.[21]

Since 1987, the Occupational Lead Registry of the California Department of Health Services has collected laboratory reports of adults with blood-lead levels of ≥ 25 µg/dL. A summary of the data from 1987–1990 shows 14,843 blood-lead level reports, representing 2,779 individuals, for all industries.[10] Construction, painting, and demolition accounted for 125 reports (about 1% of all reports received). Forty-four workers showing peak blood-lead levels were construction workers (2% of all cases). However, this industry accounted for 5% of workers with blood-lead levels between 60–79 µg/dL and 14% of workers with blood-lead levels ≥ 80 µg/dL.

Although construction workers have a relatively small fraction of all reports of lead exposure, they tend have much higher blood-lead levels. This reflects the lack of a mandate for routine biologic monitoring before the 1993 OSHA standard for lead in construction. Thus, only workers with more severely symptomatic lead intoxication tend to seek medical attention.

STUDIES IN THE CONSTRUCTION INDUSTRY

Reports of occupational lead poisoning in the medical literature include several types of construction work: bridge work, ship refurbishing, steel structure demolition or repair, bricklaying, and house painting.[1,3,7-9,11,12,17-20,23-26,29] The following studies from the California Occupational Lead Registry were developed after observing the lack of routine blood-lead monitoring in the industry and the resultant severely symptomatic cases.

Control Measure Assessment at a Demolition Site

An evaluation was conducted at a demolition project involving a large outdoor natural gas tank. The project involved the use of acetylene torches to cut apart the empty tank that had been painted for many years with a 10%-lead coating. The crew of 29 men was followed throughout the 6 months of the project and during changes in the work practices, respirator use, and personal hygiene techniques. At least nine men had initial blood-lead levels greater than 40 µg/dL. The mean blood-lead levels dropped after all of the workplace changes had been implemented.[27] This project illustrates the feasibility of conducting biologic monitoring and instituting control measures to decrease lead exposure at a construction demolition site.

Construction Industry Case Series

Over 2 years (1987–89), Waller identified 28 construction workers from the California Occupational Lead Registry: 89% were male, the average age was 43 (range 24–63), and 20 of 28 had peak blood-lead levels ≥ 40 µg/dL, with the highest blood-lead level at 130 µg/dL. Exposures included flame-cutting painted metal, scraping lead-based paint, and sandblasting lead-based paint during demolition, house painting, bridge construction, bridge maintenance, and water reservoir painting.[28] Seven of 28 construction workers were disabled for more than 9 months because of ongoing myalgias, weakness, and cognitive difficulties. In addition, six workers were hospitalized for chelation therapy, with one worker developing bilateral wrist drop. Results differed among three of the work sites investigated, where periodic blood-lead level monitoring was done. The workers from these sites had lower peak blood-lead levels, did not require hospitalization, and did not experience a subsequent disability period.

Current Occupational Lead Registry Surveillance

Although the number of reports has varied over the years, the adult blood-lead reports from 1987 through the first 6 months of 1993 show a similar yearly distribution among three blood-lead-level ranges (40–49 µg/dL, 50–59 µg/dL, and ≥ 60 µg/dL) (Fig. 1). Looking at only the construction industry, one sees relatively few cases or reports during the first 5 years, except in 1989 when reporting increased because of the demolition site investigation described earlier (Fig. 2). There were eight times and 12 times more reports or cases, respectively, in 1991 and 1992. This increase could be associated with the increased attention given to the passage of Title X and the requirement for a lead in construction standard in 1993. If the pace

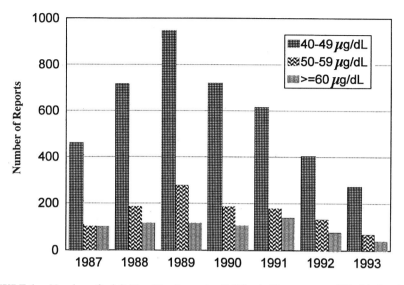

FIGURE 1. Number of adult blood lead reports, California Department of Health Services; 1993 for 6 months only.

described for the first 6 months of 1993 continues, there will be even more blood-lead level reports or cases than in 1992.

The age distribution and the predominantly male work force in construction was similar to the general industry profile for the California Occupational Lead Registry. However, the percent distribution of reports of high blood-lead levels ($\geq$ 50 µg/dL) for construction and general industries was noteworthy for the decreasing

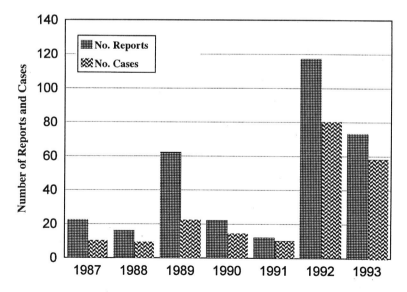

FIGURE 2. Number of construction industry reports and cases, California Department of Health Services; 1993 for 6 months only.

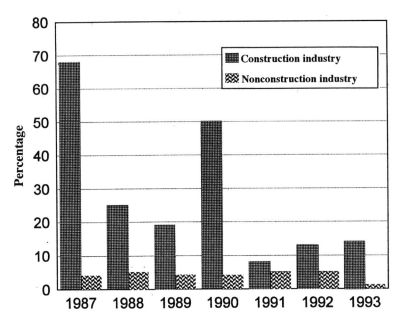

FIGURE 3.   Percent of reports ≥ 50 µg/dL blood lead, California Department of Health Services; 1993 for 6 months only.

percentage trend for construction (Fig. 3). It appears that cases in construction workers are not occurring at the same disproportionately higher blood-lead level compared with earlier years and with general industry. Perhaps the increased awareness of lead hazards and the requirement of biologic monitoring in construction are allowing the detection of lead intoxication at earlier stages. Further follow-up will be needed to assess this trend adequately.

PREVENTION OF LEAD POISONING

Prevention of lead poisoning in the construction industry is complicated by several factors. Unlike most industrial environments that include lead, the work environment on construction projects is constantly changing. Control measures must be mobile and flexible to keep up with these changes. In addition to the workers removing the lead paint, nearby workers also can have significant exposures. Potential lead exposures for both groups are increased by the need to enclose many projects to limit environmental exposures from them.

The air-lead exposure level for construction is now the same as for general industry, 50 µg per cubic meter of air as an 8-hour time-weighted average.[14] However, the standard presumes that certain construction tasks carry a high risk of exposure to lead and therefore require a very strict level of control, unless air monitoring confirms that no excess lead exposures are occurring. These high-risk work tasks include manual demolition, abrasive blasting, cleaning with power tools, use of lead mortar, spraying lead paint, and cutting or burning lead coatings or paint.

Given the rapid changes occurring on a construction site as the project progresses, this presumptive approach is reasonable. Even with rapid turnaround of air-monitoring results, such results may not be available until the project has moved or may not reflect the current intensity of activity on the project. As people involved in these projects develop more experience monitoring lead exposures during different job tasks, the application of appropriate control measures should become easier.

Although the OSHA standard appropriately emphasizes the use of engineering controls to reduce lead exposures, currently available controls are often not effective, particularly with strict enclosure of the work sites. Contractors therefore must rely on personal protective equipment and work practices to minimize exposures on these projects. Appropriate training of workers is critical to ensuring that these control programs are effective. Providing a clean area for meals and snacks and changing facilities is logistically difficult at many construction sites and a new consideration for most construction contractors.[4]

The OSHA standard also requires a medical surveillance program that includes medical examinations and biologic monitoring (see chapter 13). This program should be supervised by a physician familiar with the prevention, diagnosis, and treatment of occupational illness and injury. Under the OSHA standard, medical surveillance is triggered when air monitoring indicates exposures above 30 μg per cubic meter of air (the so-called action level) for 1 day or for an individual working in a high-risk job task (unless air monitoring documents levels below the action level). Monitoring is then required every 2 months for 6 months and every 6 months thereafter for the duration of the project. There is serious question as to whether this schedule is adequate given the potential for very high lead exposures in construction. A worker's blood-lead level can increase 40 μg/dL or more during short periods of intense exposure between periodic tests.

Removal from exposure is required for workers having blood-lead levels greater than 50 μg/dL or for other medical considerations; during removal, monitoring at least every month is required until the worker is cleared for return. Given the mobility of the work site and the limited opportunities for work not involving lead exposure at these projects, medical removal can cause considerable difficulty. The logistics of establishing an adequate medical surveillance program for these workers is also challenging. Often, workers move from one job site to another; determining who is responsible for medical surveillance of workers at a particular time can be difficult. Despite these practical difficulties and in light of the limitations of air monitoring, good blood-lead monitoring programs are critical to protecting construction workers from the adverse effects of lead exposure.

The interim final rule for lead exposure in construction is an important step toward controlling lead poisoning in construction. OSHA has highlighted ways in which lead exposure in construction is unique and has targeted those areas in the standard. This standard will apply until a final OSHA standard is developed under section 6 of the Occupational Safety and Health Act. Information collected as this standard is enforced can be used to refine and improve it in the development of a final rule. Certain areas will be key:

- First, is a blood-lead level of 50 μg/dL sufficiently protective? There is substantial medical evidence to indicate that blood-lead levels of 40 μg/dL or lower can result in overt or subclinical disease, and the reproductive system and developing fetus may be the most susceptible organ systems at lower levels. NIOSH has set as a goal the elimination of exposures that lead to blood-lead levels higher than 25 μg/dL.[13]
- Second, blood-lead levels are required every 2 months on employees under medical surveillance. However, the duration of a construction job, especially

for a residence, can be shorter. Thus, consideration needs to be given to performing an exit blood-lead level measurement if the job ends before 2 months and, also, when the tasks or location change markedly for an individual worker.

CONCLUSION

With the introduction of new legislation—Title X and the OSHA standard for lead in construction—the construction work force and industry are undergoing major changes in the way work is performed and how employees are being protected from lead exposure. We must remember the primary goal of eliminating lead use wherever possible.

If lead is in the workplace, there must be strict adherence to the prevention, control, and monitoring principles of the OSHA standard. Consideration needs to be given to the adaptation of the current lead standard to address lowering the blood-lead level for medical removal, bystander exposures to lead at the work site, exit blood-lead levels for the transient worker, unnecessary emphasis on air-lead concentrations that may not represent workplace conditions, and adequate counseling and guidance for male or female workers attempting to have a child.

As illustrated earlier, the surveillance of elevated blood-lead levels is crucial in assessing the overall condition and health of the construction work force. Evaluation of lead registry information and resultant intervention strategies should be encouraged and communicated to the construction industry and safety and health workers.

REFERENCES

1. Booher LE: Lead exposure in a ship overhaul facility during paint removal. Am Ind Hyg Assoc J 49:121–127, 1988.
2. California Employment Development Department: State of California, Sacramento, CA, 1986.
3. Campbell BC, Baird AW: Lead poisoning in a group of demolition workers. Br J Ind Med 34:298–304, 1977.
4. Center to Protect Workers' Rights: Model Specifications for the Protection of Workers from Lead on Steel Structures. Washington, DC, Center to Protect Workers' Rights, 1993.
5. Centers for Disease Control and Prevention: Preventing lead poisoning in young children: A statement by the Centers for Disease Control. Atlanta, CDC, 1991, Dept. of Health and Human Services publication 99-2230.
6. Department of Health and Human Services: Healthy people 2000: National health promotion and disease objectives. Washington, DC, Department of Health and Human Services, 1990, Dept. of Health and Human Services publication 91-50212.
7. Fischbein A, Leeds M, Solomon S: Lead exposure among iron workers in New York City: A continuing occupational hazard in the 1980s. N Y State J Med 84:445–448, 1984.
8. Himmelstein J, Wolfson M, Pransky G, et al: Lead poisoning in bridge demolition workers—Massachusetts. MMWR 38:687–694, 1989.
9. Landrigan PJ, Baker EL, Himmelstein JS, et al: Exposure to lead from the Mystic River Bridge: The dilemma of deleading. N Engl J Med 306:673-676, 1982.
10. Maizlish NA, Rudolph LA, Rokyce A, et al: Elevated blood lead in California adults, 1987–1990. Berkeley, CA, California Occupational Health Program, California Department of Health Services, 1990, publication CDHS(COHP) SR90-001.
11. Marino PE, Franzblau A, Lilis R, Landrigan PJ: Acute lead poisoning in construction workers: The failure of current protective standards. Arch Environ Health 44:140–145, 1989.
12. McCammon C, Daniels W, Hales T, Lee S. Lead exposure during lining of tanks with lead sheeting. Appl Occup Environ Hyg 7:88–91, 1992.
13. National Institute for Occupational Safety and Health: NIOSH Alert: Request for assistance in preventing lead poisoning in construction workers. Cincinnati, 1992, NIOSH publication 91-116a.
14. Occupational Safety and Health Administration: Lead exposure in construction. 29 CFR Part 1926, Interim final rule. Fed Reg 58:26590–26649, 1993.
15. Occupational Safety and Health Administration: Lead standard. 29 CFR Part 1910.1025. Washington, DC, U.S. Govt. Printing Office, 1989.

16. Occupational Safety and Health Administration/National Institute for Occupational Safety and Health: Working with lead in the construction industry. Washington, DC, OSHA/NIOSH, 1991.

17. Pagliuca A, Mufti GJ, Baldwin D, et al: Lead poisoning: Clinical, biochemical, and haematological aspects of a recent outbreak. J Clin Path 43:277–281, 1990.

18. Pollock CA, Ibels LS: Lead intoxication in paint removal workers on the Sydney Harbour Bridge. Med J Aust 145:635–639, 1986.

19. Rae CE, Bell CN, Elliott CE, Shannon M: Ten cases of acute lead intoxication among bridge workers in Louisiana. Ann Pharmacother 25:932–937, 1991.

20. Risk I, Thurman D, Beaudoin D: Lead exposures among lead burners—Utah, 1991. MMWR 41:307–310, 1992.

21. Rudolph L, Sharp DS, Samuels S, et al: Environmental and biological monitoring for lead exposure in California workplaces. Am J Public Health 80:921–925, 1990.

22. Seligman PJ, Halperin WE: Targeting of workplace inspections for lead. Am J Ind Med 20:381–390, 1991.

23. Spaedy S, Schubert TT: Inorganic lead poisoning in an adult. Am J Gastroenterol 83:581–583, 1988.

24. Spee T, Zwennis WCM: Lead exposure during demolition of a steel structure coated with lead-based paints. I. Environmental and biological monitoring. Scand J Work Environ Health 13:52–55, 1987.

25. Stockbridge H, Daniell W: Lead poisoning among bricklayers—Washington State. MMWR 40:169–171, 1991.

26. Sussell A, Tubbs R, Montopoli M: Occupational exposures during abrasive blasting removal of lead-based paint on a highway bridge. Appl Occup Environ Hyg 7:497–503, 1992.

27. Waller K, Osorio AM, Jones J, Maizlish N: Lead exposure in a tank demolition crew (in press).

28. Waller K, Osorio AM, Maizlish N, Royce S: Lead exposure in the construction industry: Results from the California Occupational Lead Registry, 1987 through 1989. Am J Public Health 82:1669–1671, 1992.

29. Zimmer FE: Lead poisoning in scrap-metal workers. JAMA 175:238240, 1961

SCOTT SCHNEIDER, CIH
ECKHART JOHANNING, MD, MSc
JEAN-LOUIS BÉLARD, MD, DES
GÖRAN ENGHOLM, MSc

NOISE, VIBRATION, AND HEAT AND COLD

From The Center to Protect
  Workers' Rights
Washington, DC (SS)
  and
Department of Environmental and
  Occupational Medicine
Mt. Sinai Medical Center
New York, New York
  and
Eastern New York Occupational
  Health Program
Latham, New York (EJ)
  and
Division of Safety Research
National Institute for Occupational
  Safety and Health
Morgantown, West Virginia (JLB)
  and
National Board of Health and
  Welfare
Stockholm, Sweden
  and
National Institute of Occupational
  Health
Umeå, Sweden (GE)

Reprint requests to:
Scott Schneider, CIH
Ergonomics Program Director
The Center to Protect Workers'
  Rights
111 Masachusetts Ave. NW
Washington, DC 20001

Safety hazards are well understood and well recognized in the construction industry. Chemical hazards in construction have been gaining in recognition in recent years, particularly since the application of the Occupational Health and Safety Administration's Hazard Communication Standard to construction in 1988. Ergonomic hazards in construction are now getting more attention. However, although physical hazards such as noise, vibration, and heat and cold affect most construction workers, little research on these problems has been published, and there has been almost no action to reduce exposures to them.

NOISE

Almost all construction workers are exposed to excessive levels of noise on the job. Most of the workers lose some or all of their hearing after years at the trade. This loss can seriously harm their effectiveness on the job and their quality of life away from work. Most of the noise is machine-generated.

Sound levels from heavy trucks, bulldozers, and front-end loaders, for instance, vary depending on vehicle size (tonnage or power), noise controls on the equipment, how well a vehicle has been maintained, and the work that the vehicle does. A powerful truck straining under a heavy load up an unpaved hill will produce more noise than an empty one driving on a level highway.

Exposure Levels

Noise levels reported from construction equipment range from about 75 dB for an electrician's drill press to 108–111 dB for a jackhammer.[6,8,12,27,59,70] Impact noise can reach high levels from bolt guns (140–160 dB) and other construction tools.

Few dosimetry studies have been done on worker exposures, but worker exposures have been reported at 85–87 dB on an 8-hour time-weighted average.[14,46,58,70] Dranitsaris found that 28% of pipefitters had 8-hour time-weighted average exposures of higher than 87 dB.[14] A smaller portion of other trades were exposed at that level, i.e., only 6% of electricians.

Hearing Loss

Testing the hearing of sheet metal workers, Kenney and Ayer[46] found significant hearing loss among workers older than 39. The hearing loss index—the average loss in both ears at 1, 2, and 3 kHz—showed that three of the four workers in their 40s and all workers between 50 and 60 had a loss of more than 25 dB.

In 1969 a new organization, Bygghälsan, was created to provide occupational health services to the Swedish construction industry. Workers were invited to have regular check-ups every 2–3 years. Over 10 years, almost 90% of the workers had at least one check-up. Each check-up included a pure-tone audiometric test with measurements at 500 Hz, 1,000 Hz, 2,000 Hz, 3,000 Hz, 4,000 Hz and 6,000 Hz. The screening level was 20 dB. Analysis of the data shows wide variation in hearing loss, reflecting variation in the levels of exposure to noise. Figure 1 compares hearing loss among office and sheet metal workers. In people examined in 1971–1980, 49.7% of sheet metal workers age 35–39 and 90% of workers age 55–59 had a hearing loss exceeding 30 dB at 4,000 Hz in the left ear. The corresponding figures for office workers employed by companies in the industry were 19.3% and 64%, respectively. The proportion of sheet metal workers and office workers with hearing loss was roughly the same at 3,000 Hz and 6,000 Hz. The results also show that hearing loss exceeding 30 dB is much less common at lower frequencies. However, a substantial difference exists between occupational groups at these frequencies. At 500 Hz, 2.6% of sheet metal workers age 35–39 and 7.0% of workers age 55–59 experienced hearing loss. The figures for office workers were 0.9% and 4.1%, respectively (Fig. 2).

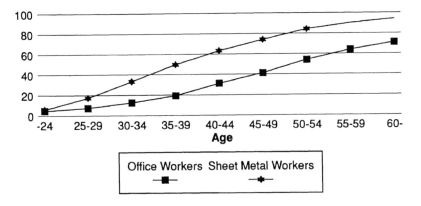

FIGURE 1.   Percentage of Bygghälsan examinees in 1971–80 with hearing loss > 30 dB at 4 kHz on the left ear.
Source: Göran Engholm, Bygghälsan; n = 18,397 office workers, 13,519 sheet metal workers.

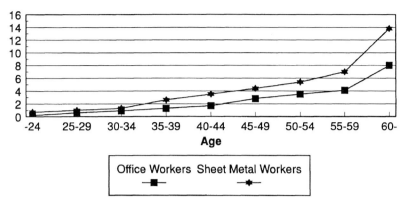

FIGURE 2.   Percentage of Bygghälsan examinees in 1971–80 with hearing loss > 30 dB at 500 Hz on the left ear.
Source: Göran Engholm, Bygghälsan; n = 18,397 office workers, 13,519 sheet metal workers.

The Workers' Compensation Board of British Columbia also began a hearing conservation program in the construction industry in the mid 1980s. A study by the board of about 5,000 construction workers showed that 49% had noise-induced hearing loss (Figs. 3 and 4). Seven percent had more than a 28-dB loss in at least one ear, and another 7.8% had a loss of 20–27 dB. They estimated that there could be as many as 10,000 claims for hearing loss among construction workers in British Columbia, which could potentially cost the industry $20 million in Canadian currency.[66] As a result, the provincial government began a hearing conservation program whereby industry paid into a fund organized by the government to provide free hearing tests for construction workers. The government administered about 176,800 tests in 1987–1991. The 32,800 tests given in 1989 showed 50% of the workers to have significant hearing loss, 22% of which was classified as severe to profound.[65] Data from 1991 show that workers generally suffer significant loss of hearing after working more than 15 years in the trade. Another significant drop-off in hearing occurs for workers with more than 25 years in the trade. Some trades with more significant exposures have higher losses. For example, carpenters had more losses than electricians, who do not use as many noisy tools. However, all trades exhibited significant hearing loss.

Noise Control

In 1972, the U.S. Congress passed the Noise Control Act, which authorized a Noise Control Office to be established in the Environmental Protection Agency in order to reduce environmental noise levels.[2] One of the main duties of the office was regulation of construction noise, which was identified as one of the leading noise problems in the country affecting not only construction workers but communities surrounding such projects. The EPA subsequently proposed and enacted regulations for the control of noise from portable air compressors (1976) and medium and heavy trucks (1976 and 1986).[83,84] The portable air compressor regulation (40 CFR 204) allows noise levels of no more than 76 dBA at 7 meters from the machines. (The symbol dBA indicates decibel level measured to approximate human hearing.) The medium- and heavy-truck regulations (40 CFR 202 and 205, effective 1988) affect newly manufactured trucks heavier than 10,000 pounds, setting an 80-dBA noise

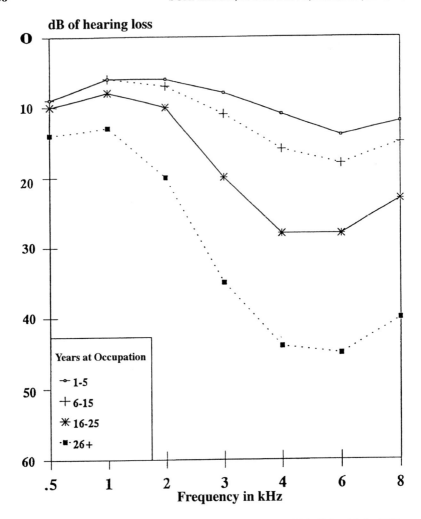

FIGURE 3.   Hearing loss among construction carpenters in British Columbia in 1991.
Source: Workers' Compensation Board of British Columbia; n = 2778.

standard measured at 50 feet from the vehicle. Although much of the work of this
office stopped when funding ended in 1981–1982, the few regulations that were pro-
mulgated had a significant effect on construction site noise levels from the regulated
equipment.

Other government agencies stepped in to help move this agenda forward. The
Bureau of Mines has always had an active noise control program. In the 1970s, it
identified several pieces of equipment used in construction and mining as major
sources of noise. The bureau then commissioned several studies on how much noise
emissions could be controlled by retrofitting the equipment. These reports focused
on controlling noise exposure to the operators. While building a quieter truck may
be the best solution, thousands of old pieces of equipment are in use, and the re-
placement rate is low. Retrofitting old equipment to make it quieter must be consid-

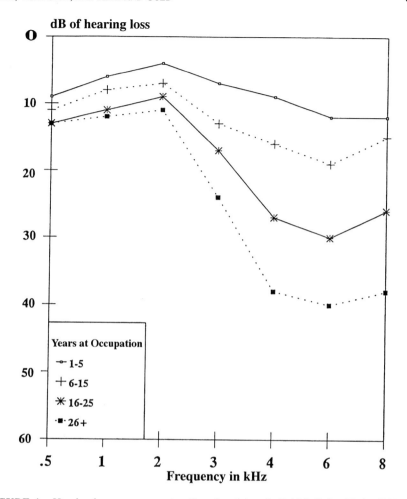

FIGURE 4. Hearing loss among construction electricians in British Columbia in 1991. Source: Workers' Compensation Board of British Columbia; n = 89.

ered an important interim measure. Two noise control manuals were produced, one for bulldozers and one for front-end loaders.[79,80] These reports demonstrate that noise from these critical pieces of construction equipment can be controlled effectively and at a reasonable cost. Bulldozer noise exposures for the operators can be reduced by about 11 dB for a cost of about $3,450–$4,300 (1994 dollars) through the procedures outlined in the manual. Front-end loader noise exposures for operators can be reduced by 11–12 dB for about $1,550–$1,620 (1994 dollars) using noise control techniques outlined in the manual.

A Society of Automotive Engineers report for the National Highway Traffic Safety Administration in 1979 looked more at controlling noise emissions from construction equipment.[77] Sound levels ranged from 80 dBA for pavers to 89 dBA for truck noise as measured at 50 feet from the vehicle. The report found that use of effective mufflers was becoming widespread in the 1970s. For equipment without mufflers, noise emissions could be reduced by 6–12 dB by adding a new muffler.

TABLE 1. Noise Controls for Construction Equipment

Equipment	Noise Controls and Reference
Pile driver	Enclosure, muffler[48]
Stone cutting saw	Noise control pad with water[73]
Handheld impact drills	Reduction of reflected sound[3]
Circular saw blades	15° tooth angle, new tooth configuration, slotted saw blades, viscoelastic damping[29]
Pneumatic tools	Muffler[75]
Pavement breaker/Rock drill	Muffler, enclosure of cylinder case and front head, moil damping[47]
Portable air compressor	Muffler, acoustic enclosures[59]
Bulldozer	"Cab liner material," enclosure, sound absorption in canopy, sealing of all openings[4,49,52]
Wheeled loader	Absorption of sound cooling air route[24]
Vibratory roller	Flexible mounting for pump compartment[24]
Joint cutter	Anti-vibration mounting fixtures[24]

For equipment with inadequate mufflers, a better muffler would reduce noise levels by 1–3 dB. Noise emissions from equipment with adequate mufflers came mainly from engine mechanical noise, hydraulic noise, and fan noise. Control of these sources primarily requires the use of sound-absorbing barriers to block transmission of the noise to the operator or other nearby workers, although care must be taken to prevent interference with the cooling system for the engine. Intake noise could be controlled by use of a plenum-type air cleaner.

Many other pieces of construction equipment have been studied by noise control engineers and noise reduction methods identified (Table 1).

Hearing Conservation Programs

A hearing conservation program in construction can be effective. Bygghälsan instituted such a program in 1974 (Figs. 5 and 6). Audiometric data from 1974 and

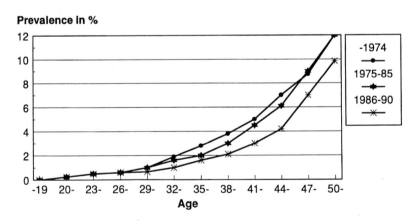

FIGURE 5. Prevalence of bilateral severe high-tone hearing loss in Bygghälsan examinees. Source: Göran Engholm, Bygghälsan; n = 134,000 in 1974 and about 55,000 per year thereafter; Total: about 1 million.

Prevalence in %

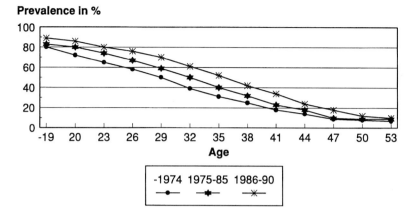

FIGURE 6. Prevalence of bilateral normal hearing in Bygghälsan examinees.
Source: Göran Engholm, Bygghälsan; n = 134,000 in 1974, and about 55,000 per year thereafter; Total: about 1 million.

1990 show a significant decrease in hearing loss among construction workers. A 10–20% increase in normal hearing prevalence was found in all groups whose workers were younger than 47 in the 1986–1990 survey. The results are based on 1 million hearing tests on construction workers over 16 years.

Audiometric testing—a key feature of any hearing conservation program—is quick, easy to perform, and inexpensive compared to required invasive procedures such as blood-lead screening and chest x-rays for asbestos. Worker training for noise and hearing protection should be no more difficult than the required training under the hazard communication standard (29 CFR 1926.59) or under other construction standards requiring training of workers about the hazards of their jobs (for example, 29 CFR 1926.21).

An effective hearing conservation program for construction would be similar to one designed for general industry,[76] but some adaptations would be required.

CURRENT REQUIREMENTS

Because of the acknowledged inadequacy of the Occupational Safety and Health Administration's limits for noise exposure for all workers and the political and economic obstacles to lowering the limits, OSHA published a hearing conservation amendment to its noise standard in 1981 to require comprehensive hearing protection programs where workers are exposed to 85 dBA or more averaged over an 8-hour day (29 CFR 1910.95 (c)). The rule requires periodic noise surveys, annual hearing tests for workers, annual worker training on noise and hearing conservation, and hearing protectors. But the rule does not apply to construction.

In the realm of hearing protection, OSHA standards for construction as of 1995 require only that contractors provide "ear protective devices" for workers and require their use whenever exposures exceed the OSHA limits and when it is not feasible to reduce exposures below those limits. Fitting of the ear protective devices must be done individually by a competent person, and plain cotton is not acceptable as a protective device (29 CFR 1926.52 and 1926.101).

Even OSHA's minimal standards in construction are rarely enforced. More than 22,700 construction inspections by federal OSHA in fiscal year 1994 yielded only 86 citations (1926.52 or 1926.101). Fines paid totaled less than $27,400.[81]

NOISE SURVEYS

Contractors need to survey sites periodically to determine where and when hearing protection is needed. To make this more convenient rather than relying on dosimetry and 8-hour averages, they could purchase an inexpensive sound-level meter and check noises at workers' ears. Any exposure above 85 dB should trigger use of hearing protectors, even if the exposure does not last all day, because the exposure may fluctuate and increase during the day or it could last all day. Sound-level measurements are also useful for determining when protection is needed. The likelihood of compliance is much greater if rational rules can be developed to minimize use of hearing protection to only when it is needed. For example, a quick check of sound levels from a noisy piece of equipment and distance from the source might yield a rule that hearing protection is required when working within 20 feet of the machine.

HEARING PROTECTION

Hearing protection should be required—based on the noise survey—when a person is operating or near noisy equipment. The type of hearing protection selected should depend on the noise exposure and on ease of use. Hearing protectors that must be rolled up and placed in the ear (such as foam plugs) would be difficult for construction work, where exposures are often intermittent. Foam plugs on a band would be more convenient because they can be removed easily, hung around the neck when not in use, and easily reinserted. Earmuffs may be easier to use for construction work, especially those that can be attached to a hard hat, which most construction workers are already accustomed to wearing. They can easily be used and removed as the demands of the job dictate. Simple rules on where and when to wear hearing protection will make compliance easier for workers and contractors. Workers must also know that contractors consider this as important through effective but fair enforcement of rational use rules.

Many construction workers have lost substantial amounts of hearing and have legitimate concerns about the effect of hearing protection on their ability to hear essential sounds on the job such as back-up alarms on heavy equipment. For this reason, the recent development and availability of active hearing protectors is an important step.[7,63] These earmuffs screen out frequencies above and below the human hearing range and selectively let human hearing frequencies (such as voice communication) in, but only to a maximum of 85 dBA. Impulse noise, like that from a bolt gun, is excluded. Such systems also can include a two-way voice communication channel so a supervisor can communicate directly with workers.[22] The National Institute for Occupational Safety and Health (NIOSH) is working on a more sophisticated system called EarTalk, which would allow communications on several channels into a set of earmuffs so members of a whole crew can be connected to each other while wearing them.

Active protectors will make the use of hearing protectors much easier and more acceptable among construction workers. The only current drawback is cost. At $125–200 a pair, they will appear too costly to many contractors. Over the long run, however, these earmuffs will be more cost-effective than disposable ear plugs. They may even be considered a "reasonable accommodation" for hearing-impaired construction workers under the Americans with Disabilities Act, in which case a contractor may be required to provide them for some workers.

HEARING TESTS

Audiometric testing each year is essential for an effective program. Workers who view their audiograms and see demonstrable hearing loss are much more motivated to use hearing protection and use it effectively. Testing also can be used to protect contractors from compensation claims if they perform both an entry and exit audiogram for each worker and can show no substantial loss from exposures on the project. Testing is convenient now that less-expensive portable audiometers can be taken to job sites. Testing need only require 5–10 minutes per person and can be done before work begins, preferably on a Monday after a weekend's rest away from occupational exposure. On many sites there is a trailer, which could be used for testing. On other sites, a mobile van equipped with an audiometer can be used. Numerous audiometric testing service companies are available that can provide such testing, and the tests are relatively inexpensive. It is essential that workers be given a copy of the test results after the test and the results explained to them.

Comparisons with past tests are also important. For this reason, a centralized system for storing and retrieving records is needed. Such a system works best in places such as British Columbia and Sweden, where contractors are assessed a fee based on hours worked or it is taken out of workers' compensation premiums and paid for centrally. With this method, all workers get free exams and all contractors have to pay. Unionized contractors currently have centralized funds jointly run with the unions to pay for some medical testing, such as asbestos exams. Centralized record-keeping would make epidemiologic studies of hearing loss and the effectiveness of hearing conservation programs possible.

WORKER TRAINING

For a hearing conservation program to be effective, workers must be trained about the hazards of noise and the need for hearing protection. Training could be held during a half-day annual generic training and supplemented by short 10-minute tool box talks on the job site similar to the way hazard communication training is done by many contractors. The generic training would discuss the general hazards of noise in construction, common noise sources and sound levels from them, the need for hearing protection and its proper use, noise control techniques, audiometric testing and how to interpret the results, and the OSHA rules. The job-site training would review this information with an emphasis on the specific hazards of the current site and rules on where and when protection is needed and the enforcement of those rules. Program evaluation and assurances that workers understand the information is needed.

Summary

The need for hearing conservation programs in construction is without dispute. That such programs can be practical and effective is also without dispute. But without an OSHA requirement for such a program, those who institute these programs will feel unfairly burdened by the costs. This is why an OSHA hearing conservation program requirement for construction is so essential.

WHOLE-BODY AND HAND-ARM VIBRATION

Intensive and prolonged exposure to mechanical vibration in construction can lead to serious safety and health problems. There are two categories of vibration, whole-body and segmental (hand-arm) vibration. With the ever-growing use and

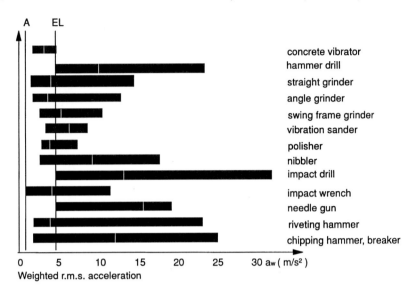

FIGURE 7.   Vibration exposure levels of construction hand tools.[18,40]
A = Action level (proposed) 1m/sec²; EL = Max exposure level (proposed) 5m/sec²

progression of motor driven equipment and tools in many construction jobs, the risk of injuries is increasing.

Machine and vehicle vibration transmitted to the entire body, so-called whole-body vibration, is associated with acute and chronic adverse health effects. Seated road and off-road vehicle operators are particularly affected by vibration transmitted

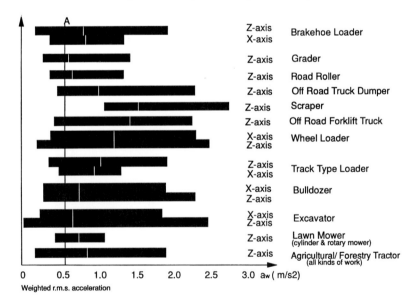

FIGURE 8.   Vibration exposure levels of construction off-road vehicles.[18,40]
A = Action level 0.5m/sec² proposed.

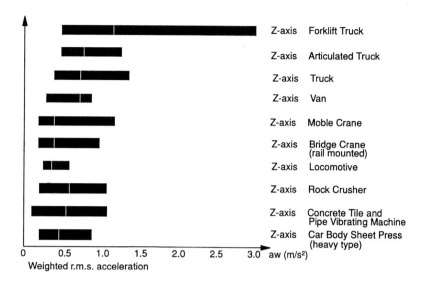

FIGURE 9. Vibration exposure levels of construction vehicles and machines.[18,40]

through the seat to the back and internal organs, especially the gastrointestinal tract (Figs. 8 and 9).

Segmental or hand-arm vibration primarily affects arms, hands, and possibly the upper spine and neck.[20,25] Pneumatic or motor-driven hand tools or machines often transmit high levels of vibration and can cause neurovascular damage and intermittent blood circulation problems with vasospasm in hands and fingers, known as white finger or Raynaud's syndrome (Fig. 7).

To protect against vibration injuries, national and international (ISO [International Standards Organization] 2631 and 5349) regulations and standards exist.[16,26,86] National standards in the U.S. have been set by American National Standards Institute (ANSI) and the American Conference of Governmental Industrial Hygienists.[1,2] OSHA has not issued a standard devoted to vibration, although the International Labor Organization recommended in 1977 (ILO Agreement No. 148 Part III, Para.1) that the "competent authority shall establish criteria for determining the hazard of exposure to vibration in the working environment and, where appropriate, shall specify exposure limits on the basis of these criteria."[35] Guidelines for vibration measurement, occupational medical surveillance, and preventive engineering or technical protection have been established in several countries. In the U.S., NIOSH has conducted epidemiologic and laboratory studies. NIOSH supports a general mandate to lower the vibration level as much as technically possible.[56,57]

In the U.S., injuries related to hand-arm vibration such as Raynaud's phenomenon, carpal tunnel syndrome, peripheral nerve damage (neuropathy), or debilitating joint injuries have been compensable only case by case. No uniform, clear legal criteria exist. For the first time in any western industrialized country, the Federal Republic of Germany in 1992 established as a compensable disease back injuries, such as disk herniations and severe spinal arthritis, caused by long-term and intensive whole-body vibration exposure at work. The German standard has been proposed as the basis for the future European Union health and safety standards and law.[18]

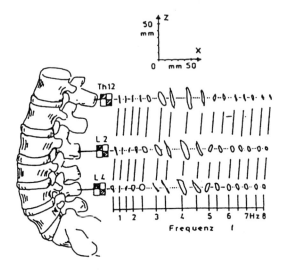

FIGURE 10. Displacement effects on vertebral bones under frequency-dependent acceleration at seat level. Spinal displacement is greatest at about 4 Hz. From Dupuis H, Zerlett G: Stresses on humans caused by mechanical vibration: Current knowledge of the effects of whole-body vibration. Bonn, Germany, Commercial Insurance Association, research division, 1984.

Whole-Body Vibration

More than 7 million workers in the U.S.—9% of the workforce—are exposed daily to whole-body vibration. A high rate of back pain, early degenerative changes of the spine (signs of excessive wear and tear), and herniated lumbar disk problems have been consistently reported among vibration-exposed occupational groups. Among seated vehicle operators, tractor drivers, truck and bus drivers, crane and earth moving equipment operators, and helicopter pilots, the rate of severe back injuries is high: 50–80%.[16,17,26,31,34,39,43,44,74] Degenerative changes such as spondylosis, osteospondylosis, osteochondrosis, and spondylolisthesis have been well documented in examinations in cadaver specimens.[16,45,71,88] However, back pain often appears long before conventional x-rays have been able to detect such changes. Poor body posture because of poor cab design, inadequate seat support, and muscle fatigue have been described as important cofactors in the pathogenesis of musculoskeletal disorders of the spine in operators or drivers.[13,16,26,68,69,78]

Two principal mechanisms of vertebral damage from vibration loads have been suggested. First, vibration-related anatomic changes may reduce the rate of nutrient supply and microvascular blood flow. This results in an abnormal tissue metabolism. Second, vibration causes continuous compression and stretching of the spinal structures and may result in structural fatigue and repeated microtrauma.

The transmitted seat vibrations are magnified by body organs, resulting in greater relative displacement, discomfort, and potentially greater mechanical damage. Construction vehicles often vibrate at the 4–8 Hz resonance range, which is critical for the human body, and vibration force at the disk or vertebra level of the vehicle operator can be 2–2.5 times greater than the measured level at the seat. This typically results in greater muscle fatigue and structural harm (Fig. 10).[10,51,55,89]

Vibration Measurement

Vibration is a vector quantity consisting of magnitude and direction. A biodynamic coordination system for measurements is used. The applicable ISO and ANSI standards consist of three exposure-time-dependent curves with frequency (Hz) and weighted acceleration (m/s² rms) coordinates.[16,25,26,36–38,85,86] If the measured-weighted acceleration in one axis or all three axes combined—the vector sum—exceeds the given ISO limits and curves, the given standard has been violated.

Typical frequency ranges for whole-body vibration are 1–80 Hz and, for hand-arm vibration, 8–1,000 Hz. Measurements are conducted using triaxial accelerometers (transducers) that are placed on the seat level, vehicle floor level, or the handles of the tools, while vibration (acceleration) levels are electronically recorded. Later, recorded data can be analyzed with computers and interpreted using the ISO time curves for allowable exposure limits. ISO standard 2631 sets limits for maximal 24-hour vibration exposure; the so-called fatigue-decreased proficiency time curves are typically used. However, because current exposure limits have mainly been based on tests with young and generally healthy individuals, the standard may not reflect typical effects for the construction industry. Based on clinical experience and epidemiologic studies, some experts argue that currently recommended vibration exposure limits set by ISO 2631 are too high and should be lowered.[30,71,72,86]

MEDICAL SURVEILLANCE AND PREVENTION

Whole-body vibration exposure can be primarily attenuated through better vehicle and operator seat engineering, which will reduce or isolate hazardous accelerations and frequencies, particularly in the important resonance range of the human body. Modern vibration attenuation seats are commercially available for many applications. However, simple retrofitting of existing vehicles without proper assessment of vehicle vibration characteristics by vibration experts may be counterproductive. Inadequate seat replacements can increase the transmitted vibration because of false damping and a resonance mismatch.

In addition to improved engineering of construction vehicles, better medical monitoring and surveillance of vibration-exposed construction workers will be necessary. Every employee with occupational exposure should have a preemployment and periodic follow-up physical, with special emphasis related to back problems. The medical evaluation should be conducted by a qualified occupational physician. Workers need to be educated about whole-body vibration risks and ways to reduce exposure, such as reduced work schedules, avoidance of heavy and forceful lifting after prolonged vehicle operations, and awkward body postures.

Engineering controls, administrative measures, and medical surveillance can partially eliminate or reduce vibration hazards. In addition, all vehicle manufacturers in the U.S. should be required to publish any vibration exposure data (vibration safety data sheets) and issue health warnings if the seat exposure levels exceed an action level of $a_w > 0.5$ m/s^2 as currently proposed by the European community.[18]

Hand-Arm Vibration Syndrome

Long-time operators of chain saws, grinders, drills, chippers, nut-hammers, and the like are often exposed to hazardous levels of shock and vibration that can lead to nerve or vascular disorders known as hand-arm vibration syndrome. Pneumatic or motor-driven heavy tools generate high-level frequency-dependent displacement that can harm the operators, especially in cold climates. Hearing loss has also been attributed to vibration exposure.[22,39,40,41,53,62]

NIOSH estimates that more than 500,000 construction workers are exposed to hand-arm vibration syndrome (white-finger disease or Raynaud's syndrome). Its prevalence among construction workers is thought to be 19–55%. The latency can range from 1–20 years before symptoms occur: the blanching of one or several fingers, or pain, tingling, or numbness, often in both hands. This typically cumulative condition is reversible in the early stages but, if not recognized in time, may result in chronic pain and neurovascular disorder, which may be difficult to treat.

The first reports of injury from the use of pneumatic tools—in mines in the U.S.—came more than 60 years ago from Hamilton and Laeke, who were governmental inspectors. The first occupational disability due to hand-arm vibration syndrome was compensated 1929 in Germany, and the syndrome was listed as an occupational disease by law in 1976 (BK 2104). In the U.S., no OSHA standard exists for the prevention of this Raynaud's syndrome; however, exposure limit guidelines have been established by the American Conference of Governmental Industrial Hygienists and by the American National Standards Institute (S3.34). In 1989 NIOSH released a criteria document for a recommended standard but did not include a specific exposure limit; instead the document recommended engineering controls and other measures to minimize exposure and improve medical detection of related problems.[56]

VIBRATION MEASUREMENT AND SYMPTOMS

Segmental vibration is measured and analyzed according to the ISO/DIN 5349 and 8662.1 recommendations with measurements of frequency (Hz), accelerations (a_w rms), and allowable duration of daily exposure somewhat similar to noise. Vibration direction is measured in three dimensions (axes x, y, and z) where the tool and hand interface. Cofactors such as temperature and noise should also be measured.

Typical clinical symptoms and signs such as aches and pain, numbness, tingling, and discoloration in the fingers have been classified into four severity stages based on the Stockholm consensus classification of 1985. Progression to stage 4 of the Stockholm classification system is considered irreversible injury (Tables 2 and 3).

Intermittent Raynaud's syndrome has been explained as a reflex spasm of the artery with a narrowing of the blood vessels that results in reduced blood flow (ischemia) and pain in the hands and fingers. Cold temperature or a humid climate can trigger this condition in a vibration-injured worker.

Vibration can also lead to direct nerve damage (neuropathy) of the upper extremities, with the typical symptoms of numbness, tingling, burning, and a "pins and needles" sensation in the nerve distribution zone on the arm. Additionally, operators of vibrating tools frequently exhibit carpal tunnel syndrome. With carpal tunnel syndrome, sensory neurologic impairments predominate, and complaints about decreased feeling and touch in the fingertips are typical. Some tool operators may be affected by a reduction in muscular strength, range of joint motion, and grip control of the tool. This can be due to direct mechanical trauma to muscles and joints. Nerve damage with a loss of nerve fibers and increase of nonfunctioning collagen has been reported.

Nonspecific but related symptoms are excessive sweating of hands, headaches, vertigo and dizziness, anxiety, and impotence. Hearing loss also is common among vibration-exposed tool operators.

MEDICAL SURVEILLANCE AND TREATMENT

None of the symptoms of hand-arm vibration syndrome are specific.[61] Proper diagnosis is based on a thorough occupational and medical history, documentation of vibrating-tool use, estimation of a cumulative vibration dose, physical examination, and few medical tests. During a medical examination, hand-arm vibration syndrome can be provoked with a cold water immersion test and then measured. Together with an exposure history such clinical tests can help with the diagnosis. The vascular constriction seems to be caused by a central sympathetic reflex in the autonomous

TABLE 2. The Stockholm Workshop Scale for Classification of Cold-Induced Raynaud's Syndrome[61]

Stage	Grade	Description
0	Mild	No attacks
1	Moderate	Occasional attacks affecting only the tips of 1 or more fingers
3	Severe	Frequent attacks affecting all phalanges of most fingers
4	Very severe	As in stage 3, with trophic skin changes in the fingertips

Note: Staging is determined separately for each hand; in the evaluation, the grade of the disorder is indicated by the stages of both hands and the number of affected fingers on each hand—for example, 2L(2)/1R(1).

nervous system and cannot be deliberately controlled or stopped by the patient. Other tests can include blood flow studies such as plethysmography, finger systolic blood pressure, and ultrasound flow measurements with a Doppler sonography. For the assessment of direct nerve damage, these evaluations typically include standard neurologic tests, electrical studies (EMG/NCS), and muscle force measurements (dynamometer). Nerve biopsy and other special laboratory tests are usually not indicated. In hand-arm vibration syndrome, damage of both the median and ulnar nerve typically can be detected; in carpal tunnel syndrome, only the median nerve will be affected.

The cumulative vibration exposure dose can be roughly calculated by taking a detailed history of hand-arm vibration exposure and by assessing machine or tool vibration levels from comparison data banks available from research reports and centers.[40,41] The typical machine vibration level (weighted acceleration m/sec^2 rms) can be multiplied by the exposure duration in years, based on total hours of machine use and patterns of daily tool use, including break schedules and job alterations.

Medical treatment of hand-arm vibration syndrome can include medications to increase and ease the blood flow in the hands and fingers (calcium channel blocker, ∂1-blocker, or blood thinner). Of primary importance, however, is stopping the exposure to vibration and initiating a medical removal or transfer as early as possible. Vasospastic disease can gradually be improved in most cases if vibration exposure is stopped and the worker's duties replaced by other tasks. If carpal tunnel syndrome is diagnosed, intensive physical therapy, antiinflammatory medications, and possibly a splint during nonworking time should be used. Surgery should be considered for carpal tunnel syndrome only when it is advanced and if conservative medical treatment has failed. If hand-arm vibration syndrome has advanced to stage 3 or 4 of the Stockholm classification, no medical treatment may be effective and the condition may be irreversible. Workers younger than 40 have a poorer prognosis.

TABLE 3. The Stockholm Workshop Scale for Classification of Sensorineural Effects of the Hand-Arm Vibration Syndrome[61]

Stages	Symptoms
0SN	Exposed to vibration but no symptoms
1SN	Intermittent numbness with or without tingling
2SN	Intermittent persistent numbness, reduced sensory perception
3SN	Intermittent or persistent numbness, reduced tactile discrimination or manipulative dexterity or both

Note: The sensorineural stage is to be established for each hand.

PREVENTION

Primary prevention or source elimination of excessive vibration and shocks is of utmost importance. This can be accomplished through better ergonomic tool design and engineering to reduce and isolate vibration energy. Vibration can be attenuated by controlling amplitude, acceleration, frequency, or impulse shock characteristics of the tool. A high power-to-weight ratio and a low torque with a cutoff rather than slip-clutch have been found to be advantageous. Heavy, difficult-to-hold, bulky tools require increased grip forces, which lead to increased coupling and vibration transfer. Tool handles and control knobs should be designed and positioned to avoid awkward wrist and hand posture and slipping surfaces. Tools should be light and allow an easy grip. Work above the shoulder or head level should be avoided.

Because no effective personal protective equipment is available, administrative and organizational strategies should be applied. Operation times of vibrating tools should be kept to a minimum and should not exceed the maximal ISO 2631 FDP or European Union exposure levels. Frequent short breaks and modified work tasks are beneficial to reduce overloading and fatigue effects.

The manufacturer and suppliers should provide vibration and frequency data sheets to facilitate calculation of daily exposure schedules for workers and supervisors. Clear warning labels and exposure-level information for the operators should be placed on the tools and equipment.

Widely advertised vibration-absorbing gloves and pads generally are not useful and should not be relied on. Special machine and tool vibration characteristics will require customized damping solutions. Inappropriate personal protective equipment can lead to an increase of vibration effects (resonance) and safety problems. Vibrating tool operators should be educated to always keep the body and hands warm with appropriate clothing and gloves. A simple leather glove can be useful to both improve the grip control and to keep the hands warm. Studies have shown that workers with large, warm hands seem to be less at risk for hand-arm vibration syndrome. Smoking should be avoided, because it also contributes to blood vessel constriction.

WORKER EDUCATION AND TRAINING

Workers need education and training in the recognition of vibration risks, and they should learn preventive techniques. All tool operators should have a preplacement examination by a qualified physician, especially if tool vibration levels are above the 1 m/sec^2 (action limit), and be enrolled in a medical surveillance program (see chapter 13). Medical examinations should be offered yearly or more often. Workers should be instructed to report early signs and symptoms of hand-arm vibration syndrome. Permissible maximal exposure levels (5 m/sec^2 in the European Union) and action levels (1 m/sec^2 in the European Union) should be established and mandated in the U.S.

Summary

Almost all vibration-related disease ought to be preventable if an effective control program is in place that includes source and vibration transfer reduction, occupational medical surveillance, and early disease detection.

EXPOSURE TO HEAT AND COLD

Despite a progressive modernization in building techniques, construction workers' dynamic and static workloads remain substantial. Many construction tasks

require continuous movements, heavy lifting, awkward postures, and exposure to in-
clement weather.[9] Consequently, it is often forgotten that exposure to hot or cold environments may not only lead to reduced work time, reduced performance, and
increased error rates,[5,42,64] but also to severe illness or fatalities due to hypothermia
or heat stress.[15]

Heat Stress

Heat stress is a situation in which the addition of environmental heat load and
metabolic heat production exceeds the capabilities of the body to maintain normal
functions without excessive strain.[33] If basic precautions to allow the body to maintain a normal temperature are not taken, a person may be at risk for heat stress when
engaging in heavy physical activity in a hot environment. Because construction
workers often work outside, they are exposed to solar radiation. In addition, humidity is an aggravating factor because it prevents sweat from properly evaporating,
thereby impairing the body's normal thermoregulation.

EXTENT OF THE PROBLEM

Data are limited on the effects of hot thermal working conditions on injury and
illness in construction workers. Robinson et al. reviewed construction workers' illness compensation cases in 1977–1985 and identified the 20 most common construction-related health conditions.[67] Heat stroke, the only heat-related illness
reported, ranked among the top ten. Heat exhaustion, which is not generally recognized as an illness in construction workers' compensation data, is, however, a major
stage of heat stress, and it may necessitate rest in a cool environment along with oral
or intravenous rehydration. Unpublished data obtained from the Preventive
Medicine Division, Office of the Surgeon General of the U.S. Army, indicate that in
1985–1989, heat exhaustion cases requiring medical attention occurred 10 times
more often than did heat stroke.[50] Informal contacts with emergency physicians suggest that the number of heat exhaustion cases could be two to three times higher because most cases are not reported but are simply treated by removing the workers
from the workplace and allowing him or her to recover in a cool area for the rest of
the day. If this 10:1 ratio of heat exhaustion cases were applied to the number of heat
stroke cases reported in the workers' compensation data, heat exhaustion would rank
as the leading cause of worker claims in heavy construction, second in special
trades, and third in general building construction.

HAZARDOUS WASTE WORK

Hazardous waste clean-up or abatement has become an important job that is
performed by construction workers in the U.S. Much of the work requires abatement
workers to be protected by encapsulating chemical-protective clothing. Various
types of workers are involved, including asbestos workers, laborers, masons, carpenters, and equipment operators. The contribution of protective clothing to heat
stress has been described by many authors.[11,21,23,33,87] This protection acts as a barrier
against worker exposure to toxic materials but also limits the body's ability to adequately evacuate heat. As a result, the potential for increased risk of heat stress is apparent.[21] Critical knowledge gaps remain, especially in the area of work-and-rest
cycles for construction workers who must wear encapsulating chemical protective
clothing to perform their tasks.[54]

Nonetheless, all construction workers must be informed that hot environments
can still be hazardous. Workers can reduce the risks of heat exposure by protecting

their body from solar radiation, increasing their water intake, and taking work breaks in the shade.[19]

Cold-Related Syndromes

In the winter, many construction workers are exposed to cold environmental conditions. Low temperatures, mud, rain, chilly winds, and drafts on building sites may trigger cold-weather-related syndromes in workers overexerted by heavy physical labor.[28] When temperatures drop below freezing, unprotected extremities increase the risk for frostbite or trench foot. Jensen reported that 64% of all injuries related to cold temperature involved the hand or foot.[42]

Workers may avoid most cold-related injuries by improving their thermal insulation through wearing layers of clothing, winter cap/hard hat liners, extra socks, and gloves. However, added clothing limits the ability of a worker to perform tasks. Generally, there is a loss of performance: physiologic, psychologic, or both.

Summary

The protection of construction workers in hot or cold environments should be based on prevention. Because the environmental conditions cannot be easily controlled at construction sites, the promotion and implementation of a few basic precautions could significantly reduce the occurrence of heat- or cold-related injury or illness.

REFERENCES

1. American Conference of Governmental Industrial Hygienists: Threshold limit values for hand-arm vibration. Cincinnati, ACGIH, 1990–91.
2. American National Standards Institute S3.34: Guide for the measurement and evaluation of human exposure to vibration transmitted to the hand. New York, ANSI, 1986.
3. Asztély J: On the control of noise emission from handheld impact drills. Inter-Noise 83:107–110, 1983.
4. Bares LF, Salyers EF: A new material systems approach for controlling heavy equipment operator noise exposure. Inter-Noise 80:495–498, 1980.
5. Barrett MV: Heat stress disorders, old problems, new implications. AAOHN J 39:369–380, 1991.
6. Bartholomae RC, Parker RP: Mining machinery noise control guidelines, 1983. Pittsburgh, PA, U.S. Dept. of the Interior, Bureau of Mines, 1983.
7. Bilsom Corporation, Lakeland, Florida: Information on #707 Impact Headset. Product Literature.
8. California State Department of Public Health, Bureau of Occupational Health and U.S. Public Health Service, Division of Occupational Health: Occupational Health Study of Heavy Equipment Operators. January 1966.
9. Center to Protect Workers' Rights: An agenda for change. Report of the National Conference on Ergonomics, Safety, and Health in Construction. Washington, DC, July 18–22, 1993.
10. Coermann R: The mechanical impedance of the human body in sitting and standing position at low frequencies. In Lippert (ed): Vibration Research. Tarrytown, NY, Pergamon Press, 1963.
11. Cohen J: Heading off heat stress. EPRI J 2:23–27, 1988.
12. Daniel JH, Burks JA, Bartholomae RC, et al: The noise exposure of operators of mobile machines in U.S. surface coal mines, 1979. Pittsburgh, PA, U.S. Dept. of Interior, 1981, Bureau of Mines information circular 8841.
13. Dieckmann D: Einfluss horizontaler mechanischer Schwingungen auf den Menschen (Influence of horizontal mechanical vibrations on humans). Int Z angew Physiol einschl Arbeitsphysiol 17:83–100, 1958.
14. Dranitsaris P: Noise dose assessment of the construction industry [masters' thesis]. Department of Chemical Engineering and Applied Chemistry, University of Toronto, Toronto, Ontario, 1982.
15. Dukes-Dobos, FN: Hazards of heat exposure. Scand J Work Environ Health 7:73–83, 1980.
16. Dupuis H, Zerlett G: The Effects of Whole-Body Vibration. Berlin: Springer Verlag, 1986.
16a. Dupuis H, Zerlett G: Beanspruchung des Menschen durch mechanische Schwingungen: Kenntnisstand zur Wirkung von Ganz-Körper-Schwingungen (Stresses on humans caused by mechanical vibration: Current knowledge of the effects of whole-body vibration). Bonn, Germany, Schriftenreihe des Hauptverbandes der gewerblichen Berufsgenossenschaten (Commercial Insurance Association, Research Division), 1984.

17. Dupuis H, Zerlett G: Whole-body vibration and disorders of the spine. Int Arch Occup Environ Health 59:323–336, 1987.
18. EC 1993: Amtsblatt der Europaeischen Gemeinschaften (Bulletin of the European Communities). Nr. C 77/12, 18.3.1993.
19. Environmental Protection Agency and Occupational Safety and Health Administration: A guide to heat stress in agriculture. Washington, DC, EPA and OSHA, 1993, EPA-750-b-92-001.
20. Farkkila M: Vibration induced injury. Br J Ind Med 43:361–362, 1986.
21. Favata EA, Buckler G, Gochfeld M: Heat stress in hazardous waste workers: Evaluation and prevention. Occup Med 5:79–91, 1990.
22. Franks JR:Personal communication to Scott Schneider, 1993.
23. Goldman RF: Heat stress in industrial protective encapsulating garments. In Levine SP, Martin WF (eds): Protecting Personnel at Hazardous Waste Sites. Boston, Butterworth, 1985, pp 215–266.
24. Gonner HW: Noise and vibration reduction on construction machinery. Ergonomics in Developing Countries: An International Symposium, November 18–25, 1985. Geneva, International Labor Office, 1987, Occupational Safety and Health Series No. 58, pp 224–237.
25. Griffin MJ: The effects of vibration on health. Southhampton, University of Southhampton, Great Britain, 1982, memorandum 632.
26. Griffin MJ: Handbook of Human Vibration. London, Academic Press, 1990.
27. Halén M: Constructional noise—a survey of noise on building ites. Bygghälsan, Stockholm, 1973.
28. Hamlet MP: Human cold injuries. In Pandolf KB, Sawka MN, Gonzalez RR (eds): Human Performance Physiology and Environmental Medicine at Terrestrial Extremes. Benchmark Press, 1988, pp 435–466.
29. Hansen WE: Reduction of the noise from circular saw blades. Inter-Noise 83:737–741. 1983.
30. Heide R: Zur Wirkung langzeitiger beruflicher Ganzkörper-vibrationsexposition [dissertation]. (Consequences of long-term occupational exposure to whole-body vibration). Humboldt Universität, Berlin, German Democratic Republic, 1977.
31. Heliövaara M, Knekt P, Aromaa A: Incidence and risk factors of herniated lumbar intervertebral disc or sciatica leading to hospitalization. J Chron Dis 40:251–258, 1987.
32. Heliövaara M: Occupation and risk of herniated lumbar intervertebral disc or sciatica leading to hospitalization. J Chron Dis 40:259–264, 1987.
33. Hénanc R: La chaleur en milieu militaire (Heat in the military environment). In Manuel de Médecine du Travail Appliquée aux Armées. (Handbook of Occupational Medicine Applied to Military Activities). Publication 2030 DEF/DCSSA/2/TECH, Office of the Surgeon General, Paris, 1981, pp 14–35.
34. Hulshof C, v Zanten B: Whole-body vibration and low-back pain. Int Arch Occup Environ Health 59:205–220, 1987.
35. International Labour Office: Noise and vibration in the working environment. Geneva, ILO, 1976, Occupational Safety and Health Series No. 33.
36. ISO 2631: Evaluation of human exposure to whole-body vibration. Part 1: General requirements. Geneva, International Standards Organization, 1985.
37. ISO 8662.1: Hand-held portable power tools—Measurement and the assessment of human exposure to hand-transmitted vibration. Geneva, International Standards Organization, 1988.
38. ISO 5349: Mechanical vibration. Guidelines for the measurement and the assessment of human exposure to hand-transmitted vibration. Geneva, International Standards Organization, 1986.
39. ISSA: Vibration at the Workplace. International Colloquium of the International Section of ISSA for Research on Prevention of Occupational Risk, Vienna, 1989.
40. ISSA/Christ E, et al: Vibration at Work. International section "Research". Institut National de Recherche et de Securite (INRS), Paris, 1989.
41. Jacobson B: Vibration hand-held machines in the construction industry. Safety Science 15:367–373, 1992.
42. Jensen R: Worker's compensation claims related to heat and cold exposures. Professional Safety 29:19–24, 1983.
43. Johanning E: Survey results of back disorders and health problems in subway train operators exposed to whole-body vibration. Scand J Work Environ Health 17:414–419, 1991.
44. Johanning E, Wilder D, Landrigan P, Pope M: Whole-body vibration exposure in subway cars and review of adverse health effects. J Occup Med 33:605–612, 1991.
45. Junghanns H: Die Wirbelsäule in der Arbeitsmedizin (The spine in occupational medicine). Stuttgart, Hippokrates, 1979.
46. Kenney GD, Ayer HE: Noise exposure and hearing levels of workers in the sheet metal construction trade. Am Ind Hyg Assoc J 28:626–632, 1975.
47. Kessler FM: Pavement breaker/rock drill noise control methods. Inter-Noise 78:329–336, 1978.

48. Kessler FM, Schomer PD: Pile driver noise control. Inter-Noise 80:321–324, 1980.
49. Kovac JG, Bartholomae RC, Bockosh GR: Bulldozer noise control. Inter-Noise 80:457–460, 1980.
50. Lipnick R: Letter of February 8, 1993, R. Lipnick, United States Army, Office of the Surgeon General, Division of Safety Research, NIOSH.
51. Magid EB, Coermann R: The reaction of the human body to extreme vibrations. Proc Inst Environ Sci 135, 1960.
52. Marraccini LC: Experiments in bulldozer retrofit noise control. Inter-Noise 84:181–184, 1984.
53. Miyashita K, Morioka I, Tanabe T, Takeda S: Symptoms of construction workers exposed to whole-body and local vibration. Int Arch Occup Environ Health 64:347–351, 1992.
54. Moran J: Personal protective equipment. Appl Ind Hyg 4:7–9, 1988.
55. Müller EA: Die Wirkung sinusförmiger Vertikalschwingungen auf den sitzenden und stehenden Menschen. (The effect of sinusoidal vertical vibration on sitting and standing human beings) Arbeitsphysiologie 10:459–476, 1939.
56. National Institute for Occupational Safety and Health: Criteria for a recommended standard occupational exposure to hand-arm vibration. NTIS, 1989, PB90-168048.57. National Institute of Occupational Safety and Health: Vibration syndrome. Springfield, VA, National Technical Information Service, 1983, Current Intelligence Bulletin 38, publication 83-110.
58. Ottoboni F, Milby T: Occupational disease potentials in the heavy equipment operator. Arch Environ Health 15:317–321, 1967.
59. Patterson WN: Portable air compressor noise diagnosis and control. Inter-Noise 74:519–524, 1974.
60. Pawlik PU: Substrategy for construction noise abatement. Washington, DC, Office of Noise Abatement and Control, EPA, 1981, report EPA/550/9-82-151.
61. Pelmear PL, Taylor W: Hand-arm vibration syndrome. J Fam Pract 38(2):180–185, 1994.
62. Pelmear PL, Taylor W, Wasserman DE (eds): Hand-Arm Vibration. New York, Van Nostrand Reinhold, 1992.
63. Peltor Corporation, East Providence, Rhode Island: Information on Tactical 7 hearing protectors. Product Literature.
64. Ramsey JD, Morrissey, S: Isodecrements curves for task performance in hot environments. Appl Erg 9:66–72, 1978.
65. Roberts ME: 1989 Hearing test results in the construction industry. British Columbia Workers Compensation Board, 1990.
66. Roberts ME: Potential for noise-induced hearing loss claims in the building construction industry. Vancouver, British Columbia Workers Compensation Board, 1985.
67. Robinson C, Venable H, Stern F, et al: The assessment of hazards in the construction industry. Proceedings of the Eighth International Symposium on Occupational Health Epidemiology. Arch Mal Prof 12: 601, 1991.
68. Sandover J: Dynamic loading as a possible source of low-back disorders. Spine 8:652–658, 1983.
69. Sandover J: Vibration, posture and low-back disorders of professional drivers. Department of Human Science, Loughbrough University of Technology, Great Britain, DHS report 402, 5/1981.
70. Schneider S, Susi P: Final Report—An Investigation of Health Hazards on a New Construction Project. Washington, DC, Center to Protect Workers' Rights, 1993, report OSH1-93.
71. Seidel H, Heide R: Long-term effects of whole-body vibration: A critical survey of the literature. Int Arch Occup Environ Health 58:1–26, 1986.
72. Seidel H, Blüthner R, Bräuer D, et al: Whole-body vibration and the spine—Mechanisms, health risk and hygienic evaluation. Second Workshop on Criteria for the Evaluation of Effects of Whole-body Vibration on Man. International Labour Organization, Moscow, 1988.
73. Shaw S, Halliwell NA: Stone cutting saw: Control using the water supply. Inter-Noise 83:147–150, 1983.
74. Spear RC, Keller C, Behrens V, et al: Morbidity patterns among heavy equipment operators exposed to whole body vibration. Cincinnati, NIOSH, 1976, Dept. of Health Education, and Welfare publication 77-120.
75. Stojanowski WJ, Troszok A, Niewczas BM: Aerodynamic noise eliminator of the pneumatic tools. Inter-Noise 83:163–166, 1983.
76. Suter AH, Franks JR (eds): A practical guide to effective hearing conservation programs in the workplace. Cincinnati, NIOSH, 1990, U.S. Dept. Health and Human Services publication 90-120.
77. Toth WJ: Noise abatement techniques for construction equipment. Springfield, VA, National Technical Information Service. Society of Automotive Engineers Report to the U.S. Dept. of Transportation, National Highway Traffic Safety Administration, 1979, report DOT-TSC-NHTSA-79-45.
78. Troup JDG: Driver's back pain and its prevention—A review of the postural, vibratory and muscular factors, together with the problem of transmitted road-shock. Appl Erg 9:207–214, 1978.

79. U.S. Department of the Interior, U.S. Bureau of Mines, Pittsburgh Research Center: Bulldozer noise control. By Bolt Beranek and Newman, Inc., Contract J0177049, May 1980.
80. U.S. Department of the Interior, U.S. Bureau of Mines, Pittsburgh Research Center: Front-end loader noise control. By Bolt Beranek and Newman, Inc., Contract J0395028, June 1981.
81. U.S. Department of Labor, Occupational Safety and Health Administration: Enforcement data (personal communication), 1993.
82. U.S. Environmental Protection Agency: Noise Control Act of 1972 as amended by the Quiet Communities Act of 1978, December 1978.
83. U.S. Environmental Protection Agency: Noise Emission Standards for Transportation Equipment—Medium and Heavy Trucks. 41 FR 15537-15558, April 13,1976. (and subsequent actions in 1979 (44 FR 67659), 1981 (46 FR 8497), 1982 (47 FR 7186), 1985 (50 FR 25516) and 1986 (51 FR 850)).
84. U.S. Environmental Protection Agency: Portable Air Compressors—Noise Emmission Standards. 41 FR 2161-2182, January 14, 1976.
85. Wasserman DE: Control aspects of occupational hand-arm vibration. Appl Ind Hyg 8(4):22–26, 1989.
86. Wasserman DE: Human aspects of occupational vibration. In Salvendy G (ed) Advances in Human Factors/Ergonomics 8. Amsterdam, Elsevier, 1978, pp 1–188.
87. White MK, Hodous TK: Reduced work tolerance associated with wearing protective clothing and respirators. Am Ind Hyg Assoc J 4:304–310, 1987.
88. Wickström G: Effect of work on degenerative back disease. A review. Scand J Work Environ Health 4(suppl1):1–12, 1979.
89. Wilder DG, Woodworth BB, Frymoyer JW, Pope MH. Vibration and the Human Spine. Spine 7:243–254, 1982.

SCOTT SCHNEIDER, CIH
LAURA PUNNETT, ScD
THOMAS M. COOK, PhD, PT

ERGONOMICS: APPLYING WHAT WE KNOW

From the Center to Protect
  Workers' Rights
Washington, DC (SS)
  and
Department of Work Environment
University of Massachusetts
Lowell, Massachusetts (LP)
  and
Biomechanics/Ergonomics
  Laboratory
University of Iowa
Iowa City, Iowa (TMC)

Reprint requests to:
Scott Schneider, CIH
Center to Protect Workers' Rights
111 Massachusetts Avenue NW
Washington, DC 20001

Ergonomics is concerned with the match between job requirements and worker capabilities. It is the science of fitting the job to the worker, designing workplaces, equipment, tools, and work methods that minimize the risk of injury or illness. To a lesser extent, ergonomics may deal with fitting the worker to the job through job selection and, occasionally, worker training, but this approach is generally less effective.

One primary application of ergonomics to construction trades is the prevention of injuries and illnesses that affect the musculoskeletal system. These injuries and illnesses are often referred to collectively as work-related musculoskeletal disorders, or WMD. These sprains, strains, and related problems can be acute or chronic, in the latter case resulting from weeks, months, or years of accumulated microtrauma. The chronic problems are known as cumulative trauma disorders, repetitive strain injuries, or repetitive motion injuries. A distinction is often made between acute musculoskeletal *injuries* and chronic *illnesses,* although the distinction may be more illusory than real. For example, upper extremity cumulative trauma disorders such as carpal tunnel syndrome are usually classified by the Bureau of Labor Statistics as illnesses. However, back disorders are classified by many people as injuries even though they may be preceded by long-term exposure to heavy lifting, repetitive bending, or other ergonomic exposures.[7] Regardless of the nomenclature, work-related musculoskeletal disorders are becoming increasingly recognized as widespread and costly problems in construction and other industries.

In the United States, work-related illnesses reported to the Bureau or Labor Statistics for all employment increased nearly two and a half times in 1986–1991.[6] Most of the new cases in these 6 years were classified as "diseases associated with repeated trauma," which increased from 18% of the total cases in 1981 to 61% in 1991. Additionally, low back injuries are estimated to account for about 16% of all compensable injuries in the workplace and about one third of all workers' compensation costs.[32]

In construction, the rate for work-related cumulative trauma in 1991 was 3.1 cases per 10,000 full-time workers, second only to cases of skin disorders among work-related illnesses.[7] In a study of self-reported work-related complaints over 1 year among 526 unionized construction workers, Cook et al. found the prevalence of musculoskeletal complaints to be 75% in the low back, 41% in both the neck and wrist/hands, 40% in the knees, and 28% in the feet.[11] In 1994, Hunting et al. reported on a survey of electricians showing that about half had back or hand/wrist symptoms at least three times in the previous year or one episode lasting longer than 1 week during the previous year.[15] About 82% of the workers had at least one symptom in the past year, while 52% reported 2 or more symptoms.

Work-related medical and compensation costs for WMD in the U.S. are estimated to be between $20 billion and $40 billion each year.[20] In addition, indirect costs resulting from absenteeism, retraining, lost productivity, and other hidden consequences are estimated to be more than double the direct costs. The effects of these disorders in human suffering and disrupted lives, at home and at work, cannot be measured in monetary terms.

ERGONOMIC RISK FACTORS IN CONSTRUCTION WORK

The physical aspects of a job that increase the risk of WMD in construction are similar to those identified in other industries. These risk factors include *repetition* of a same motion; manual forces that are excessive or prolonged, such as heavy lifting or frequent or prolonged grasping; *postures* that are awkward or maintained for extended periods; *pressure* from hard surfaces or sharp edges on the body; *vibration* from tools and machinery; and *environmental factors* such as extremes of temperature and humidity.[25]

These risk factors are integral parts of many construction jobs as they are currently configured. Lifting and carrying heavy materials, working with the hands overhead or below knee level for extended times, and being exposed to vibration and extreme environmental conditions are common.[28] In one recent study, construction workers identified the most troublesome elements of their jobs as maintaining awkward postures for prolonged times (69% of respondents), working in adverse environmental conditions (67%), having to work "very hard" (44%), and having to reach overhead (43%).[11] However, few construction jobs have been studied extensively to document the frequency or intensity of ergonomic risk factors. One exception is a series of studies by Wickström et al. that sought to document the extent of back injuries among workers tying concrete reinforcement rods together.[27] The authors reported a larger percentage of concrete-reinforcement workers suffering harmful effects from difficult work postures than any other group. Several investigations of injury data and worker symptoms and complaints are underway to develop trade-specific injury profiles and to provide more detailed assessments of ergonomic risk factors within the construction trades. Although few full-scale epidemiologic studies have been conducted among construction workers, the high rates of musculoskeletal complaints and the presence of known ergonomic stressors have been documented in the industry.[28] It is therefore appropriate to ask how these problems can be corrected even while further research is carried out.

Who's Responsible For Ergonomics

Regardless of whether they understand the term *ergonomics,* a wide range of people make decisions affecting the number and severity of ergonomic risk factors to which construction workers are exposed. Architects, designers, and project owners determine the materials, methods, and procedures that will be needed to complete a project. Their choices influence the postures, repetitions, forces, and other factors to which workers will be exposed. Contractors and subcontractors clearly have a major impact on how project plans are translated into a final product. Through their decisions about the flow of materials, the sequencing and coordination of tasks, scheduling, and other factors, contractors can directly influence the ergonomic risk factors on a job site.[21]

Suppliers of materials, tools, and machinery also influence risk factors for WMD through the design, packaging, and delivery methods they adopt. Such factors include the weight of a load to be lifted or the time and effort required to find a particular item in a bundle of parts.

Construction workers use their bodies at work in ways that affect the likelihood of illness and injury. For reasons discussed below, it can be argued that they may be victims of unfortunate circumstances; nevertheless, workers have a major contribution to make in reducing WMD because they alone know all the constraints involved in completing a job.

Regulators also make, or fail to make, decisions that affect ergonomic risk factors in construction.

Organizational and Psychosocial Factors

In construction, change does not come easily and occurs in the context of certain psychosocial and economic realities. The ever-changing mix of employees and employers (contractors) tends to fragment accountability and incentives for controlling ergonomic risk factors in the workplace. Contractors who may never see or be held responsible for the long-term effects of their workers' exposure to ergonomic risk factors have little incentive to modify work practices or purchase new tools or equipment to reduce hazards.

For instance, whole-body vibration puts operators of construction equipment at high risk for back problems. Solutions exist. Vibration-dampened ergonomically designed cabs produce much lower stress on the musculoskeletal system.[1] But, because these are cumulative injures from chronic exposure and workers change jobs frequently, contractors have little incentive to retrofit or replace old cabs or pay extra for better cab designs. Unless workers are experiencing WMD problems, contractors do not recognize the need. Here the fluid nature of the construction industry and the chronic nature of WMD collide to produce inaction.

In addition to the ergonomic risk factors that contribute to WMD, injury and illness rates are influenced by economic factors.[18] During recessions or when unemployment is high in a particular area, workers may be more likely to risk injury, not to report injuries and illnesses, and to work while injured. They may need the work, fear losing their jobs, or may be concerned about not being hired on a future job. Even in good economic times, some construction jobs, such as drywall installation, may be compensated on a piece-rate basis, which often encourages workers to perform faster and for longer hours than can be sustained without risk of injury or illness. Paradoxically, safety incentive programs, in which employees are rewarded for working a certain number of days without a lost-time accident, may encourage workers to underreport illnesses and injuries and to continue working with pain and discomfort until their conditions are more severe and even disabling.[17]

Proposed changes to reduce WMD must also deal with psychosocial factors. Construction work is considered to occur in a "rough and tumble" culture that encourages workers to get the job done at any physical cost. Such a climate tends to foster overexertion, when workers feel pressure from peers and supervisors to push beyond reasonable limits. Scheduling and production pressures may tend to speed up the work, and workers may cut safety corners to complete the work faster. Supervisors and contractors may not recognize or be willing to accept the possibility that workers may be more productive over the long-term by working more slowly but steadily. Furthermore, limited opportunities to participate in decisions about one's own work process are believed by some to increase workers' physiologic susceptibility to the effects of physical stressors.[5]

Another economic and psychosocial factor, the transient nature of construction employment, impedes efforts to pinpoint and control the causes of injuries and illnesses or to assess the efficacy of ergonomic interventions. With many different subcontractors moving on and off a site, there is rarely a central authority for safety and health as there is in many larger industrial settings. One contractor may create hazards for another's employees. Most often there is no responsible person on a work site who knows about ergonomic risk factors and is authorized to correct situations before they result in injury or illness.

CONTROLS FOR ERGONOMIC RISK FACTORS

Once the ergonomic risk factors associated with particular work tasks are identified and understood, the approaches to controlling or modifying the risk factors are engineering controls, administrative controls, and the use of personal protective equipment.[20]

Engineering Controls. Engineering controls are measures that are taken to physically modify the forcefulness, repetitiveness, awkwardness, vibration levels, physical pressures, or environmental extremes associated with performing a job. Examples of engineering controls include modifications of materials, tools, machinery, and work surfaces. Engineering controls are usually the most effective long-term approach to reducing risks for WMD. However, in a highly dynamic work environment such as a construction site, finding feasible engineering controls may be difficult.

Administrative Controls. Administrative controls, such as rest breaks, changing work organization, or worker training, are an important part of any program intended to reduce WMD among construction workers.

Personal Protective Equipment. The third approach, the use of personal protective equipment, is considered much less reliable than administrative or engineering controls for preventing WMD. The ergonomic value of backbelts, wrist splints, and vibration-absorbing gloves is largely unproved.[21]

THE ERGONOMICS PROCESS AND THE TEAM APPROACH

Experience in industrial settings over the last 10–15 years has shown that the most successful strategy for making ergonomic improvements is to use a team approach and develop a process for identifying and solving problems.[31] This approach is analogous to several highly successful management methods, such as total quality management. Using TQM to reduce WMD in the construction industry may be more difficult but more necessary than it is in industrial settings.

The ergonomics process is an ongoing cycle of identifying high-risk tasks, analyzing the tasks for ergonomic risk factors, proposing a solution for reducing the risk factors, implementing the intervention, and evaluating the solution. The cyclical nature of the process is important for two reasons. First, the process is rarely perfect the first time, and one or more repetitions are almost always necessary to fine-tune the details of the proposed improvement. At times, a proposed solution may be tried and abandoned entirely in favor of an alternative. Second, the process must be cyclical and continuous because of ongoing changes in designs, materials, tools, machinery, and work methods. These changes are especially prevalent in construction, where a job site may change dramatically in a short time.

Who should be involved in this ergonomics process? Experience in industry and common sense indicate that everybody who can influence or be influenced by proposed ergonomic interventions should have input in the decision making if it is to have the highest probability of success.[31] Too many times, impressive engineering solutions to ergonomic problems have gone unused due to failure to consult workers or supervisors. In addition to workers and contractors, the team could include suppliers, manufacturers, owners, and others, depending on the problem to be addressed.

Examples of Ergonomic Interventions in Construction

Ergonomic interventions to control WMD can range from the very simple to the more elaborate. Modifications can be costly, but in many cases they cost little or nothing. Many ergonomic improvements actually save time and money. There are lessons to be learned from successful and unsuccessful ergonomic interventions.

Stresses related to **drywall installation** have been reduced using a number of job modifications.[26] Simple handles have been developed for carrying one or two sheets of drywall to reduce stress on the hands and shoulders. Dollies for moving drywall have been developed that are narrow, for getting through small doorways, but that can be tipped sideways to create a table for cutting the drywall and will allow for picking it up at waist height. Mechanical lifts exist to raise and hold drywall overhead to reduce shoulder stress.

One study found that workers fastening drywall became fatigued and significantly slowed their work pace late in the workshift.[1a] Experiments with frequent 10- to 15-second breaks, or micropauses, indicated that workers could maintain their productivity throughout the day and ultimately be more productive.

In some regions, drywall dimensions have been reduced from 4 feet wide (120 cm) to 3 feet wide (90 cm) to reduce the weight of the board, making it easier to carry and lift.[4] This intervention will need to be closely evaluated because this change could also result both in increased repetitions and dust exposure for drywall fasteners and tapers.

A tool has been developed to allow **concrete reinforcement** workers to tie rods from a standing height.[12] This technique is widely used in Europe and is intended to reduce the load on the back that results from working in a bent posture and the stress on the wrist from repeated twisting of the wires. However, the Swedish-developed tool weighs 15–18 pounds, and U.S. workers complain it is too heavy. The tool is so different from current practice in the U.S. that many workers initially reject it as no improvement to their current technique. Because the tool requires the use of different muscle groups than do current work methods, there is a need for an acclimation period of 2–3 weeks before workers can decide whether the tool provides an improved work method for them. This tool is apparently most useful for bridge decks, which must be tied at every junction for long runs.

Painting overhead can place strain on the arms and shoulders from pressing a long pole with a roller on it against the ceiling. The worker must maintain a tight grip on the pole to support it and press upward to apply the paint. One successful and inexpensive intervention in Sweden has been the use of a "painter's disk," a simple plastic flange that screws onto the pole just above the handle. The weight of the pole and roller can then be supported by the flange, reducing the required grip force.[9] Neck stress, another ergonomic problem associated with painting overhead, has been addressed with an inflatable neck pillow that is worn behind the neck and attached by suspenders to the pants.[22]

Laying of masonry blocks is known to cause back injuries. The weight of the blocks and awkward postures used to handle them are obvious risk factors. In Germany, masonry blocks are manufactured with handholds to make them easier to lift, and a limit has been set on the weight of blocks that one person is allowed to lift.[16] Blocks heavier than 25 kg (55 lb) must be lifted by a hoist. Blocks weighing 7.5–25 kg (16.5–55 lb) must be lifted using two hands; only blocks weighing less than 7.5 kg (16.5 lb) may be lifted one-handed. Even stricter standards exist in Sweden, where one-handed lifts may be used only for blocks weighing up to 3 kg (6.6 lb); two-handed lifts are required for blocks weighing 3–12 kg (6.6–26.4 lb).[2] Blocks weighing 12–20 kg (26.4–44 lb) may be lifted only between knee and shoulder heights (0.5–1.5 m), and blocks heavier than 20 kg must be lifted mechanically.

In general, **materials handling** is a major risk factor for ergonomic injuries on job sites. Better coordination of materials shipments and storage has been suggested as a way to reduce injury rates.[22] For example, materials should be stored as close as possible to where they will be used. In Germany, a just-in-time delivery system for bricks has been developed and implemented with the cooperation of the brick manufacturers, contractors, and unions.[19] This modification requires much more coordination between the trades. Better planning must be evaluated for possible negative consequences such as speeding up the pace of the work.

Proper **physical conditioning** has been shown to help prevent injuries. In Sweden, an exercise program was introduced to allow workers 10 minutes of paid time to limber up before beginning work.[10] Workers who participate in this program say they feel better and healthier and have fewer aches and pains than those who don't. The program gives workers time to socialize and plan their day, which has a beneficial psychological impact. Similar exercise programs have been instituted by several construction companies in the U.S. in the past few years.

Training is a common administrative control strategy for reducing WMD. Training in "proper lifting" techniques has been a main emphasis of many worker training programs, but few data support this approach as an effective method for back injury prevention.[23] In fact, the method of lifting most widely taught (with the knees, keeping the back straight) may be more dangerous in some situations. However, training that helps workers develop strategies for recognizing and avoiding dangerous working conditions may have much broader benefits. Workers can benefit from understanding what causes WMD and what factors in the workplace put them at higher risk for injury and illness.

Introducing New Technologies in Construction

Technology can have a dramatic impact on people's jobs—positive and negative. Construction practices have changed considerably in the past 20 years. For example, the number of poured concrete structures is increasing. Walls are almost entirely drywall construction. Hot asphalt roofing is often replaced with single-ply roofing. Sheet-metal duct work is mostly built off-site using computer-aided design and plasma-arc cutters. Some housing sections are made on assembly lines and bolted together on site.

Although none of these changes were made with any thought toward their ergonomic impact on workers, current technologic capacity includes the ability to design tools and equipment specifically with ergonomic factors in mind. The situation is analogous to car manufacturers who emphasize design-for-assembly as an important aspect of the overall production process. Workers should be involved in the design, testing, and implementation of any new technology. Workers know the intricacies of their jobs and the potential problems best. They are often the best source for ideas on how to redesign equipment to meet their needs. Worker involvement in redesign will lead to greater acceptance later.[30]

Workers are often skeptical of new technology and may have good reason.[3] It is not unusual for ergonomic improvements to be "sold" to employers as a way to reduce injuries and increase productivity. This can pose a dilemma for workers. Increases in productivity can lead to a need for fewer workers. In an economic climate in which as many as 50% of construction workers may already be unemployed, workers may not be receptive to technological innovations that increase productivity and reduce the amount of needed labor. However, even if the number of workers required for a job declines, if a company becomes more competitive and obtains more work as a result, employment by the company might remain constant. Workers may reject or resist change unless they see benefits, such as fewer accidents, a longer work life, reduced pain and suffering, or increased productivity that can maintain employment levels.

Another important aspect of new technology in construction is also related to employment levels: the skill level required to use the technology. The easier it is to use, the faster it will be accepted. A danger exists that new technology, in reducing the skill level required to do a job, may lessen job security of highly trained, more experienced workers. Ideally, new technology should give workers more skills.

If a new technology is substantially different from current work methods or requires markedly different skills, workers will need training and time to acclimate to the new methods. If the new technology helps workers and allows them to work in a manner similar to what they are accustomed to, it will be accepted more easily. Workers often must be convinced of the hazards of doing the work in the traditional way. For example, battery-powered screwdrivers are similar to the electric screwdrivers commonly used in the industry, but they weigh less and are more portable and, thus, preferable ergonomically. Once manufacturers began making models with smaller and more durable, longer-life batteries, they were widely accepted in construction.

Construction workers often buy their own hand tools. The payback time often needs to be short, because individual workers may not be able or willing to make long-term investments for uncertain benefits. The same economic concerns are faced by contractors who may be asked to make large investments in new equipment.

There is a lack of information about which new technologies or tools to use. Despite the marketing efforts of many tool manufacturers, there is no such thing as an "ergonomic tool" that is good for every task. Tools must be assessed in the context of the work for which they will be used. Their efficacy depends on their appropriate use. A bent-handle hammer, for instance, has been suggested as an ergonomic intervention for carpenters.[29] However, although it might not help with nailing concrete forms, it might be useful for nailing roofing materials.

IMPLEMENTING WHAT WE KNOW

Once effective ergonomic control measures are identified, three levels of implementation can be used: education, regulation, and engineering.

Education about how risks of WMD can be reduced is important at all levels. Suppliers, owners, contractors, supervisors, and workers all need to know how the work site can be improved to reduce WMD. Given the financial and personal costs associated with WMD, individuals at each level should have ample motivation for implementing ergonomic improvements. Ergonomic improvements to prevent WMD also can help make jobs more accessible to already-injured workers. In the U.S., the Americans with Disabilities Act, which requires reasonable accommodation for injured workers, could have a significant impact on construction work sites in the future.

However, experience has shown that regulation is often necessary to assure widespread adoption of safer and less risky work practices. Both OSHA and the American National Standards Institute are developing standards intended to reduce ergonomic risk factors and their consequences. The construction industry knows the importance of conducting job hazard analyses as part of project planning; perhaps ergonomic impact will someday be incorporated into these analyses.

A national strategy to prevent WMD in construction must be multifaceted. It must focus on the development of engineering controls and interventions and their dissemination in the workplace. Secondly, it must lead to implementation of effective administrative strategies. Third, a national strategy must promote a research effort focused primarily on identification of common ergonomic problems and effective solutions. NIOSH has a control technologies branch that has developed many control technologies, such as for woodworking machinery, and it could be useful in devising interventions for construction.[13]

Fourth, an essential part of an effective national strategy to reduce WMD must be information dissemination. Databases like the Solutions database from the Canadian Center for Occupational Safety and Health can provide information about solutions that have been devised for occupational safety and health problems.[8] Use of the news media, including articles in union and contractor publications, presentations at conferences, and television programs, can play an important role in raising awareness of ergonomic issues and possible solutions. Innovative mechanisms are needed for information dissemination such as "construction extension services" similar to those that exist for agriculture. Construction technology centers need to be developed similar to those being establishing for manufacturing industries by the National Institute for Standards and Technology. Economic incentives such as tax credits or low-interest loans could be used to stimulate the adoption of new technology.

Innovations that cannot be implemented site-by-site, such as redesigned concrete blocks or ergonomically better rotary tower crane cabins, will need to involve manufacturers, materials engineers, owners, contractors, workers, and, in some instances, regulatory agencies.

REFERENCES

1. Andersson B, Norlander S, Wos H: Evaluation of muscular stress in construction machine operators: An EMG study. Appl Occup Environ Hyg 10:161–169, 1995.

1a. Andersson P: Manuellt skruvningsarbete utan och med mikropauser: An EMG-studie (Manual screw tightening with and without micropauses) [English abstract]. Bygghälsan Bulletin 91-09-16, 1991, p 39.

2. A pillow to cushion the neck. Working Environment in Sweden 1992.

3. Bernard E: Information technology: Old problems, new tools, and new possibilities for a healthy workplace. In Brown MP, Froines JR (eds): Technological Change in the Workplace-Health Impacts for Workers. Los Angeles, University of California at Los Angeles, 1993, pp 9–22.

4. Björklund M, Helmerskog M, Nordberg/Bohlin M, et al: 90 sheets for the 90s [English abstract]. Bygghälsan Bulletin, September 16, 1991, pp 35–36.

5. Bongers PM, deWinter CR, Kompier MAJ, Hildebrandt VH: Psychosocial factors at work and musculoskeletal disease. Scand J Work Environ Health 19:297–312, 1993.

6. Bureau of Labor Statistics: Occupational Injuries and Illness in the United States by Industry, 1991. Washington, DC, U.S. Dept. of Labor, 1993, bulletin 2424.

7. Bureau of Labor Statistics: Recordkeeping Guidelines for Occupational Injuries and Illnesses. Washington, DC, U.S. Dept. of Labor, 1986.

8. Canadian Center for Occupational Health and Safety: Solutions. Hamilton, Ontario, Canadian Center for Occupational Health and Safety.

9. Cederqvist T: Jämförande studie av erfordrad muskelkraft i underarmen vid innertaksmälning utan och med avlastningsstopp—an EMD-studie (Comparative study of needed muscular strength in the lower arm during painting of ceilings with and without a painter's disk). Bygghälsan Report, April 1984.

10. Cederqvist T, Gustafson B, Jonsson H, Lindström H: Prevention of muscuo-skeletal injuries in the Swedish construction industry: Experience from five years of a pre-work warm-up program. In Proceedings of the 12th Triennial Congress of the International Ergonomics Association, Vol 2. Toronto, Human Factors Association of Canada, 1994, pp 60–62.

11. Cook TM, Zimmerman CL: A symptom and job factor survey of unionized construction workers. In Kumar S (ed): Advances in Industrial Ergonomics and Safety IV. Bristol, PA, Taylor and Francis, 1992.

12. GLIM Aktiebolag Company: Glim-Scan Clip Chairs. Product literature, GLIM Aktiebolag Company, Norrköping, Sweden.

13. Hampl V, Johnston OE: Control of wood dust from horizontal belt sanding. Am Ind Hyg Assoc J 46:567–577, 1985.

14. Hammarskjöld E: Blocks and bricks of masonry—weight recommendations—A new Swedish standard [English abstract]. Bygghälsan Bulletin 1987-05-01, 1987, p 18.

15. Hunting KL, Welch LS, Cuccherini BA, Seiger LA: Musculoskeletal symptoms among electricians. Am J Ind Med 25:149–163, 1994.

16. Kaiser R, Linke-Kaiser G: Verbesserung der Arbeitsbedingungen im Mauerwersbau (Improving work conditions for masons). Ergomed 16:14–25, 1992.

17. Lessin, N: Testimony on the Comprehensive Occupational Safety and Health Reform Act (HR 1280)-given 7/21/93 before the House subcommittee on Labor Standards, Occupational Safety and Health. New Solutions 4:76–85, 1994.

18. Levitt RE: The organization of work in construction. In Helander M (ed): Human Factors/Ergonomics for Building and Construction. New York, Wiley & Sons, 1981, pp 217–277.

19. Linke-Kaiser G: Presentation at the National Conference on Ergonomics, Safety and Health in Construction, Washington, DC, June 20, 1993.

20. National Institute for Occupational Safety and Health: A National Strategy for Occupational Musculoskeletal Injuries—Implementation Issues and Research needs—1991 Conference Summary. Cincinnati, Dept. of Health and Human Services, 1992, NIOSH publication 93-101.

21. NIOSH Back Belt Working Group: Workplace Use of Back Belts—Review and Recomendations, May 1994. Cincinnati, Dept. of Health and Human Services, 1994, NIOSH publication 94-122.

22. Niskanen T, Lauttalammi J: Accident prevention in materials handling at building construction sites. Construction Management and Economics 7:263–279, 1989.

23. Nordin M, Crites-Battie M, Pope MH, Snook SH: Education and training. In Andersson GBJ, Frymoyer JW, Chaffin DB (eds): Occupational Low Back Pain: Assessment, Treatment and Prevention. St. Louis, Mosby-Year Book, 1991, pp 266–276.

24. Noro K, Imada A (eds): Participatory Ergonomics. Bristol, PA, Taylor and Francis, 1991.

25. Putz-Anderson V: Cummulative Trauma Disorders: A Manual for Musculoskeletal Diseases of the Upper Limbs. New York, Taylor and Francis, 1988.

26. Rosenlund E: Bra Byggredskap (Good construction tools). Rygg Institutet, Sundsvall, Sweden, 1989.
27. Saari J, Wickström G: Load on back in concrete reinforcement work. Scand J Work Environ Health 1(suppl):13–19, 1978.
28. Schneider S, Susi P: Ergonomics and construction: A review of potential hazards in new construction. Am Ind Hyg Assoc J 55:635–649, 1994.
29. Schoenmarklin RW: The effect of angled hammers on wrist motion. Proceedings of the 32nd Annual Meeting of the Human Factors Society 1:651–655, 1988.
30. Slaughter ES: Builders as source of construction innovation. Journal of Construction Engineering and Management 119:532–549, 1993.
31. Vink P, Lourijsen E, Wortel E, Dul J: Experiences in participatory ergonomics: Results of a roundtable session during the 11th IEA Congress, Paris, July 1991. Ergonomics 35:123–127, 1992.
32. Webster BS, Snook SH: The cost of 1989 workers' compensation low back pain claims. Spine 19:1111–1116, 1994.

JAMES L. WEEKS, ScD, CIH
D. J. McVITTIE

CONTROLLING INJURY HAZARDS IN CONSTRUCTION

From the Division of Occupational
  and Environmental Medicine
George Washington University
Washington, DC (JLW)
  and
Construction Safety Association
  of Ontario
Toronto, Ontario
Canada (DJM)

Reprint requests to:
James L. Weeks, ScD
GWU Medical Center
Suite 201
2300 K Street NW
Washington, DC 20037

Gustave Boenickhausen-Eiffel [was] a man whose every rivet slid smoothly into its respective hole. [He was] a man who erected the 8,000 ton tower without a single accident to its 250 workers, its only 250 workers. [He] promised, and did deliver, the finished Tower in two years, two months and five days, on time for the opening of the [Paris] Exhibition [of 1889].[24]

The lost-time injury rate among construction workers is the highest among all major industrial sectors in the United States (Fig. 1). Moreover, this rate, based on estimates by the U.S. Bureau of Labor Statistics (BLS), is likely an underestimate because it is based on data only from employers with more than 10 employees;[34] data from the 1990 U.S. Census show that 82% of construction contractors employ fewer than 10 employees and that small firms tend to have higher accident rates.[30] The rate of fatal injuries is also elevated[14] and is a close second to that in underground coal mining. BLS reported 924 fatal injuries in construction in 1993,[33] 15% of the total number of fatalities in all industries, but construction workers comprise only about 5% of the private sector work force. Although the work-related death rate in construction appears to have declined in the past 15 years, the rate of nonfatal lost-time injuries has not.[31,34,35] As a consequence of this poor safety performance, workers' compensation rates and other consequences of accidental injury are especially high for this industry.[2,11–13] The average workers' compensation premium in 1994 was $28.62 per $100 of payroll.[4] In the U.S. and Great

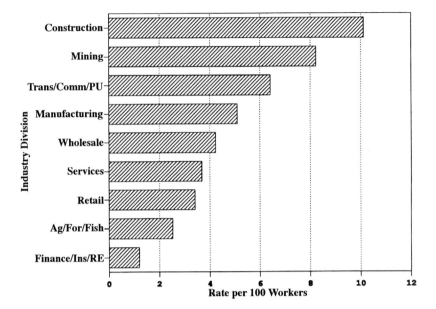

FIGURE 1. Rate of occupational injuries by industry division, selected states, 1981–86. The states included are Alaska, California, Colorado, Delaware, Hawaii, Indiana, Iowa, Kentucky, Maryland, Missouri, Nebraska, Oregon, Washington, Wisconsin, and Wyoming. (From Kisner and Fosbroke,[14] based on Bureau of Labor Statistics Supplementary Data System.)

Britain, little progress has been made to reduce the overall rate of disabling injury in construction.[25] Nevertheless, many construction contractors and employers in the U.S. have exemplary safety records, with injury rates at or below the national average for all employers.[19] In Ontario, Canada, injury rates for 1975–1990 were reduced by 20% and death rates from 19.3 to 10.2 per 100,000.[3]

This chapter identifies preventive strategies for specific types of injuries and identifies features of employers and workers that are associated with low injury rates. The information is based on published reports from the U.S. government and the scientific literature.

PHYSICAL AND BEHAVIORAL CAUSES OF INJURIES

There are two broad concepts concerning the causes of occupational injuries. The first is physical; the second, behavioral or social. Traumatic injuries occur when an individual falls, strikes a physical object, is struck by or crushed by an object, comes into contact with a source of energy (e.g., electrical or thermal), is buried by a cave-in, or overexerts himself or herself. For example, a fall from a height onto a surface sufficient to cause injury may result from a worker losing his or her balance on a slippery working surface. A foreign body can become lodged in the eye if a tool propels it toward a worker who is not wearing protective eyewear. To prevent injury, it is essential that the physical causes be controlled. Thus, it is essential to keep working surfaces clean and dry, to place guards on certain tools, to wear protective eyewear, and take other measures. Because the physical environment of a construction project changes rapidly, controlling physical hazards is an ongoing task. One long-overlooked physical factor affecting injury rates is the set of decisions made by architects and design engineers. How a project is designed and, by implication, how the work is designed can clearly affect injury rates (see Table 1 on page 409).

Behavior, on the other hand, is more difficult to change. Some employers do not provide adequate training for their employees and do not stress and reward safe practices, and some workers do things that are patently dangerous. Why? The question of why people do the things they do has been the preoccupation of philosophers, theologians, and social scientists for thousands of years. Its durability suggests the absence of a clear answer.

Even though the physical hazards that injure are usually known, behind every injury—except for those resulting from natural catastrophes—is the problem of behavior. How did a known hazard develop, and how did a worker or workers get in harm's way and become injured? The interaction of physical hazards and behavior results in injury.

Moreover, the absence of knowledge about how to control the physical environment is not a significant problem. Many codes of practice detail measures for controlling the physical environment for almost every conceivable situation in construction.[1,5,7–11,14] Some codes describe what organizational or social arrangements would work at a construction project (Table 1).[16,18]

Whatever may be lacking in efforts to prevent injuries in construction, it is not the absence of codes of practice. A major focus of these codes is to define how to control the physical environment, i.e., how to use certain tools or machines or conduct certain procedures. For the most part, these codes, if implemented, would prevent many injuries and fatalities. Their existence is ample testimony that the knowledge for working safely exists.

The codes of practice for construction are implemented in several ways. The rules of the Occupational Safety and Health Administration (OSHA) are legally enforceable, and employers are subject to fines and other penalties if they fail to comply. Enforcement of OSHA regulations is limited by OSHA's having a small number of inspectors relative to the number of construction projects under its jurisdiction. In fact, OSHA has a minor presence on a construction site compared with the rate of inspections by many local building departments to determine structural integrity and safety of a project and to grant work or occupancy permits (see chapter 15).

Adherence to the code of the U.S. Army Corps of Engineers is achieved by requiring contractors to have safety programs, low injury rates, and other means. Failure to comply can result in termination of a contract. Similar features are used

TABLE 1. Selected Safety Standards for Construction[18]

OSHA Construction Standards (29 CFR 1926)

U.S. Army Corps of Engineers Safety and Health Requirements Manual, 1992

The U.S. Bureau of Reclamation Construction Safety Standards, 1987

The U.S. Department of Energy Construction Project Safety and Health Management Order 5480.9, 1993

The American National Standards Institute Basic Elements of an Employer Program to Provide a Safe and Healthful Work Environment (ANSI A10.33), 1991

American National Standard for Construction and Demolition Operations—Safety and Health Program Requirements for Multi-Employer Projects (ANSI A10.33), 1992

The Associated General Contractors Manual of Accident Prevention in Construction, 1992

The International Labor Organization Code of Practice, Safety and Health in Construction, 1992

The Council of the European Communities Directive 92/57/EEC, Implementation of Minimum Safety and Health Requirements at Temporary Mobile Construction Sites, 1992.

by the Department of Energy. Codes of the American National Standards Institute, Associated General Contractors, and International Labor Organization are voluntary but can be invoked as standards of practice in a variety of environments.

In light of the presence of knowledge and codes combined with the absence of their being implemented at enough job sites, one can assume that the most important safety problem for the construction industry is not how to make the physical environment safe but, instead, how to manage the social environment so that workers implements their knowledge of how to work safely.

It has been known for years that trenches can cave in and trap and kill. We also have known how to prevent cave-ins (shoring, trench-boxes, or sloping the walls) and what conditions are likely to result in collapse (unstable soil and water). Yet as many as 100 cave-in deaths occur each year in the U.S.[26,27]

Similarly, use of a ground-fault circuit interrupter is standard with the use of portable electrical hand tools. Yet in 1984–86 in the U.S. construction industry, there were 789 fatal electrocutions, at least 12% of which would have been prevented if the tool had had a ground-fault circuit interrupter.[28] Fatalities caused in other ways associated with powered hand tools also are preventable with the application of existing knowledge of safe work practices.[29] All safety codes address problems of shoring trenches and using ground-fault interrupters. The knowledge and the technology for controlling these physical hazards exists, but behavior by contractors and workers does not conform to the knowledge often enough to prevent these deaths.

Electrocutions also occur when a vehicle or metal ladder comes in contact with an elevated power line. Proximity warning devices can be attached on crane booms to warn operators. Risk of contact is practically eliminated if power lines are underground rather than elevated. It might be possible to request that a utility company temporarily relocate, deenergize, or shield existing wires.

Falls are the leading cause of deaths in construction. They can be prevented with the use of safety harnesses or belts attached to lanyards and lifelines and the erection of stable and sturdy work platforms. Better perimeter protection for roofs and floor edges can also reduce the need to rely on fall-arrest systems. In some instances, this could require changes in building codes. Safety nets should be used in some situations. Risk of injury when workers are struck by vehicles, especially when the vehicles are reversing, could be reduced with the use of sensors (ultrasonic, infrared, or microwave), convex mirrors for the vehicle operator, or closed-circuit television. The flow of traffic could be altered with a drive-through lane to eliminate the need for vehicles to back up. Similarly, vehicular and pedestrian traffic can be separated. Back-up alarms have not proved particularly effective in reducing risk; a worker with hearing loss (a common problem for construction workers) may not hear the alarm, and a worker who does hear an alarm may tune it out by failing to distinguish it from other background noises.

Given the knowledge of how to control the physical environment, we will address the more practical question of what some employers do to have significantly better safety records than others. Below, we discuss the experience of several construction employers and several factors that have been evaluated in the scientific literature.

ACHIEVING GOOD SAFETY RECORDS

Contractors in the United States

The most comprehensive and current review of safety in construction was conducted by Meridian Research under contract to OSHA.[19] Meridian identified, analyzed, and compared codes of practice and reviewed the performance of several large construction employers. Brief summaries follow, based on Meridian's findings.

All of the codes required that a person at a job site be identified as responsible and that the person be held accountable by measuring their performance based on injury incidence rates or a similar measure. All of the codes provided for hazard abatement; self-inspection; accident investigation, reporting, and analysis; and recording and reporting of injuries and illnesses. Having first-aid capability was recommended for seven of these programs; hazard analysis and evaluation of fitness for duty in six; and employee involvement in four.

However, the fundamental test of the utility of safety programs is whether they lower injury rates. For the industry as a whole, including all but small employers, the lost-time injury rate was about 6 lost-time injuries per 200,000 hours worked per year in 1991. Some construction employers report lost-time injury incidence rates of about 2 per 200,000 hours worked per year, a rate that is lower than the national average for all employers (not just those in construction) of 3.7 lost-time injuries per 200,000 hours in 1991.[34] Some employers in construction have divisions with 1 million hours worked and no lost-time injuries.

How do some employers achieve such low rates? Codes of practice are implemented in several ways. The Corps of Engineers requires its contractors to comply with the its code and that this requirement be included in the contract. In addition, the corps reviews and evaluates plans before each phase of a project and during a project. The corps requires a job-hazard analysis before every job, examines accident reports, often conducts on-site inspections, and reviews—at a higher level—the work of the on-site inspectors. For large projects, the corps' inspector is continuously on-site. Failure at any stage can result in work stoppage or cancellation of a contract.[36]

The BE&K Construction Company, based in Birmingham, Ala., maintains records on the injury rates of each of its managers. The managers, in turn, are held accountable by higher management. The company's injury rate is reported as a third of the industry average.

The Bechtel Construction Company, San Francisco, works only with contractors who have implemented safety programs and who have low injury rates. Programs are negotiated with each subcontractor and included in the contract. If a subcontractor does not comply, the contract may be canceled. Bechtel has won the National Constructors Association Annual Accident Prevention Award for 35 of the past 36 years.

Brown & Root Braun, the petroleum and chemicals business unit of Brown & Root, Inc., has an effective fall protection program employing remotely activated pin extractors and full-body-protection harnesses. The pin extractor makes it possible for the operator to disconnect rigging from a distance without having to climb or be lifted.

Gulf States of Baton Rouge, La., has adopted a Continuous Improvement Process by which all employees are responsible for instituting change. All incidents are investigated and reported to the corporate level within 24 hours, ongoing training is emphasized, and contractors are selected based in part on their injury incidence rates from the OSHA log. Drug testing is conducted before employment, after accidents, and randomly.

M.B. Kahn Construction, Columbia, S.C., has a written safety program with in-house competition between divisions for the best safety record. There is a quarterly newsletter, a rank ordering of superintendent and project managers by the safety performance in their divisions, employee recognition, an annual awards breakfast, and safety awards raffle. Their medical incidents were reduced from 28 in 1987 to 9 in 1991, but the report did not give the number of people at risk.

The Mecklenburg County (N.C.) Engineering Department reduced its injury rate by half and costs by 92% with the use of quality circles, incentives for low injury rates, and a team safety program.

Monsanto Chemical, St. Louis, adopted Business Roundtable recommendations and decentralized management, placing responsibility with site managers. A comprehensive safety program includes safety in every contract, daily audits, on-site safety coordinators, permits for hazardous work, training, awards, and accident investigations and reports. The OSHA recordable (lost-time) injuries were 4.0 (per 200,000 hours) in 1985 and 2.3 in 1989.

The Pizzagalli Construction Co. of Burlington, Vt., emphasizes site-specific training, awards and incentives for good performance, drug and alcohol testing following accidents, fines for contractors who do not comply with safety provisions, inspection of personal safety equipment, and management commitment to safety. Annual worker compensation costs were reduced by 76% from 1986–1988.

Shamrock Farrell, Houston, reviews every accident, conducts daily tool-box safety talks, has weekly safety training sessions whenever workers go to a new site, and gives gift certificates to reward excellence. A free flow of information is stressed. Shamrock reports low workers' compensation costs and increased productivity.

Shell Oil has adopted total quality management with comprehensive construction safety programs, including designing safety into products and processes, selecting contractors only with an experience modification rating of 1.0 (about average) or less, and requiring weekly and quarterly safety reports. Accidents are reported to management within 48 hours. Shell's 1989 incidence rate for OSHA reportable injuries was one tenth the national average, with the lost work day rate declining steadily since 1985.

These programs have several noteworthy features. First, there is ample evidence of a management commitment to safety. Although each organization expresses this commitment in its own way, management commitment is a sine qua non for a successful safety program.

Secondly, results are measured. Costs and injury incidence rates are calculated and used as a management tool for measuring performance. This practice has been stressed elsewhere.[17]

Thirdly, safety is a common feature in contracts with subcontractors. Linking safety to this common and fundamental institutional commitment—the contract— helps to demonstrate a serious commitment to safety.

Fourth, the savings derived from a successful injury control program are significantly more than what is expended to implement a safety program. Meridian estimates that savings across the industry could be as high as $16 billion annually if features of these programs were adopted and enforced. Savings would come in the form of decreased workers' compensation premiums and payments, less time lost because of accidents and injuries, and increased productivity.

Lastly, there is great diversity among these programs. Some employers focus attention on specific hazards, while others take a more global approach. Some provide mostly positive incentives, others mostly negative. This diversity suggests that, aside from some general features noted above, no single program is most effective. Paying attention to safety in any of many ways helps to make work safer.

The Meridian report has its weaknesses. Many of the employers were large organizations or companies whose primary business was something other than construction, such as petrochemicals. The selection of employers was not representative of construction industry employers. Secondly, the review was based on employers' self reports, which were not independently audited to determine their completeness or veracity. Thirdly and more importantly, changes in injury rates could have occurred for many reasons having nothing to do with a safety program. Because young and inexperienced workers tend to have more accidents and injuries than older workers, a decline in an injury rate could result from a decline in the proportion of younger workers in the groups being evaluated. For instance, when workers are laid off during a recession, the inexperienced workers are often laid off first, and injury rates fall.[32] Changes in methods, materials, equipment, or processes also often result in increased injury rates simply because workers are not familiar with them.

Despite its flaws, the Meridian survey demonstrates that injuries in construction are not inevitable and that it is possible, given organizational commitment, to work in construction safely. The Meridian report[19] concluded:

> These case studies and qualitative assessments of the practices of some major organizations active in construction demonstrate that introducing safe management practices can have dramatic impacts on accident and injury rates. In addition, the experience of many firms and organizations indicates that the costs of implementing such programs are only a fraction of those associated with work-site accidents. In summary, worker protection programs that are characterized by *management commitment, employee involvement, work-site analysis, hazard prevention and control,* and *safety and health training* offer the best hope of breaking the cycle of injury, death, and spiraling costs that threatens to overwhelm this industry (emphasis added).

Contractors in Ontario

Work-related injury and death rates for construction in Ontario are substantially lower than in the U.S. Given the strong similarities of the work forces and the materials, equipment, and processes used, the difference is worth examination. There is some difference in the definition of lost-time injuries and the methods for calculating rates, but that difference—whereby Ontario has no waiting period for benefits while some states have waits of several days—does not explain the gap. Premiums for coverage in Ontario are generally lower than in the U.S., but benefits paid in Ontario are generally higher than in the U.S.

Although the workers' compensation systems and safety and health regulations are roughly similar with regard to work practices and equipment, the construction industry in Ontario appears to benefit from features that do not exist or are not as readily available in the U.S. The differences include cooperative labor-management ventures in safety and health: site health and safety committees, sectorwide and industrywide health and safety committees, occupational health and safety services provided through an industry-directed organization, and a higher rate of inspection by regulatory bodies. These activities or programs resemble the "good practices" described in the Meridian Research report on U.S. employers.

PUBLIC HEALTH AND SOCIAL SCIENCE INVESTIGATIONS

Public health and behavioral scientists have investigated some aspects of construction worker injuries, which are briefly summarized below. Findings are diverse.

Landeweerd et al.[15] examined whether construction work attracted people who tended to be more willing to take risks than others. He used questionnaires designed to test a theory of risk homeostasis: that individuals adhere to a target level of risk that they consider acceptable. One interpretation of the theory is that if an employer made a concerted effort to make the workplace safer, workers would continue to gravitate to the presumably higher level of risk that was acceptable, thus leading to a higher rate of injury. Landeweerd et al. also found that the workers' risk-taking tendency was not related to their injury rate and was not related to self-reported safety behavior, and their behavior was more risk-averse than that of a group of skiers, a group assumed to be willing to take risks. In brief, the overall theory that construction workers as a group were more willing to take risks was not supported.

Niskanen[20] surveyed 207 road maintenance workers to determine the attitudes and safety practices of workers and immediate supervisors.[20] He found that the attitudes of coworkers, their judgments, the attentiveness and the attitude of supervisors, and the method of instructing the workers in safety had a significant effect on worker attitudes toward safety. The workers felt that the supervisor's management methods had the greatest effect on safe work habits. Paradoxically, many workers believed that risk-taking was part of their job.

Dedobbeleer and German[5] conducted a survey at nine nonresidential construction sites in the Baltimore metropolitan area. The study was designed with a multicausal model explaining the occurrence of accidents and injuries. According to the model, workers' safety practices depend on (1) predisposing factors for each worker (knowledge and attitudes about safety, perceived susceptibility, and witnessing an injury), (2) enabling factors that allow safety aspirations to be realized (safety training and appropriate tools), and (3) reinforcing factors that provide rewards and penalties for safe or unsafe behavior (top management's, foremen's, and coworkers' attitudes toward safety and enforcement or their attention to safe procedures). From the model, predisposing factors [(1) above] are beyond the employers' control but (2) and (3), enabling and reinforcing factors, can be controlled. If (1) is known, it might be useful in managing (2) or (3).

Data for this model were analyzed using multiple linear regression. Age, attitude toward safety performance, perceived control over personal safety, absence of a serious injury record, and exposure to training all affected worker adherence to safety regulations. Highlights of the findings include that about a third of the workers had sustained a serious injury in the past 5 years, more than a third had never been exposed to a safety training program, and 30% cited their own experience as the way they learned safety practices. Most (60%) were union members. About half of the workers did not report receiving site-specific training, and 30% reported the absence of regular safety meetings. One third reported that their foreman either never or only occasionally pointed out hazards and unsafe practices. One fifth felt under pressure all the time. Workers' self-reporting of practices and the researchers' subsequent verification of the reports of unsafe practices by observing the workers on the job were highly correlated.

Factors that the researchers found to be associated with worker compliance with safety regulations were the "predisposing" variables of age, an absence of serious injuries at work, the worker's attitude toward safety performance, and control over one's own safety on the job and the "enabling factors" of exposure to safety training and having received safety instruction at initial employment. No reinforcing variable was significantly related to safety performance.

Age was strongly related to safety performance, with younger workers exhibiting less knowledge about safe practices and poorer safety performance. This relationship between age and performance or injury rates is practically ubiquitous, according to the authors. The authors suggest mandatory safety training before employment as a response to this problem.

Salminen et al.[22] examined organizational factors related to 99 serious injuries in southern Finland in 1988–89. The 73 surviving victims and their foremen were interviewed personally and asked to evaluate nine factors influencing the occurrence of an accident: the wage system, the need to save time, work timetables, professional pride, curiosity, lack of caution, and attitudes and practices of coworkers, foremen, and customers. The need to save time, work timetables, and lack of caution were clearly related to the occurrence of these accidents; the others were not. The larger firms in this sample had lower injury rates than the smaller firms.

To evaluate the "defensive attribution hypothesis" Salminen[23] studied the same group of serious accidents. According to the hypothesis, the person injured in an accident is more likely to attribute the cause to an external factor while foremen and uninvolved coworkers attribute the cause to the victim. The hypothesis was upheld in this group, suggesting, not surprisingly, that what a person says about an accident is affected by his or her own involvement.

CONCLUSION: SAFE WORK CONDITIONS ARE PRACTICABLE

Several common themes run throughout the reports and studies considered here. Positive attitudes toward safety by workers and management are mutually supportive, and their attitudes tend to rise and fall together. Site and periodic tool-box training are essential. However, what should be taught, how to teach it, and by and for whom have not been analyzed.

Experience was an important factor affecting workers' performance, suggesting that experience is indeed a good teacher and that a sizable portion of "training" occurs informally as "experience." Workers untrained by experience are at greater risk of injury. This finding illustrates both the inadequacy of current formal training and the strong effect of experience on workers' learning to work safely. It should be possible to take advantage of this naturally occurring training and to incorporate it into more formal training. The finding also reinforces the need for more training for younger and less experienced workers.

According to at least one study, injuries occur because of a combination of workers' feeling rushed and a lack of caution. As a corollary, workers benefit by having more control over their work, and control is often a product of unionization.[6,21]

To summarize, the features that result in lower injury rates are:
• Management commitment
• Employee involvement
• Work-site analysis
• Hazard control
• Safety and health training

Each of these factors means different things to different people. A management group that claims it is committed may be perceived by construction workers as paying mere lip-service to safety instead of incorporating safety into all its functions, including meetings, contracts, architectural design, and personnel decisions. Employee involvement may mean compliance with safety rules to some and a nuisance to others. To others, it could mean employee participation in drafting and adopting safety rules, or it could mean union involvement in training and safe work practices.[6,22] Hazard control could mean casual distribution of lanyards to prevent falls rather than a comprehensive program involving not only lanyards but also organizing work to minimize the time spent at risk of falls. Training could mean casual "tool-box" meetings and an abstract statement of principles with admonitions to "be careful out there,"or it could be site-specific with specific objectives using the knowledge and information from the workplace.

The clear messages are that safe construction work is possible and that many codes of practice exist. What is needed is a commitment by both employers and workers to implement them.

REFERENCES

1. Burati JL, Matthews MF, Kalidini SN: Quality management in the construction industry. J Constr Engineer Manage 117:341–359, 1990.
2. Chaney P: The hidden costs of jobsite accidents. Constructor 73:40–41, 1991.
3. Construction Safety Association of Ontario: 1993 Annual Report. Toronto, Canada, 1993.
4. Cost fever breaks: Engineering News Record, Sept 26, 1994, p 40.
5. Dedobbeleer N, German P: Safety practices in the construction industry. J Occup Med 29:863–868, 1987.
6. Dedobbeleer N, Champagne F, German P: Safety performance among union and non-union workers in the construction industry. J Occup Med 32:1099–1103, 1990.
7. DeJoy DM: Attributional processes and hazard control management in industry. J Safety Res 16:61–71, 1985.
8. DeJoy DM: Supervisor attributions and responses for multi-causal workplace accidents. J Occup Accid 9:213–223, 1987.
9. Denton DK: Safety Management: Improving Performance. New York, McGraw-Hill, 1982.
10. Fellner DJ, Sulzer-Azaroff B: Increasing industrial safety practices and conditions through posted feedback. J Safety Res 15:7–21, 1984.
11. Fullman JB: Construction Safety, Security, and Loss Prevention. New York, John Wiley & Sons, 1984.
12. Gorman EJ III: Workers compensation: Labor/management proposals to reduce injuries and illness. In Proceedings of the National Conference on Construction Health and Safety. Seattle, September 25–27, 1990.
13. Hinze J, Applegate L: Cost of construction injuries. J Constr Engineer Manage 117:537–550, 1990.
14. Kisner SM, Fosbroke DE: Injury hazards in the construction industry. J Occup Med 36:137–143, 1994.
15. Landerweerd JA, Urlings IJM, deJong AHJ, et al: Risk taking tendency among construction workers. J Occup Accid 11:183–196, 1990.
16. Lanier E: Reducing injuries and costs through team safety. Prof Safety 7:21–25, 1992.
17. Levitt RE, Samelson NM: Construction Safety Management. 2nd ed. New York, John Wiley & Sons, 1993.
18. Mattila M, Hyodynmaa M: Promoting job safety in building: An experiment on the behavior analysis approach. J Occup Accid 9:266–267.
19. Meridian Research: Worker protection programs in construction: Final report. Silver Spring, MD, Meridian Research, 1994, OSHA contract J-9-F-1-0019.
20. Niskanen T: Assessing the safety environment in work organization of road maintenance jobs. Accid Anal Prev 26:27–39, 1994.
21. Robinson J: Workplace hazards and workers' desires for union representation. J Lab Res 9:238–249, 1988.
22. Salminen S, Saari J, Searela KL, Rasanen T: Organizational factors influencing serious occupational accidents. Scand J Work Environ Health 19:352–357, 1993.
23. Salminen S: Defensive Attribution hypothesis and serious occupational accidents. Psychol Rep 70(3 PT 2):1195–1199, 1992.
24. Salvadori M: Why buildings stand up-the strength of architecture. New York, WW Norton, 1980.
25. Snashall D: Safety and health in the construction industry. BMJ 301:563–564, 1990.
26. Stanevich RL, Middleton DC: An exploratory analysis of excavation cave-in fatalities. Prof Safety 33:24–28, 1988.

27. Suruda A, Smith G, Baker SP: Deaths from trench cave-ins in the construction industry. J Occup Med 30:552–555, 1988.
28. Suruda A, Smith L: Work-related electrocutions involving portable power tools and appliances. J Occup Med 34:887–892, 1992.
29. Trent R, Wyant W: Fatal hand tool injuries in construction. J Occup Med 32:711–14, 1990.
30. U.S. Department of Commerce, Census Bureau: County Business Patterns, U.S., 1991. Washington, DC, U.S. Govt. Printing Office, 1991.
31. U.S. Department of Health and Human Services, National Institute for Occupational Safety and Health: Fatal Injuries to Workers in the United States, 1980–1989: A Decade of Surveillance. Washington, DC, U.S. Govt. Printing Office, 1993, NIOSH publication 93–108.
32. U.S. Department of Labor: The American Workforce. Washington, DC, U.S. Govt. Printing Office, 1993
33. U.S. Department of Labor, Bureau of Labor Statistics: National Census of Fatal Occupational Injuries, 1993. Washington, DC, August 10, 1994.
34. U.S. Department of Labor, Bureau of Labor Statistics: Occupational Injuries and Illnesses in the United States by Industry, 1991. Washington, DC, U.S. Govt. Printing Office, 1993, bulletin 2424.
35. U.S. Department of Labor, Bureau of Labor Statistics: First National Census of Fatal Occupational Injuries reported by BLS. October 1, 1993, news release.
36. U.S. Department of Labor, Occupational Safety and Health Administration, Office of Construction and Engineering: Construction Lost-time Injuries: The U.S. Army Corps of Engineers Data Base, 1984–88. Washington, DC, U.S. Govt. Printing Office, 1990.

JAMES L. WEEKS, ScD, CIH

CONTROLLING OCCUPATIONAL HEALTH HAZARDS IN CONSTRUCTION

From the Division of Occupational
and Environmental Medicine
George Washington University
Washington, DC

Reprint requests to:
James L. Weeks, ScD
GWU Medical Center
Suite 201
2300 K Street
Washington, DC 20037

Construction workers are exposed to a wide variety of airborne and dermatologic chemical hazards and to many physical hazards. The social organization of the industry also includes features that are inherently stressful. Airborne hazards include asbestos, crystalline silica, lead, welding emissions, roofing and pavement tar, engine exhaust, and organic solvents used in paints, adhesives, caulking compounds, and other applications. Dermatologic hazards include cement, organic solvents, epoxy resins, and physical wear and tear associated with manual labor and materials handling. Physical hazards arise from awkward or heavy manual materials handling, poorly designed tools, awkward work postures, repetitive motions, noise, vibration, risk of electrical shock, heat, cold, ionizing and nonionizing radiation, adverse weather, and working under hyperbaric conditions.

Construction workers as a whole die more frequently than expected from lung cancer,[23,28] gastric cancer,[23,19] sinonasal cancer,[27,60] chronic lymphocytic leukemia,[21] and nonHodgkins lymphoma (see chapter 3).[54] Among construction workers, noise-induced hearing loss is more common than expected, as is the incidence of alcoholism and alcohol-related morbidity and mortality,[10,29,33,43,46,48] and the suicide rate.[40] Causes of these elevated rates for construction workers as a group are only partially understood. Some of the social disruptions common to construction work, such as chronic unemployment and absences from family, and resulting stress may contribute to health problems.

Occupational causes of elevated morbidity and mortality rates among construction workers in special trades are understood better than they are among construction workers as a whole because exposure in each trade is more uniform. For example, asbestos insulation workers, plumbers, pipe fitters, and other workers exposed to asbestos have elevated risks of asbestosis, lung cancer, and mesothelioma.[47] Roofers have an excess risk of lung cancer from emissions from roofing tar.[51] Welders have an excess risk of lung cancer and chronic obstructive lung disease from welding emissions.[24,51] Painters exposed to organic solvents experience neurologic[34,39] and neuropsychiatric[61,63] disorders and a higher than expected fatality rate from falls.[35,58] Air flow obstruction is more common among painters.[55] Lead poisoning occurs often among bridge maintenance workers because of their exposure to lead-based pigments used historically to paint bridges.[18,38,44,49,59] Workers applying concrete with compressed air experience a decline in lung function.[36]

This chapter describes, evaluates, and illustrates generic and conventional industrial hygiene methods for controlling occupational hazards affecting construction workers, hazards that may cause some of the excess morbidity and mortality. Stress is not considered. Case studies identifying and controlling exposure to asbestos, lead, crystalline silica, and additives to cement are discussed. Results from the epidemiologic research noted above illustrate the need for better understanding of other hazards and, to the extent that researchers can identify specific hazards, they also indicate which hazards should be controlled.

INDUSTRIAL HYGIENE IN CONSTRUCTION

The conventional practice of industrial hygiene consists of four core activities: anticipation, recognition, evaluation, and control of hazards at work.[14,62] Although this chapter is primarily concerned with hazard controls, the first three activities provide important information for deciding whether and when to implement controls. Moreover, because of the construction industry's different physical and social environment, implementing any of these core activities in construction requires considerable adaptation.

Anticipation of Hazards

Anticipation of hazards requires consideration of hazard exposure and control early and often in the characteristic phases of a construction project, including conceiving the project, acquiring financing, acquiring land, making detailed architectural plans, hiring prime and subcontractors, breaking ground and preparing the site, laying a foundation, erecting and topping off, finishing the interior, finishing the exterior, and holding a grand opening or ribbon-cutting. Each phase has unique opportunities and hazards that should be recognized and controlled (Table 1). For instance, financing could be made contingent on a specified level of performance (positively and negatively) with respect to injuries or illnesses, and organization for safety could be an integral part of contracts with prime contractors and subcontractors. Some of these phases—ground breaking, topping off, and grand opening— are ceremonial events that present unique opportunities for publicly recognizing past performance, injuries, and commitments to control hazards. Hazards that might occur in the excavation and construction of a project should be systematically considered and steps taken to control them.

There are many variations of these phases, depending, for instance, on whether the project is a building, highway, or tunnel and whether it is new construction, renovation, or demolition. Regardless, detailed planning is conducted at virtually every

TABLE 1.   Hazards and Opportunities to Promote Health and Safety in the Life Cycle of a Typical New Construction Project

Phase	Potential Hazards, Opportunities
Conception, design	Opportunities: architects to design structures that are safe to build, to maintain, and to occupy For renovations and demolitions, identify hazards if possible
Hiring prime and subcontractors	Opportunities: invitation to bid and contracts contingent on a successful safety program; contactors to coordinate programs before starting work
Hiring workers	Opportunities: hire experienced and trained workers, train those that are not; safety provisions in labor-management contract, involve workers in making work rules and methods; site-specific training; regular safety meetings
Ground breaking	Opportunities: to speak about safety during ceremony
Site preparation	Hazards: noise; vibration; cave-in; unknown underground hazards; adverse weather Opportunities: regular walk-through inspections
Making forms, pouring foundation	Hazards: cement eczema; traumatic injury; musculoskeletal strain; cave-ins; creosote and other chemicals; adverse weather Opportunities: regular walk-through inspections
Erecting: general	Hazards: falls; traumatic injury; musculoskeletal strain (static postures); noise; adverse weather Opportunities: regular meetings; tool box meetings, safety training, accident investigating, collect and analyze data, regular walk-through inspections
Erecting: concrete	Hazards: leading edge fall hazard; building and stripping forms; cement eczema; laying, walking on re-bars
Erecting: steel	Hazards: falls; traumatic injury; musculoskeletal strain; noise; heat; cold; welding emissions and ultraviolet radiation; adverse weather
Topping off	Opportunities: speak for safety during ceremony, pay tribute to injured
Mechanical installations	Hazards: traumatic injury; falls; musculoskeletal strain; fiberglass; welding emissions and ultraviolet radiation; solvent vapors Opportunities: regular walk-through inspections
Exterior finishing	Hazards: falls, solvent vapors, pigments, glues; electrical hazards; adverse weather Opportunities: regular walk-through inspections
Interior finishing	Hazards: falls; knee trauma; dust; solvent vapors; traumatic injury; electrical hazards; adverse weather Opportunities: regular walk-through inspections
Landscaping	Hazards: noise; musculoskeletal strain, fertilizer dermatitis, traumatic injury; adverse weather Opportunities: regular walk-through inspections
Grand opening or ribbon cutting	Opportunities: speak for safety during ceremony, pay tribute to injured

phase, at every organizational level, and every day for every construction site regardless of its size or nature. For hazards to be anticipated and controlled early, workplace hazards must be considered in the planning process.

Anticipation of hazards is possible because of the large amount of existing knowledge about many chemical and physical hazards in construction. For instance, we do not need a detailed investigation to determine that lead is potentially hazardous or to question whether exposure at a given work site should be evaluated and controlled.

Anticipation of hazards is necessary because exposure to many hazards in construction is fleeting, occurring on one job briefly and being repeated on another project. By the time a hazard is recognized, the hazard and the conditions that produced it probably will have changed. Therefore, hazards should be anticipated and controlled before they become obvious. If existing knowledge is used, hazard control can be integrated into existing planning processes. Without planning, preventable injuries may occur,[50] and the hygienist or safety director is forever responding to developments on a job site—"one fire drill after another," as one safety director put it—rather than controlling hazards from the beginning.

Recognition of Hazards

Hazards can be identified and controls evaluated with medical surveillance systems, a well-established public health practice (see chapter 13). Surveillance is the

> ...[o]n-going scrutiny, generally using methods distinguished by their practicality, uniformity, and frequently their rapidity, rather than by complete accuracy. Its main purpose is to detect changes in trend or distribution in order to initiate investigative or control measures.[37]

Surveillance need not be limited to identifying disease or injury. Surveillance systems can be used to identify hazards and, thus, to enable primary prevention. Disease surveillance depends on the occurrence of disease and, for workers already affected, requires secondary prevention. For instance, to prevent silicosis in construction, it would be useful to know who provides abrasive blasting services and whether and how frequently they use sand as the abrasive. Roofing contractors could be identified to develop and implement controls on roofing tar emissions. Employers who install steel reinforcing bars could be identified and changes in work practices considered to reduce the occurrence of musculoskeletal disorders.

Chemical hazards at a work site can be recognized by maintaining an inventory of the materials and methods used on that site and by medical surveillance (see chapters 7 and 13). A materials and methods inventory that can be useful for detecting hazards should include when, how often, and how much of whatever chemical is used and how often specific physical hazards are encountered. Data sheets analogous to OSHA's material safety data sheets could be a convenient and useful means of keeping an inventory of physical hazards. Small computers would facilitate the organization of and access to such information. The size of computer memories continues to expand substantially so that storing and retrieving information from a computerized data set is possible and convenient for even the smallest contractor.

Construction methods create significant physical hazards that result in musculoskeletal and other disorders. Hazards associated with tools and work practices are best recognized and evaluated by directly and systematically observing and recording workers' activities combined with assessing symptoms or manifest physical impairment.

Evaluation of Hazards

Hazard evaluation often occurs along with recognition and can be accomplished by several means. The conventional industrial hygiene practice for evaluation of airborne chemical hazards is to measure their concentration, frequency, and duration and to compare results with established exposure limits. Exposure limits may be mandatory or advisory. For most chemicals, the exposure limit applies to a full-shift time-weighted average. A limited number of chemicals also have ceiling limits never to be exceeded or short-term (usually 15-minute) exposure limits (STELs). In practice, sampling to assess compliance almost always consists of taking a full-shift sample. On a typical construction site, however, the conditions of exposure may vary widely for the worker and for any workers nearby or downwind. Consequently, full-shift sampling has limited value. To evaluate hazardous exposures using ceilings or STELs, one would need to use real-time monitoring or short-term sampling during an excursion to evaluate the short-term or peak exposure.

There are two problems with taking ceiling or STEL samples. To take a sample to compare an exposure with a ceiling or STEL, one would need to know beforehand when and where an exposure would occur. Otherwise, it would be nearly impossible to plan a sampling strategy.

Another problem is that the scientific foundation of STEL or ceiling samples varies considerably;[64] they are not infallible guides to what is safe. The ceiling limit for carbon monoxide in construction, for instance, is 400 ppm, a level that produces headaches and impaired neurologic function[51] and, thus, is clearly inadequate. For hazards without STELs or ceilings, there may be irreversible chronic effects resulting from many episodes of acute exposure. Grossly excessive but short-term exposure to crystalline silica, for which there is no short-term limit, can cause acute silicosis,[47] a rapidly fatal affliction. Because STELs or ceilings are intended to prevent acute health effects, if characteristic acute effects occur and if they are caused by an identified exposure at a work site, one can conclude, with no sampling at all, that exposure was (and may still be) excessive.

Construction work has many tasks for which hazards may be obscured by taking full-shift samples. Hazards can be missed, not only because a worker may be exposed to them for only part of a shift, but also because there may be several tasks and hazards to which a worker is exposed on one shift that contribute to risk of illness. Conventional exposure assessment must be adapted to this peculiarity of the industry.

One method for exposure assessment among construction workers is task-based exposure assessment. This is a strategy of measuring exposure to potential hazards associated with specific tasks for the duration of the task rather than measuring exposure for any individual worker for the duration of a shift. By measuring exposure this way, it is possible to identify sources and specific exposures and, thus, to be more efficient in implementing controls. Furthermore, for tasks that have been evaluated this way, it is possible to estimate the amount and variety of exposure to any worker and determine needed controls.

Control of Hazards

Controls can be conceptualized by considering the source of hazards, the environment into which they are released, and the workers that are exposed to them. Following from this scheme are three generic types of controls: applied at the source, in the environment, or at the worker. These types also give us a hierarchy of effectiveness: the controls closest to the source are most often the most effective and most efficient ones. Positive engineering controls applied at the source eliminate the hazard from the workplace; environmental controls limit the release of a hazard into the worker's environment; controls applied to the worker consist of personal protective equipment that protects individual workers or administrative controls that limit the duration of worker exposure with changes in work scheduling.

In some cases, approaches are combined. For instance, typical controls for radiant physical hazards such as noise, radiant heat, or ionizing or nonionizing radiation include a combination of reducing the elapsed time of exposure and increasing the distance between the worker and the source.

POSITIVE ENGINEERING CONTROLS

Positive engineering consists of using less hazardous products or work methods. The aim is to prevent a hazard from being created and released into the environment. The hazard can be eliminated from the process or job, its release can be prevented, or the objective of a given task may be met in a different way than originally intended. For instance, water can be used as a solvent for paints instead of organic solvents, nonsilica abrasives can replace sand in abrasive blasting, drywall panels can be reduced in size and shape, redesigned tools can reduce musculoskeletal stress, or noise, or vibration. Positive engineering can be as simple as a manhole cover being round; regardless of how it falls, it cannot fall down the manhole and injure the occupants. Blades reconfigured on a planer can significantly reduce noise.

All occupations, including the construction trades, involve a large number of tasks and processes, each of which may be hazardous. As a result, there are many needs and opportunities for positive engineering, each of which must be designed for each task. Workers often have a rich cache of ideas on how to make tasks less hazardous, and they have an obvious interest in evaluating modifications to their jobs, regardless of the origin of the proposed change. Therefore, workers should be included in any effort to invent ways to reduce hazards. Positive engineering requires ingenuity, open-mindedness, and a willingness to consider alternative methods. It also requires a commitment to safety at least as strong as a commitment to productivity.

ENVIRONMENTAL CONTROLS

Environmental controls are techniques designed to remove, dilute, or contain hazards after they have been generated and released into the environment. The typical environmental control for airborne hazards is local exhaust ventilation that removes contaminated air from the worker's breathing zone. Some tasks that produce airborne hazards are totally contained, a procedure that protects people outside of the containment but that increases exposure for anyone who must work within it.

One way to protect against radiant physical hazards such as noise, radiant heat, or ionizing or nonionizing radiation is for the source to be shielded, which is an environmental control. Air conditioning is a form of environmental control for heat and humidity and, in some instances, for airborne hazards and noise.

There are two problems with environmental controls on the construction site. First, they usually must be added on to a hazardous task, thus making it necessary to manage another machine on the site. Construction tasks are done at varying locations and the physical environment of a construction work site is constantly changing. Indeed, the reason for construction is to change the physical environment. For most construction tasks, workers and equipment must move on when the work is done. Therefore, any environmental control would need to be portable and be able to adapt to changes in the environment. As a consequence, there is significant resistance from workers and/or contractors to using environmental controls on a job site. Resistance may result more from perception than reality; large pieces of equipment such as generators, air compressors, and welding rigs are routinely and frequently moved from one place to another on a job site. Environmental controls could be among them.

The second problem, which follows from the first, is that few practical environmental controls are suitable for a construction project. Emissions from roofing tar, a known cause of lung cancer, are difficult to control with any kind of ventilation. There are no ventilation controls for spray painters on a scaffold. Exhaust ventilation for abrasive blasting is cumbersome. Some environmental controls that do exist include portable ventilation for welding and sanding, the ability to shield ultraviolet radiation from welding, and containment devices that can control airborne hazards.

There is a clear need for research and development of environmental controls for selected hazardous tasks in construction. In the meantime, in the absence of feasible environmental controls (due, in part, to the absence of a market for them), we must rely more on positive engineering and worker-centered controls.

WORKER-CENTERED CONTROLS: PERSONAL PROTECTIVE EQUIPMENT

Worker-centered controls generally consist of personal protective equipment (PPE) and administrative controls. PPE includes any device worn or used by an individual worker and designed to protect that individual worker. There is much PPE for construction workers: hard hats, work shoes, gloves, welders' helmets, safety glasses, abrasive blasting helmets, lanyards for work at heights, respirators for spray painting, dust masks for sanding drywall, hearing muffs or plugs, and others. Many workers carry tools or supplies on belts or in pouches. PPE is a promising approach in that it is already commonplace. Although it appears to be simple, effective use of PPE requires consideration of many factors.

Use of personal respirators or hearing protectors, for example, requires more than merely making them available. Exposure needs to be monitored, devices must be fit properly for each worker, workers need training and education about hazards and the protective devices, and the devices need to be inspected and maintained (see chapter 9).

PPE also has many inherent weaknesses. Some devices are unacceptable to workers because they are uncomfortable, interfere with communication, or provide ineffective protection. Face masks limit peripheral vision. PPE is often provided without consideration of all the tasks necessary to make it effective. As a result, PPE frequently provides little real protection and produces a negative attitude toward their use. Construction workers often work under conditions, such as in confined spaces and awkward positions, that make using PPE difficult. Construction work is often physically strenuous and can be made more so with PPE. Finally, neither bystanders nor occupants of buildings under renovation are protected at all. The problem of bystander exposure is one strength of environmental controls and of positive engineering; not only do the controls protect the workers immediately involved in a hazardous task, they usually also protect bystanders.

PPE is considered active inasmuch as each worker must wear, attach, or otherwise activate the controls. Positive engineering, on the other hand, is a passive means of control that does not require activation. Environmental controls can be active or passive, depending on their design. Environmental controls that must be moved and set up for each task are considered active. In general, passive methods of controlling health and safety hazards are preferred to active methods because they are inherent in the task and do not depend on activation by individual workers.

In spite of the problems with PPE, there are times when it is essential and can save lives.[5] In general, these times occur when there is no alternative to PPE while better controls are being developed or implemented. Air-supplied respirators are essential, for example, in confined spaces with either an oxygen deficiency or hazardous concentration of a toxic substance. If misuse of PPE generates a negative attitude, this could result in workers not using it in situations when it is clearly needed, resulting in illness, injury, or death.

Administrative controls are any measures that do little to reduce the concentration of a hazard but do reduce either the duration or frequency of exposure for individual workers. For example, hazardous jobs can be done on off shifts, or workers can be rotated out of certain tasks. For projects that are already complex administratively, adding additional objectives may meet resistance in the absence of a compelling need.

Controlling for Specific Substances

CONTROLLING FOR ASBESTOS

The considerable amount of knowledge that exists about the adverse health effects of asbestos is sufficient to anticipate the need for controls in any situation where it is encountered (see chapter 6). There are many situations, such as removal of asbestos from buildings, in which controls are mandatory given only the presence of the mineral.[12] Ignorance of the hazards of asbestos is not a reasonable explanation for the absence of controls. For asbestos removal, positive engineering in the form of substitute materials is not possible.

Controls for removal usually consist of a combination of work practices, environmental controls, and PPE. In general, safe asbestos removal requires trained workers who seal and isolate the work area, post warning signs, wear full-body protection and, in some instances, use positive-pressure respirators. Asbestos is usually removed while it is enclosed, when possible, or wet. The removed asbestos must be placed in a sealed bag for disposal. Curtains, enclosures, and bags must be strong enough to avoid tearing and bursting.

Safe removal requires environmental and medical monitoring. These requirements have not always been in place. In past years, many workers were not informed of the hazards, despite accumulating evidence concerning its disease-producing potential. This resulted in lax standards for controlling exposure and in many preventable cases of asbestos-related disease. The first exposure limit for asbestos was set at 12 fibers per cubic centimeter (f/cm^3) in 1946. This limit has been progressively lowered to the current permissible exposure limit of 0.1 f/cm^3 set by OSHA in 1990.

Many workers or their survivors affected by these diseases have successfully bypassed the exclusive remedy of workers' compensation systems and have sued asbestos processors as third parties. These suits have created sufficient liabilities that manufacturers have sought protection under bankruptcy laws. These liabilities have created a significant economic disincentive for its continued use and, thereby, have reduced the risk of exposure in new construction in the United States. Although the motivating factor was to reduce costs, the effect has been the implementation of positive engineering, with increasing restrictions on the use of asbestos, and the use of substitute materials such as synthetic fibers.[12]

The principal markets for new application of asbestos are in developing countries. In construction in the U.S., exposure to asbestos now occurs almost wholly during asbestos removal or renovation, demolition, ship-breaking or repair, and repair of other structures in which asbestos has been used.[8,30] Exposure to asbestos can reasonably be anticipated in old buildings where it is used on many pipes, tiles, and siding. In these work settings and, in the absence of controls, construction workers engaged in repair, renovation, asbestos removal, or demolition will likely be exposed.

Synthetic vitreous fibers (also referred to as man-made mineral fibers—MMMF) appear to be a suitable substitute material for most applications. Questions remain about the pathogenic potential of these fibers, and research is continuing.[7,16,22,25,26,42] Although epidemiologic and laboratory investigations have been mostly negative, rats exposed to synthetic fibers by inhalation have developed mesothelioma.[20]

Controlling asbestos exposure includes and conspicuously ignores several elements necessary for control. The failure to anticipate hazards laid the foundation for excessive and unnecessary exposure resulting in disease and death.[12] Positive engineering is evident in eliminating additional installation of asbestos and using synthetic fibers as a substitute. Environmental controls and PPE are used in combination to prevent worker and bystander exposure.

CONTROLLING FOR LEAD

Lead is widely used for several reasons, including its electrical conductivity, lubricant effects, and color. Consequently, workers in many trades have been exposed (see chapter 8).

The hazards of lead exposure have been known for centuries. Effects include encephalopathy, peripheral neuropathy, kidney disease, lead colic, impaired heme synthesis, and impaired reproductive capacity.[51] Among construction workers, lead poisoning has been reported among bridge repair and renovation workers[38,59,49] and bricklayers using mortar with a lead additive.[57] Lead paint in new construction has been reduced, but other uses, such as in soldering, plumbing, and electrical installations, continue.

Certain work tasks carry a high risk of exposure to airborne lead. During these tasks, strict control and monitoring of exposure are essential. In construction, the principal sources of exposure occur in repair, renovation, and demolition. Tasks with a high risk for lead exposure include lead-based paint removal by abrasive blasting, power tool cleaning or burning, spraying of lead paint, and flame cutting of lead-painted metals. With these tasks, the primary route of absorption is inhalation. Ingestion is also a possibility if workers' hands become contaminated and they subsequently eat or smoke without washing.[57]

Bystanders, whether workers or others, are at risk of exposure from tasks that generate airborne lead. For example, in the course of removing lead-based paint from a bridge, nearby communities have been exposed.[44] To prevent dispersion into the community, the work and the worker were contained in an enclosed booth. This increased exposure to the worker, necessitating use of a positive pressure air-supplied respirator and full-body protective gear. Workers can also be exposed by taking lead home on their hair or clothing. The provision of time and space for on-site change and shower facilities can help prevent this form of bystander exposure.

Many instances of overexposure to lead have been detected by some form of medical surveillance, for example by workers' compensation data, health hazard evaluations by the National Institute for Occupational Safety and Health (NIOSH), or the use of a state-based heavy-metal registry.[56,38,41] These data, when compiled in a timely fashion, have been essential for treatment and management of affected workers and for identifying employers and tasks that pose a controllable risk.

Control of exposure can be anticipated in most instances. Bridges with a 20-year-old coat of paint most likely have lead-based pigment; plumbing in old buildings usually contains lead, as does solder. If lead content is not known, it can be determined easily with a variety of hand-held direct-readout instruments. Lead absorption in any worker can be attributed in part to a failure to anticipate hazards.

In new construction, positive engineering has reduced exposure considerably. Lead-based pigments have been replaced, organic lead has been eliminated from gasoline, and the lead content in solder has been reduced.

Environmental controls have been used on lead removal projects, mainly to prevent bystander exposure. Workers have encountered increased exposure and consequently have needed to wear supplied-air respirators and other personal protective devices. This is an instance in which environmental controls were developed and achieved their stated objective.

CONTROLLING FOR CRYSTALLINE SILICA

Crystalline silica is the most abundant material in the earth's crust. The health effects of crystalline silica have been known since antiquity (see chapter 6).[53] The most prominent is silicosis, most often a chronic fibrosis of the lung with characteristic nodules of fibrotic tissue often surrounding a particle of silica.[47] Silicosis may be complicated with simultaneous pulmonary tuberculosis. It can be progressive and continue after exposure has ceased. Acute silicosis is a fulminant and progressive process that results soon after short-term but grossly excessive exposure. Lung cancer, resulting directly from exposure to silica or indirectly from silicosis, is also a possible effect.[45,47]

In construction, exposure to airborne respirable silica can occur during abrasive blasting or from cutting concrete that contains sand or silica-containing rock—during tunnel or highway construction and other excavation work. In abrasive blasting operations, the source of respirable silica is sand, the most common abrasive used for blasting. It is readily available, inexpensive, hard, and resistant to chemical corrosion and to high temperatures.[31] However, it is entirely crystalline silica, and the abrasive blasting produces a high concentration of fine airborne particles.[6]

The conventional method of protecting abrasive-blasting workers is use of a continuous-flow air-supplied helmet that covers the entire torso and protects from both inhalation and rebounding particles. NIOSH recommends a type CE positive-pressure air-supplied respirator as a superior means of personal protection. OSHA regulations (29 CFR 1910.94(a)) require employers in manufacturing to use the abrasive-blasting helmet and to institute other measures designed to protect employees; however, there are no such regulations covering workers in construction. Abrasive blasting helmets reduce exposure to sand but only when workers are trained and properly fitted and when the helmets are used and maintained properly.

The alternate method of preventing exposure from abrasive blasting is to prohibit the use of sand and to use other abrasives. Sand for abrasive blasting has been restricted in the United Kingdom since 1949. Belgium, Germany, and Sweden have also prohibited or restricted the use of sand. Substitute abrasives that have minimal amounts of silica include garnet, nickel slag, copper slag, coal slag, and steel grit. Although the cash outlay for these abrasives is greater than for sand (about $44 per ton for coal slag and $36 per ton for sand),[31] the health risks, and therefore costs, are considerably less. Alternative abrasive materials introduce their own hazards apart from silica so that workers still need some form of protection from the inhalation hazard and from flying particles.

Bystander exposure can be a significant problem, especially on construction sites. Although a sandblasting crew may be well protected, other workers in the vicinity, particularly those downwind, can be exposed to high levels. One review estimated that workers as far as 2,400 feet downwind may be overexposed.[6]

Controls for exposure to silica during tunneling can be accomplished with wet drilling methods, use of ventilation to remove dust-contaminated air, restrictions on reentry following blasting (which would also be necessary to reduce exposure to toxic gaseous byproducts of blasting), and use of enclosing cabs for vehicle operators. However, cabs protect only the operators.

Medical monitoring to detect the harmful effects of exposure to crystalline silica is useful but primarily as a means of secondary prevention. Silicosis is irreversible and sometimes progressive. Because silicosis is usually chronic, by the time the disease is detected, little can be done to reverse it; however, its progression can be slowed in most cases. The site where exposure occurred should be identified to determine if there are additional cases and the work environment inspected to evaluate current exposure. Information may not be available on employers when the disease is discovered, especially if the construction firms were small.

CONTROLLING FOR CHROMATES

Contact dermatitis has been a consistent finding among workers exposed to cement (see chapter 7).[11,15,17,52] Water-soluble hexavalent chromate compounds have been identified as the cause and, in 1980, were removed from cement in Sweden. In 1981 in Denmark, ferrous sulfate was added to the mix to transform water-soluble to water-insoluble chromate (i.e., reduction of $Cr6+$ to $Cr3+$), thus reducing its ability to cause dermatitis.[2] Although the prevalence of irritant contact dermatitis declined, workers with allergic cement eczema showed no improvement. This change added about 1% to the cost of cement but was balanced by a reduction in needs for medical treatment.[3] The addition of ferrous sulfate was evaluated by patch testing among workers with known sensitization to chromate 9 and the data analyzed by multivariate analysis for additional risk factors.[13] Gloves and barrier creams were ineffective for preventing this condition.[1] Absences as a result of chromate allergies declined with reduced use.[33]

This chronicle of identifying and evaluating causes of dermatitis among cement workers illustrates the fundamental utility of systematic analysis of causes followed by corrective action and follow-up evaluation. It also provides a basis for anticipating similar problems in the future, should chromate compounds be used. Personal protective devices proved ineffective, and positive engineering was used in the form of a less-toxic compound. It is not clear from these sources whether environmental controls were feasible or considered.

SUMMARY

Industrial hygiene is the anticipation, identification, evaluation, and control of occupational health hazards. Strategies for controlling hazards consist of positive engineering to eliminate the source of the hazard, environmental controls to remove the hazard from the environment, and protective and administrative measures intended to protect individual workers. These control strategies form a hierarchy of effectiveness and efficiency, in the order listed. This conventional definition of industrial hygiene needs to be adapted to some of the unique features of the construction industry, which is a constantly changing physical and social environment with intermittent exposures to chemical and physical hazards.

Some methods for identification and control have been adapted for use in construction. However, in notable instances, known hazards such as asbestos, crystalline silica, and lead were neither anticipated nor controlled, resulting in preventable diseases. Positive engineering has been used for new construction involving asbestos, lead, and chromates in cement. Synthetic fibers can be substituted for asbestos, there are substitutes for lead, and other compounds may substitute for chromates in cement. Substitution is feasible for the use of sand in abrasive blasting but not possible in some instances of abrasive blasting: when renovating old buildings or bridges and when digging into the earth's crust. Some environmental controls are feasible (such as wet drilling into silica-containing rock) but not always implemented.

Developing and implementing controls is hampered by several weaknesses in regulations. Only recently has OSHA's lead standard been applied to construction. Regulations covering abrasive blasting (29 CFR 1910.94(a)) are weak, and there is no standard covering respiratory protection for construction. Neither medical nor exposure monitoring is required.

FUTURE NEEDS

There are several ways to better protect the occupational health of construction workers. For instance, restricting or prohibiting the use of sand in abrasive blasting would reduce exposure to crystalline silica among sandblasters and bystanders, where such restrictions do not exist. Regulations requiring wet drilling would help to reduce exposure to respirable silica among highway construction workers and tunnel workers.

Education and training is needed in every level of the industry,[4] from unskilled and apprentice workers to top management and owners. This education should include the health effects of common hazards, methods for controlling them, and the costs of allowing the hazards to produce disease.

One practical use of task-based exposure assessment, as described here, is that, for tasks that have been evaluated, we can anticipate exposure and initiate controls from the beginning of such tasks.

The controls described in this chapter emphasize substitution (a form of positive engineering) and personal protection. Few environmental controls exist. Task-based evaluations and controls appear to be a promising method of identifying, evaluating, and controlling hazards. There is a need to further identify tasks or parts of tasks that result in hazardous exposures and to research and develop effective and feasible environmental controls. Hazards for which they might be used include welding emissions, solvent vapors from paints and other chemicals, emissions from road paving and roofing, and others. Hazards encountered during demolition or renovation deserve special attention.

The many contracts in construction, which involve financing, property rights, the specialty trades, suppliers, and vendors, could be used along with other measures to create incentives and commitments to improve working conditions and reduce the risk of occupational illnesses and injuries.

REFERENCES

1. Avnstorp C: Risk factors for cement eczema. Contact Dermatitis 25:81–88, 1991.
2. Avnstorp C: Follow-up of workers from prefabricated concrete industry after the addition of ferrous sulfate to Danish cement. Contact Dermatitis 20:365–371, 1989.
3. Avnstorp C: Prevalence of cement eczema in Denmark before and since the addition of ferrous sulfate to Danish cement. Acta Derm Venereol (Stockh) 69:151–155, 1989.
4. Behrens VJ, Brackbill RM: Worker awareness of exposure: Industries and occupations with low awareness. Am J Ind Med 23:695–701, 1994.

5. Bishop PA, Nunneley SA, Constable SW: Comparisons of air and liquid personal cooling for intermittent heavy work in moderate temperatures. Am Ind Hyg Assoc J 52:393–397, 1991.
6. Brantley CD, Reist PC: Abrasive blasting with quartz sand: Factors affecting the potential for incidental exposure to respirable silica. Am Ind Hyg Assoc J 55:946–952, 1994.
7. Brown RC, Davis JM, Douglas D, Gruber UF, et al: Carcinogenicity of the insulation wools: Reasessment of the IARC evaluation. Regul Toxicol Pharmacol 14:12–23, 1991.
8. Brown SK: Asbestos exposure during renovation and demolition of asbestos-cement clad buildings. Am Ind Hyg Assoc J 48:478–486. 1987.
9. Bruze M, Fregert S, Gruvberger B: Patch testing with cement containing iron sulfate. Dermatol Clin 8:173–176, 1990.
10. Burkhart G, Schulte PA, Robinson C, et al: Job tasks, potential exposures, and health risks of laborers employed in the construction industry. Am J Ind Med 24:413–425, 1993.
11. Burrows D: Chromate dermatitis. In Maisbach HI (ed): Occupational and Industrial Dermatology. 2nd ed. Chicago, Year Book, 1987, pp 406–420.
12. Castleman BI, Ziem G: Asbestos: Medical and Legal Aspects. 2nd ed. Clifton, NJ, Prentice-Hall, 1986.
13. Christophersen J, Menne T, Tanghi P, et al: Clinical patch testing data evaluated by multivariate analysis; Danish Contact Dermatitis Group. Contact Dermatitis 21:291–299, 1989.
14. Clayton GD, Clayton FE, Allen RE, Patty FA, (eds): Patty's Industrial Hygiene and Toxicology. 4th ed. New York, John Wiley & Sons, 1991.
15. Dannaker CJ, Shite TR, Rycroft RJG: Long term prognosis in occupational chromate allergy: An attempted 18 year follow-up study. Contact Dermatitis 21:59, 1989.
16. Enterline PE: Carcinogenic effects of man-made vitreous fibers. Ann Rev Public Health 12:459–480, 1991.
17. Farm G: Changing patterns in chromate allergy. Contact Dermatitis 15:298–299, 1986.
18. Fischbein A, Leeds M, Solomon S: Lead exposure among iron workers in New York City. A continuing occupational hazard in the 1980s. N Y State J Med, 84:445–448, 1984.
19. Gonzalez CA, Sanz M, Marcos G, et al: Occupation and gastric cancer in Spain. Scand J Work Environ Health. 17:240–247, 1991
20. Grandjean P, Bach E: Indirect exposure: The significance of bystanders at work and at home. Am Ind Hyg Assoc J 42:819–824, 1986.
21. Hall NE, Rosenman KD: Cancer by industry: Analysis of a population-based cancer registry with an emphasis on blue-collar workers. Am J Ind Med 19:145–159, 1991.
22. Hesterberg TW, Miller WC, McConnell EE, et al: Chronic inhalation toxicity of size-separated glass fibers in Fischer 344 rats. Fundam Appl Toxicol 20:464–476, 1993.
23. Keller JE, Howe HL: Cancer in Illinois construction workers: A study. Am J Ind Med 24:223–230 1993.
24. Kilburn KH, Warshaw RH: Pulmonary functional impairment from years of arc welding. In Proceedings of VII International Pneumoconiosis Conference, Part II. Pittsburgh, August 23–26, 1986, NIOSH publication 90-108.
25. Kojola WM, Moran JB: Exposure limits for man-made mineral fibers. Position of the Building and Construction Trades Department, AFL-CIO. Appl Occup Environ Hyg 7:724–733, 1992.
26. Lippman M: Asbestos and other mineral fibers. In Lippman M (ed): Environmental Toxicants. Human Exposures and their Health Effects. New York, Van Nostrand Reinhold, 1992, pp 30–75.
27. Luce D, Leclerc A, Morcet JF, et al: Occupational risk factors for sinonasal cancer: A case-control study in France. Am J Ind Med 21:163–175, 1992.
28. Morabia A, Markowitz S, Garibaldi K, Wynder EL: Lung cancer and occupation: Results of a multicentre case-control study. Br J Ind Med 49:721–727, 1992.
29. Olkinuora M: Alcoholism and occupation. Scand J Work Environ Health. 10(6 Spec No):511–515, 1984.
30. Fischbein A, Luo JC, Rosenfeld S, et al: Respiratory findings among ironworkers: Results from a clinical survey in the New York metropolitan area and identification of health hazards from asbestos in place at work. Br J Ind Med 48:404–411, 1991.
31. Gerskevitch MF, Groce DW, Hearl FJ: Assessment of abrasive blasting substitutes for silica [ISSC manuscript]. Morgantown, WV, Division of Respiratory Disease Studies, National Institute for Occupational Safety and Health, 1993.
32. Goh CL: Sickness absence due to occupational dermatoses in a prefabrication construction factory. Contact Dermatitis 15:28–31, 1986.
33. Harford TC, Parker DA, Grant BF, Dawson DA: Alcohol use and dependence among employed men and women in the United States in 1988. Alcohol Clin Exp Res 16:146–148, 1992.
34. Houck P, Nebel D, Milham S Jr: Organic solvent encephalopathy: An old hazard revisited. Am J Ind Med 22:109–115, 1992.

35. Hunting KL, Matanowski GM, Larson M, Wolford R: Solvent exposure and risks of slips, trips, and falls among painters. Am J Ind Med 20:353–370, 1991.
36. Kessel R, Redl M, Mauermayer R, Praml GJ: Changes in lung function after working with the shotcrete lining method under compressed air conditions. Br J Ind Med 46:128–132, 1989.
37. Last JM: A dictionary of epidemiology. New York, Oxford University Press, 1983.
38. Lead exposure among lead burners. MMWR 41:307–310, 1992.
39. Lindstrom K: Changes in psychological performances of solvent-poisoned and solvent-exposed workers. Am J Ind Med 1:69–84, 1980.
40. Liu T, Waterbor JW: Comparison of suicide rates among industrial groups. Am J Ind Med 25:197–203, 1994.
41. Maizlish N, Rudolph L, Sutton P, et al: Elevated blood lead in California adults, 1987: Results of a statewide surveillance program based on laboratory reports. Am J Public Health 80:931–934, 1988.
42. Man-made mineral fibres and radon. IARC Monographs on the Evaluation of Carcinogenic Risks to Humans. Vol 43. Lyon, France, IARC, 1988.
43. Mandell W, Eaton WW, Anthony JC, Garrison R: Alcoholism and occupations: A review and analysis of 104 occupations. Alcohol Clin Exp Res 16:734–746, 1992.
44. Marino PE, Fransblau A, Lilis R, Landrigan PJ: Acute lead poisoning in construction workers: The failure of current protective standards. Arch Environ Health 44:140–145, 1989.
45. Merlo F, Costantini M, Reggiardo G, et al: Lung cancer risk among refractory brick workers exposed to crystalline silica: A retrospective cohort study. Epidemiology 2:299–305, 1991.
46. Muscat JE, Wynder EL: Tobacco, alcohol, asbestos, and occupational risk factors for laryngeal cancer. Cancer 69:2244–2251, 1992.
47. Parkes WR: Occupational Lung Disorders. 3rd ed. Oxford, England, Butterworth-Heinemann, 1994.
48. Pollack ES, Ringen K: Risk of hospitalization for specific non-work-related conditions among laborers and their families. Am J Ind Med 23:417–425, 1993.
49. Rae CE, Bell CN Jr, Elliott CE, Shannon M: Ten cases of acute lead intoxication among bridge workers in Louisiana. DICP 25:932–937, 1991.
50. Richter ED, Kretzmer D: Prevention through pre-review in occupational health and safety. Am J Public Health 70:157–161, 1980.
51. Rom WN (ed): Occupational and Environmental Medicine. 2d Edition. Boston, Little, Brown & Co, 1992.
52. Rosen RH, Freeman S: Occupational contact dermatitis in New South Wales. Aust J Dermatol 33:1–10, 1992.
53. Rosner DM, Markowitz G: Deadly Dust. Princeton, NJ, Princeton University Press, 1989.
54. Scherr PA, Hutchison GB, Neiman RS: Non-Hodgkin's lymphoma and occupational exposure. Cancer Res 52(19 suppl):5503S–5509S, 1992.
55. Schwartz DA, Baker EL: Respiratory illness in the construction industry. Airflow obstruction among painters. Chest 93:134–137, 1988.
56. Seligman PJ, Helperin WE: Targeting of workplace inspections for lead. Am J Ind Med 20:381–390, 1991.
57. Stockbridge H, Daniel W: Lead poisoning among bricklayers—Washington State. MMWR 40:169–171, 1991.
58. Suruda AJ: Work-related deaths in construction painting. Scand J Work Environ Health 18:30–33, 1992.
59. Tharr D: Occupational exposures during abrasive blasting removel of lead-based paint on a highway bridge. Appl Occup Environ Hyg 7:497–499, 1992.
60. Vaughan TL: Occupation and squamous cell cancers of the pharynx and sinonasal cavity. Am J Ind Med 16:493–510.
61. Welch L, Kirshner H, Heath A, et al: Chronic neuropsychological and neurological impairment following acute exposure to a solvent mixture of toluene and methyl ethyl ketone (MEK). J Toxicol Clin Toxicol 29:435–445, 1991.
62. Weeks JL, Levy BS, Wagner GR: Preventing Occupational Disease and Injury. Washington, DC, American Public Health Association, 1991.
63. Yamano Y, Tokutaka T, Kagawa J, Ishizu S: Subjective symptoms and blood findings in painters exposed to organic solvents. Sangyo Igaku 33:527–532, 1991.
64. Ziem GE, Castleman BI: Threshold limit values: Historical perspectives and current practices. J Occup Med 31:910–918, 1989.

LAURA WELCH, MD
PEKKA ROTO, MPH

MEDICAL SURVEILLANCE PROGRAMS FOR CONSTRUCTION WORKERS

From the Division of Occupational
  and Environmental Medicine
George Washington University
Washington, DC (LW)
  and
Tampere Regional Institute of
  Occupational Health
Tampere, Finland (PR)

Reprint requests to:
Laura Welch, MD
George Washington University
Suite 201
2300 K Street NW
Washington, DC 20037

Medical surveillance is the ongoing systematic collection, analysis, and interpretation of health and exposure data. Surveillance data from a range of sources are used to determine the need for occupational safety and health actions and for more specific medical intervention, to guide these interventions, and to evaluate them. Surveillance can be the collection of morbidity and mortality data from secondary sources, such as OSHA logs or medical records. The term medical surveillance refers specifically to examination of individuals expressly for the purpose of detecting health effects, and it includes examinations both at the initial point of employment and periodic monitoring.

OVERVIEW

The goal of an initial examination is to identify any medical condition that puts a worker at risk from anticipated occupational exposures or job tasks. In addition, an initial examination can serve as a baseline against which exams after the beginning of exposure can be compared. Before such an examination program begins, the investigators must be sure that the information collected will be useful, and not unnecessary, data; it can be misleading to have adverse health data that are not predictive of job ability or job-related health effects. In choosing tests to determine baseline function, the investigators also need to know how closely each test measures the function they want to measure and how stable that measure is over time in the absence of exposure. All of these factors are then combined into a choice of tests to use in an initial examination.[19,23]

Periodic medical surveillance programs follow and involve the assessment of symptom complaints, physical findings, and laboratory values to determine whether there is a deviation from the expected norm or from baseline data. In addition to following individual workers, medical surveillance programs can be used to look for trends in groups of workers. For an individual worker, the periodic examination ensures that his or her health status has not changed since the baseline examination and, if it has, allows early intervention. For individuals with abnormal findings on history, physical examination, or laboratory testing, a periodic exam affords the opportunity to closely monitor the worker's health status after an intervention has been made.

SURVEILLANCE AS PREVENTION

A medical surveillance program is one of three stages of prevention. *Primary prevention* includes engineering controls such as product substitution, administrative controls, or changes in work practices. In *secondary prevention,* a disease process can be detected early with screening, at a stage when disease can be halted or slowed. Medical surveillance is secondary prevention. It complements risk communication and industrial hygiene controls, especially when the hazard of concern cannot be eliminated. *Tertiary prevention* is the treatment of disease to delay progression or prevent disability.

Medical surveillance should be based on basic principles of screening.[19] The outcome the program is designed to detect should be alterable; something can be done if an abnormality is found. The action taken should focus on eliminating or reducing exposure, providing medical treatment of the individual, and, when controls are not feasible or accommodation is not possible, removing the employee from the exposure. In occupational medicine there is a benefit to screening even for diseases that are not treatable; in many circumstances, a case is a sentinel event pointing to other at-risk workers so that secondary prevention can be used to trigger primary prevention. In addition, screening tests should be easy to administer, valid, and reliable. The sensitivity and specificity of the tests should be known and be of an acceptable level to reduce false negatives and false positives. Further diagnosis and treatment also should be available and acceptable.

"Positive" surveillance findings should trigger an industrial hygiene investigation and a review of control strategies. Because medical surveillance serves as a second line of protection, after exposure reduction, it is used in settings where exposures may occur that exceed the exposure threshold for health effects. It also may be used where there may be susceptible populations at risk even from exposures controlled to a level set by regulation or by feasible technology. Because a surveillance program is designed to detect exposure-related effects, one of the first actions taken if the program shows a likely health effect of exposure is an investigation of the potential for exposure.

The Role of Biologic Monitoring

There can be an important role for biologic monitoring in the follow-up investigation of a positive finding. Biologic monitoring can define individual exposure levels; this is particularly useful if the substance is absorbed through the skin and air monitoring poorly reflects total exposure or dose. Other actions should include a more detailed medical evaluation and an evaluation of other risk factors for the health effect. This additional testing, in combination with the review of control strategies, allows a determination of whether the health effect is related to the exposures and of steps that are needed to reduce exposure.

Limitations of Surveillance

Medical surveillance is one step in secondary prevention, and investigators must remember its proper place in the hierarchy of controls. Surveillance is not an alternative to primary prevention. It should not be used as a way to support the use of personal protective equipment in lieu of primary prevention.

Medical surveillance programs collect confidential medical information and place special obligations on medical providers. A conflict of interest may arise more often in the practice of occupational medicine than in other areas of medicine. The codes of ethics of the American Association of Occupational Health Nursing, the American College of Occupational and Environmental Medicine, and the Association of Occupational and Environmental Clinics emphasize the primacy of the confidential relationship between the patient/worker and the health care provider (Table 1).

TABLE 1.   Codes of Ethics of Three Occupational Health Organizations

American Association of Occupational Health Nurses Code of Ethics

1. The occupational health nurse provides health care in the work environment with regard for human dignity and client rights, unrestricted by considerations of social or economic status, national origin, race, religion, age, sex or the nature of the health status.
2. The occupational health nurse promotes collaboration with other health professionals and community health agencies in order to meet the health needs of the workforce.
3. The occupational health nurse strives to safeguard the employee's right to privacy by protecting confidential information and releasing information only upon written consent of the employee or as required or permitted by law.
4. The occupational health nurse strives to provide quality care and to safeguard clients from unethical and illegal actions.
5. The occupational health nurse, licensed to provide health care services, accepts obligations to society as a professional and responsible member of the community.
6. The occupational health nurse maintains individual competence in occupational health nursing practice, recognizing and accepting responsibility for individual judgments and actions, while complying with appropriate laws and regulations (local, state, and federal) that impact the delivery of occupational health services.
7. The occupational health nurse participates, as appropriate, in activities such as research that contribute to the ongoing development of the profession.

American College of Occupational and Environmental Medicine Code of Ethical Conduct

This code establishes standards of professional ethical conduct with which each member of the American College of Occupational and Environmental Medicine (ACOEM) is expected to comply. These standards are intended to guide occupational and environmental medicine physicians in their relationships with: the individuals they serve; employers and workers' representatives; colleagues in the health professions; the public and all levels of government, including the judiciary.
Physicians should:

1. Accord the highest priority to the health and safety of individuals in both the workplace and the environment;
2. Practice on a scientific basis with integrity and strive to acquire and maintain adequate knowledge and expertise upon which to render professional service;
3. Relate honestly and ethically in all professional relationships;
4. Strive to expand and disseminate medical knowledge and participate in ethical research efforts as appropriate;
5. Keep confidential all individual medical information, releasing such information only when required by law or overriding public health considerations, or to other physicians according to accepted medical practice, or to others at the request of the individual;

(Continued on following page)

TABLE 1.   Codes of Ethics of Three Occupational Health Organizations *(Cont.)*

American College of Occupational and Environmental Medicine Code of Ethical Conduct

6. Recognize that employers may be entitled to counsel about an individual's medical work fitness, but not to diagnoses or specific details, except in compliance with laws and regulations;
7. Communicate to individuals and/or groups any significant observations and recommendations concerning their health or safety; and
8. Recognize those medical impairments in oneself and others, including chemical dependency and abusive personal practices, which interfere with one's ability to follow the above principles, and take appropriate measures.

Association of Occupational and Environmental Clinics (AOEC) Patient Bill of Rights

Our Clinic is a member of the Association of Occupational and Environmental Clinics (AOEC). As an AOEC member, we are committed to provide you prevention-oriented, compassionate, quality health care. This includes evaluation of your health problem; treatment or referral to appropriate treatment; aid in helping you understand the cause and nature of your illness; and recommendations to prevent further problems.

As a patient of our clinic, you have a right to:
1. Know and consent to all tests and procedures before they are performed.
2. Know the results of all tests and procedures.
3. Obtain a copy of your medical records, if requested.
4. Obtain a description of all financial relationships between this clinic and any employer or group to which you belong or from which you are eligible to receive services, should you be concerned about a possible conflict of interest.

As an AOEC clinic, we promise to:
1. Not release medical information about you to anyone outside this clinic without your express written permission, except in that we may be required to release your records:
   a. If you request payment for these services by another party, such as a workers' compensation insurance company, health insurance company or your employer.
   b. If subpoenaed due to a legal action.
   c. If required by public health authorities to report an occupational disease or if an emergency is found to exist, and information in your record is necessary to prevent illness in others.
   d. For continuous quality improvement review or medical research (after removal of any information that would identify you).
2. Help you obtain information about workers' compensation, social security, disability, and other health and welfare benefits.
3. Help you obtain information about laws protecting you and your health and safety on the job.
4. Provide information on local, state/provincial, and federal/national (e.g., OSHA, Canadian Centre for Occupational Health and Safety) health and safety services available to you including workplace inspections.
5. Help you improve health and safety at your worksite.
6. Provide legal testimony of our findings, if necessary.

Although health examinations are widely used in occupational health programs, neither their scientific basis nor cost benefit are well documented. More data are needed on the sensitivity and specificity and predictive value of many commonly used screening tests. In considering the role of medical examinations, one must remember that examinations for construction workers serve needs beyond purely medical ones; the educational, legal, and socioeconomic aspects of health examinations are quite important. Health examinations serve as a point of ongoing contact between professionals and workers, who can exchange important health and safety-related information. This is particularly important in construction, because the work site is not fixed.

TYPES OF EXAMINATIONS

A medical monitoring program can fill several roles simultaneously. The most important are to determine fitness for duty, to determine health effects related to specific exposures, and to provide health education and health promotion.

The Fitness-for-Duty Exam

At present, examinations before the beginning of work in the United States (for firms employing 15 or more people) are subject to regulation under the Americans with Disabilities Act. In construction, a large proportion of contracting firms are not large enough to fall under this jurisdiction. According to this relatively new regulation, fitness-for-duty examinations should be performed before placement rather than before employment. This means that a worker is offered a job contingent on passing a medical examination and, if he or she does not meet the fitness requirement of the job, the employer should attempt to accommodate the worker in another job for which he or she is qualified. What accommodation is provided is defined by the term *reasonable*, and an employer can argue that certain accommodations would present an undue burden. In many construction occupations and with many employers, it is unlikely that a worker who did not meet the initial fitness requirements could be accommodated in another job. However, as new case law is established, there may be a requirement for job redesign or other accommodations in the construction industry.

Health Effects Related to Specific Hazards

Physical strain, noise, and dusts are well-recognized causes of occupational diseases in construction workers; almost all crafts have some exposure to these hazards. Chemical exposures are generally limited to certain occupations and vary by the type of construction (see chapter 7).

To design an effective substance-specific or disease-specific monitoring program for construction workers, we need to know the nature and extent of hazardous exposures, which workers have those exposures, what diseases the exposures cause, and which workers are at risk from exposure or from personal factors (such as smoking, which multiplies the risk of disease from asbestos exposure). We need then to know the utility of the tests and their predictive value. In construction, the nature and extent of exposures and the morbidity of construction workers have not been well characterized. The literature reveals that construction workers experience work-related musculoskeletal disorders, contact dermatitis, and noise-induced hearing loss. Exposure to respiratory hazards is also widespread. Construction workers engaged in bridge repair have a disproportionate burden of lead poisoning. These data can be used to suggest a targeted medical surveillance program for construction workers (surveillance for lead is discussed in chapter 8).

REGULATORY REQUIREMENTS

Regulatory requirements for monitoring workers for these hazards differ between the United States and the European Union. In the U.S., the Occupational Safety and Health Administration has authority to set separate standards for the construction, maritime, and agricultural industries and for general industry. Although most of the standards that have specific requirements for medical surveillance apply fully to construction, there are specific places where OSHA standards differ for construction and general industry. OSHA has 21 standards that require medical monitoring in general industry; 13 of them apply to construction workers (Table 2). In addition, OSHA requires a comprehensive medical examination for work at hazardous waste sites or in lead abatement, with a broader examination than any examination designed for exposure to one specific substance.

Analyzing existing OSHA standards that require any medical evaluations, examinations, or tests (Tables 2 and 3), Silverstein[25] defined 24 features of a comprehensive

TABLE 2. Scoring of Medical Provisions of the 13 OSHA Standards that Apply to Construction

Substance Covered by Standard	Standard Citation	Total Score	Quality Score	Screening Score	Surveillance Score
Acrylonitrile	29 CFR 1910.1045	.46	.29	.67	.20
Arsenic, inorganic	29 CFR 1910.10108	.48	.21	.75	.40
Asbestos*	29 CFR 1910.1001	.52	.36	.83	.30
Benzene	29 CFR 1910.1028	.67	.64	.92	.50
Carcinogens†	29 CFR 1910.1003 to 1016	.25	.00	.50	.30
Dibromochloropropane	29 CFR 1910.1044	.42	.21	.75	.30
Ethylene oxide	29 CFR 1910.1047	.44	.14	.75	.30
Formaldehyde	29 CFR 1910.1048	.56	.14	.92	.60
Hazardous waste operations	29 CFR 1910.120	.40	.14	.67	.30
Lead	29 CFR 1910.1025	.67	.64	.92	.50
Methylenedianiline	29 CFR 1910.1050	.52	.14	.92	.40
Respirator program	29 CFR 1910.134	.15	.07	.42	.20
Vinyl chloride	29 CFR 1910.1017	.40	.14	.75	.40
	Mean	.41	.26	.65	.31
	Standard deviation	.22	.20	.30	.21

* The asbestos standards for construction and general industry differ; the score on this table applies to the standard for general industry (see Table 4).
† The OSHA carcinogen standard covers 4-nitrobiphenyl, a-naphthlamine, methyl chloromethyl ether, 3,3'-dichlorobenzidine and its salts, bischloromethyl ether, b-naphthylamine, benzidine, 4-aminodiphenyl, ethyleneimine, b-propiolactone, 2-acetylaminoflourene, 4-dimethylaminoazobenzene, and n-nitrosodimethylamine.
‡ The lead standards for construction and general industry differ; the score on this table applies to the standard for general industry (see Table 4).
Adapted from Silverstein M: Analysis of medical screening and surveillance in 21 occupational safety and health administration standards: Support for a generic medical surveillance standard. Am J Indust Med 26:283–295, 1994.

occupational medical program and created subscales from these 24 features to assign a score to each standard for quality control, screening utility, and surveillance utility. Screening utility defines the characteristics most relevant to the delivery of individual clinical services, and the surveillance utility defines the elements needed for evaluation of aggregate data and preventive actions based on these data. This analysis is useful in looking at the merit of the standards that apply in construction.

In some cases, there are differences between the general industry standard and the one for construction; asbestos, noise, and lead are three examples. Compared with the standard for general industry, the asbestos standard for construction is less specific in its requirement for medical surveillance and therefore would receive a lower score if analyzed separately. Many OSHA safety and hygiene standards other than these do apply to construction but do not specify medical surveillance.

Requirements in the European Union

As in the U.S., the European Union has specific directives for the prevention of health hazards associated with specific exposures. The directives outline the minimum level of preventive activities and give recommendations for health examinations and

TABLE 3. Scoring Rules for Medical Program Elements in OSHA Standards

Program Element	Score = 0	Score = 1	Score = 2
1. Physical examination	None	Required, but nonspecific	Required, with specific elements
2. Medical history	None	Required, but nonspecific	Required, with specific elements
3. Occupational history	None	Required, but nonspecific	Required, with specific elements
4. Laboratory tests	None	Required, but nonspecific	Required, with specific elements
5. Examination schedule	Baseline only or emergency/complaint only	Baseline + periodic	Baseline + periodic + emergency/complaint
6. Eligibility	Non-specific	Linked to qualitative exposure assessment	Linked to quantitative exposure assessment
7. Provider credentials	None	Professional degree specified	Degree + specialized training or experience
8. Laboratory certification	None	Certification required	Certification + proficiency testing
9. Guidelines for interpretation of results	None	Minimal	Comprehensive
10. Test result norms for comparison	None	Norms specified	Norms specified + required comparisons with baseline
11. Guidelines for treatment or care	None	Minimal	Comprehensive
12. Facilities and equipment	None	Minimal specifications	Comprehensive specifications
13. Provider training: Standard specific	None	Minimal	Comprehensive
14. Protocols for examinations and tests	None	Minimal	Comprehensive
15. Employee records: Contents	None	To include tests or exams or other material	To include tests, exams and other material
16. Employee records: Confidentiality and privacy	None	Limits on information about non-occupational conditions	Explicit protections for confidentiality and privacy
17. Physician-written opinions	None	Required, but nonspecific	Required, with specific elements
18. Employee records: Preservation and storage	Less stringent or specific than 29 CFR 1910.20	Equivalent to 29 CFR 1910.20	Exceeds 29 CFR 1910.20
19. Access to medical records	Less stringent or specific than 29 CFR 1010.20	Equivalent to 29 CRF 1910.20	Exceeds 29 CFR 1910.20
20. Fitness-to-work recommendations	None required	Required, but nonspecific	Required, with specific guidelines
21. Counseling and referrals	None	Provision of results required but without specific guidelines	Provision of results + specific guidelines for counseling or referrals

(Continued on following page)

TABLE 3.   Scoring Rules for Medical Program Elements in OSHA Standards *(Cont.)*

Program Element	Score = 0	Score = 1	Score = 2
22. Medical-removal provisions	None	Medical removal requirements specified	Medical removal requirements + medical removal protection benefits
23. Epidemiology	None	Aggregate data description required	Aggregate data analysis required
24. Environmental intervention	None	Provider walk-through or inspection required	Workplace evaluations or changes required

From Silverstein M: Analysis of medical screening and surveillance in 21 occupational safety and health administration standards: Support for a generic medical surveillance standard. Am J Ind Med 26:283–295, 1994; with permission.

surveillance. Each European country may implement stricter legislation. There are two general principles for medical surveillance in the European Union. First, the doctor responsible for the health surveillance of the workers must be familiar with the exposure conditions or circumstances of each worker. Second, health monitoring must be conducted in accordance with the principles and practices of occupational medicine and must include at least:

• Records of a worker's occupational and medical history
• A personal interview
• Biologic monitoring, where appropriate.

In the European Union, Belgium, France, Germany, The Netherlands, and Sweden have specialized nationwide occupational health service networks for construction workers.

SURVEILLANCE FOR AILMENTS COMMON TO CONSTRUCTION

Prevention of Musculoskeletal Disorders
At present, the only significant medical finding that predicts an applicant's risk of low back pain is a prior history of low back pain.[5,6] The severity of the previous symptoms, length of absence from work, and short intervals between the episodes have been identified as potential risk factors.[17] Lumbar x-rays have no predictive value.[13] However, the predictive value of a history of back injury for future back problems is too low to be useful in a preemployment setting, and factors of the job are more important risks. For example, in a prospective study of nurses, Videman found that a prior back injury carried a relative risk of another injury (odds ratio 1.73) but that work exposures such as daily exposure to lifting (OR 2.19) or working in specific service areas (OR 4.26) were more important.[28]

Preemployment or preplacement strength testing may be beneficial if it has been designed on the basis of exact observations on the demands of the future work, but this remains to be proven in a range of circumstances.[13] Several studies have found that workers performing jobs that equal or exceed their isometric strength testing values are up to three times more likely to suffer a low back injury than stronger workers.[7–9,15,26] However, the positive predictive value of strength testing is only 20% in a situation in which the relative risk for a weaker worker is threefold and the incidence of low-back injury is 10%. The positive predictive value increases to only 53% with a relative risk of 10, meaning that if this were used as a preplacement screening test one person who would not suffer an injury would be denied employment in order to exclude one who would have a low back injury.

Testing must be directly correlated to the job. In a large study at Boeing Corporation, Battie found that nonspecific strength testing was of no value.[4] Many of the studies that show a benefit of strength testing followed the workers for no longer than a year; it remains to be seen if the benefit of strength testing lasts with long-term exposure to lifting hazards.

There is a benefit to ongoing medical surveillance of workers in jobs that expose them to physical stresses at work, even if worker selection cannot prevent musculoskeletal injuries and illnesses. The goal is to detect musculoskeletal symptoms early and both treat the worker and modify the work. A program that performs periodic symptom surveys and uses them to identify work factors that can be changed has been shown to be effective.[18] Standard clinical practice also dictates that an occupational medical service provide occupational rehabilitation, assignment of alternate-duty jobs, and modification of jobs to fit permanently injured workers.

Prevention of Noise-Induced Hearing Loss

Noise-induced hearing loss is one of the most common occupational diseases among construction workers in industrialized countries. In Finland, 30 cases are reported for each 10,000 construction workers, and the true rates are likely to be higher.[27] Since hearing loss is reversible in the first 3–4 years after the beginning of noise exposure, the development of occupational hearing loss can be controlled with consecutive yearly audiometric tests. To assure the quality of the measurements, tests should be carried out according to the ISO standard 1999.[14] If the audiometric curve indicates a dip between 3,000–4,000 Hz under 40 dB and this dip disappears after the person has been in a noise-free environment for 2–3 days, the result indicates overexposure to noise. Noise reduction or a complete hearing conservation program should be undertaken.

Some factors are thought to increase the susceptibility of workers to noise-induced hearing loss. Diabetic neuropathy and hypercholesterolemia have been associated with an increased risk.[22] Whole-body vibration has an additive effect,[21] and smoking may be additive. Aminoglycoside antibiotics and some antihypertensive medications may also be risk factors for noise-induced hearing loss.[1]

Prevention of Lung Disease

Dust exposure might cause pneumoconiosis (from asbestos or silica), allergic diseases such as asthma and rhinitis (from wood or chemicals), or irritative symptoms (from manmade mineral fibers). Carefully carried pulmonary function tests—forced expiratory volume (in 1 minute) and forced vital capacity (FEV_1 and FVC)—are the basic references for further observations. Susceptibility to occupational lung diseases cannot be evaluated with pulmonary function tests, but pulmonary function tests along with a chest radiograph are the basic monitoring tools used in surveillance for work-related lung diseases. The measurement procedure and equipment should be standardized and calibrated to avoid errors due to variation; the standards set by the American Thoracic Society are recommended for this purpose.[2,20]

The most reproducible pulmonary function tests are FEV_1 and FVC, which can be measured with simple and reliable spirometers. Regular PFTs should be carried out for workers who are exposed to harmful dusts, especially workers in renovation, demolishing, and stone cutting. The recommended interval for PFTs is once per year.

There are two primary roles for PFTs in a surveillance program for construction workers: first, as part of a respiratory protection program and, second, to detect health effects of respiratory hazards at an early stage. Harber[12] outlines the use of spirometry in surveillance: (1) when legally mandated, as for asbestos; (2) for identification of individuals with early disease so they can be removed from exposure and the job can be modified; (3) in hazard identification, using the results from a group of exposed workers to determine if a hazard exists; (4) in preplacement testing in the U.S. (equivalent to preemployment testing in Europe); and (5) for health promotion, to encourage smoking cessation. For the second- and third-listed uses to be effective, exposures need to be well characterized. Based on the data presented in chapter 6, it would be reasonable to recommend periodic PFTs for workers exposed to silica and asbestos and for all welders, at a minimum.

In addition, information on smoking cessation is an important part of secondary prevention of occupational lung diseases and should be included in connection with health examinations.

Prevention of Dermatitis

Chemical exposure occurs most commonly during the finishing stage of building projects. Insulation materials, glues, and paints are potential hazardous exposures. Skin irritation, erythema, and blistering have been described in roofers from exposure to coal tar pitch derivatives (see chapter 7).[11] In both preplacement and periodic examinations, respiratory and skin symptoms and their relation to a worker's earlier exposures must be documented carefully. Materials containing isocyanates and epoxy resins are the most potent allergens encountered by construction workers, and exposure to cement products is common in some crafts.

Prevention of allergic diseases is primarily a hygienic rather than a medical procedure. Patch tests are not recommended in the context of medical surveillance, because they may sensitize the person;[16] they should be reserved for diagnostic use only. Atopic individuals are usually more susceptible to irritant contact dermatitis and to occupational asthma due to organic dusts (flour and animal epithelium) but not that which is caused by epoxy resins or isocyanates. For instance, if a job applicant has manifest atopic symptoms or signs, the risk for asthma or allergic dermatitis must be evaluated carefully against potential exposure in the job. In Sweden it is recommended that people with atopy or dyshydrotic eczema be excluded from jobs in which they might be exposed to potent allergens such as epoxy resins, but the positive predictive value of such a history is quite low. The possible recommendations to the individual and the employer must include specific instructions for personal protection and for technical prevention whenever economically or practically feasible. For instance, adding ferrous sulfate to cement, which reduces water-soluble chromium to an insoluble form, seems to be the most efficient way to prevent chromium-induced dermatoses among construction workers. The Scandinavian experience indicates that low-chromium cement (< 2 ppm hexavalent chromium) diminishes the risk of allergic hand dermatitis among construction workers.[3,24]

Personal hygiene at work is an important factor to be considered in the prevention of allergic dermatitis. Hand washing and the appropriate use of gloves are known to be effective in preventing contact dermatitis. The construction environment poses special challenges, because provision of water for hand washing is more difficult that in general industry. The OSHA interim lead standard for construction specifies that hand washing facilities and/or shower facilities be available at the end of a work shift, and OSHA has determined that this is technically feasible on construction sites. Such protection, if extended to all construction, could reduce contact dermatitis.

HEALTH MAINTENANCE AND HEALTH PROMOTION

Cancer and cardiovascular diseases are strongly associated with lifestyle. Smoking, poor nutrition, and a sedentary lifestyle are the most important risks for these diseases. Opinions differ about the effectiveness of health promotion during routine surveillance examinations. Depending on the approach and follow-up, however, positive results can be achieved.

Construction workers smoke more than the average working-age population. One of the most effective preventive procedures that can be performed in context of health examinations is smoking cessation counseling and therapy. Smoking cessation not only decreases the risk of cancer and cardiovascular diseases but also markedly decreases the risk of some work-related diseases such as asbestos-induced pulmonary carcinoma. It also has been suggested that smokers are more susceptible to occupational hearing loss and to work accidents. Depending on the cessation program's approach, the 1-year cessation rate varies between 10–30% of participants or, according to Clayton, is as high as 90%.[10] With nicotine chewing gum and patch therapies, 1-year cessation rates vary from 20–40%.

Information about nutrition, alcohol consumption, and physical health promotion may be included in surveillance examinations. Physical training, if a worker can be motivated for permanent change, requires little investment and allows gains in other areas of health. A common attitude among construction workers is that the physical demands of their job satisfy their need for physical exercise, which, unfortunately, is not true.

Organization of a Medical Surveillance Program

Because of the tendency of construction workers to have several jobs and employers each year, medical surveillance cannot be approached in the way it is applied in general industry; that would result in a construction worker having multiple preplacement examinations each year but little annual surveillance. If the medical data reside with an employer or his/her designate, as specified in current OSHA standards, each examination stands alone, and the opportunity to examine changes over time in an individual or in a group is lost. In such cases, medical surveillance is reduced to a litmus test for employment, and the public health benefits achieved by surveillance may be lost completely. This also can lead to unnecessary costs and risk to the worker for unnecessarily repeated tests, such as x-rays. Change can only be accomplished through an OSHA standard for construction.

At its best, effective medical surveillance in construction would require the creation of a suprastructure above the individual job or contractor. For the section of the industry that is organized into unions, unions could cooperate with employers to integrate the data collected, ensure that a worker not undergo repeated preplacement chest x-rays each year, and look for longitudinal trends in an individual and in specific trades. This is a large task, requiring expertise that many construction unions do not have. It also does not solve the problem for the majority of construction workers who are not unionized. Sweden created Bygghälsan out of the recognition that the construction industry as a whole needed a labor-management program to apply public health in construction. The Bygghälsan program is

TABLE 4.   Comparison between Medical Surveillance Provisions of Selected Standards for General Industry and Construction

Lead Standards

General Industry	Construction
Full medical surveillance triggered by air monitoring above an action level of 30 µg/m³ for more than 30 days.	Initial medical surveillance triggered by air monitoring above an action level of 30 µg/m³ but *without* a 30-day trigger. Initial medical includes blood-lead level and zinc protoporphyrin, but no physical exam.
Includes blood-lead level and zinc protoporphyrin initially and surveillance every 6 months for employees exposed above the action level for 30 days/year.	Initial medical surveillance also triggered by work in defined high-risk tasks if air sampling is not available.
If blood-lead level is at or above 40 µg/dL, blood-lead level test must be performed every 2 months until 2 consecutive samples are below 40 µg/dL.	Full medical surveillance triggered by blood-lead level above 40 µg/dL or air sampling above action level of 30 µg/m³ for 30 days/year.
Medical removal when 3 consecutive sample blood-lead level tests, on average, exceed 50 µg/dL.	If initial blood-lead level exceeds 40 µg/dL or exposure exceeds action level of 30 µg/m³, blood-lead level every 2 months for the first 6 months, then every 6 months as long as blood-lead level is below 40 µg/dL. If blood-lead level is at or above 40 µg/dL, frequency is every 2 months.
	Medical removal when one blood-lead sample confirmed, with a second sample within 2 weeks, exceeds 50 µg/dL.

Noise Standards

General Industry	Construction
Hearing conservation standard is a companion to the noise standard.	Same permissible exposure level for noise as in general industry, but a hearing conservation program is not required.

Abestos Standards

General Industry	Construction
Requires an x-ray on prescribed schedule.	X-ray is at discretion of the examining physician.
Requires a medical examination on termination of employment.	No termination examination required.

one model of effective medical surveillance for construction workers in the United States.*

SUMMARY

In summary, the basic medical examination and carefully documented work and medical history are essential parts of the health examinations of construction workers. To achieve their best potential in preventing occupational and chronic diseases, the examinations should be conducted by professionals who know the working conditions in construction and have a positive attitude toward preventive medicine. One important aspect of these examinations is the opportunity to trigger workplace investigations, followed by exposure reduction. Simultaneously, such examinations provide an opportunity for heath education of the worker and an education about work-related health problems for the health care provider.

---

* Editor's note: In the early 1990s, a declining economy and changing political circumstances led to a restructuring of the Bygghälsan program. Currently, the program's future structure and operations are still unclear.

REFERENCES

1. Alberti PW: Scott-Brown's Otolaryngology. In Kerr AJ (ed): London: Butterworth, 1987.
2. American Thoracic Society: Standardization of spirometry—1987 update. Am Rev Respir Dis 136:1285–1298, 1987.
3. Avntorp C: Prevalence of cement eczema in Denmark before and since addition of ferrous sulfate to Danish cement. Acta Derm Venerol (Stockh) 69:151–155, 1989.
4. Battie MC, Bigos SJ, Fisher L, Wortley MD: The inability of strength testing to predict future industrial back problems. Int Soc Stud Lumbar Spine 1987.
5. Biering-Sorensen F: The prognostic value of the low back history and physical measurements. Copenhagen, University of Copenhagen, 1983.
6. Bigos SJ: Back injuries in industry; a retrospective study; II Injury factor; III Employee-related factors. Spine 11:246–256, 1986.
7. Chaffin DB: Human strength capability and low back pain. J Occup Med 16:248–254, 1974.
8. Chaffin DB, Herrin GD, Keyserling WM: Pre-employment strength testing. An updated position. J Occup Med 20:403–408, 1978.
9. Chaffin DB, Herrin GD, Keyserling WM, Foulke JA: Pre-employment strength testing in selecting workers for materials handling jobs. Cincinnati, NIOSH Physiology and Ergonomics Branch, 1977, NIOSH technical report, NIOSH contract CDC-99-74-61.
10. Cooper M, Clayton R: Stop-smoking program using nicotine reduction therapy and behavior modification for heavy smokers. JADA 118:47–51, 1989.
11. Emmett EA: Cutaneous and ocular hazards of roofers. Occ Med State Art Rev 1:307–322, 1986.
12. Harber P, Lockey JE: Pulmonary function testing in pulmonary prevention. Occ Med State Art Rev 6:69–79, 1991.
13. Himmelstein JS, Andersson GBJ: Low back pain: Risk evaluation and preplacement screening. Occup Med State Art Rev 3:255–269, 1988.
14. ISO: Acoustics: Determination of occupational exposure and estimation of noise-induced hearing impairment. Geneva, International Organization for Standardization, 1990, pp 335–353.
15. Keyserling WM, Herrin GD, Chaffin DB: Isometric strength testing as a means of controlling medical incidents on strenuous jobs. J Occup Med 22:332–336, 1980.
16. Lammintausta K, Maibach HI: Dermatologic considerations in worker fitness evaluation. Occup Med State Art Rev 3:341–350, 1988.
17. Lloyd DC, Troup JDC: Recurrent back pain and its predicition. J Soc Occup Med 33:66–74, 1983.
18. Lutz G, Hansford T: Cumulative trauma disorder controls; the ergonomics program at Ethicon, Inc. J Hand Surg 12A:863–866, 1987.
19. Matte TD, Fine L, Meinhardt TJ, Baker EL: Guidelines for medical screening in the workplace. Occup Med State Art Rev 5:439–456, 1990.
20. McKay RT, Lockey JE: Pulmonary function testing: Guidelines for medical surveillance. Occup Med State Art Rev 6:43–57, 1991.
21. Pinter I: Hearing loss of forest workers and tractors operators. Report EPA 550/9-73-008 315–327, 1973.
22. Pykko I: Risk factors in the genesis of sensioneural hearing loss in Finnish forestry workers. Br J Ind Med 439–446, 1989.
23. Rempel D: Medical surveillance in the workplace: Overview. Occup Med State Art Rev 5:435–453, 1990.
24. Roto P, Sainio H, Reunala T, Laippala P: Addition of ferrous sulphate to cement and risk of chromium dermatitis among cosntruction workers. Contact Dermatitis (in press).
25. Silverstein M: Analysis of medical screening and surveillance in 21 occupational safety and health administration standards: Support for a generic medical surveillance standard. Am J Ind Med 26:283–295, 1994.
26. Troup JDG, Martin JW, Lloyd DCEF: Back pain in industry. A prospective survey. Spine 6:61–69, 1981.
27. Vaaranen V: Annual report of occupational diseases. Helsinki, Institute of Occupational Health, 1993.
28. Videman T, Nurminen T, Tola S, et al.: Low back pain in nurses and some loading factors of work. Spine 9:400–404, 1984.

KNUT RINGEN, DrPH, MHA, MPH
EARL POLLACK, ScD
JOHN F. FINKLEA, MD, DrPH
JAMES MELIUS, MD, DrPH
ANDERS ENGLUND, MD

HEALTH INSURANCE AND WORKERS' COMPENSATION:

The Delivery of Medical and Rehabilitation Services for Construction Workers

From the Center to Protect
  Workers' Rights
Washington, DC (KR, EP, JF)
  and
Division of Occupational Health
  and Environmental Epidemiology
New York State Department of
  Health (JM)
  and
Department of Health and Social
  Affairs
National Board of Occupational
  Safety and Health
Solna, Sweden (AE)

Reprint requests to:
Knut Ringen, DrPH, MHA, MPH
The Center to Protect Workers'
  Rights
111 Massachusetts Ave. NW
Washington, DC 20001

Little is known about the delivery of health services to construction workers in the United States. Thirty years ago, the Tennessee Valley Authority developed mobile health centers to provide occupational and preventive medicine to construction workers building its major power plants, dams, and other projects, but the published papers that described these programs did not include any evaluation of process or outcome.[3,4]

In the U.S., the cost of health care for construction workers is generally covered by two completely different insurance systems. In the first, members of construction trade unions are covered, in most instances, by a health and welfare fund maintained by a local chapter of the union. These health insurance plans cover only medical problems that are not work-related. However, most nonunion workers are not covered, and many union members' coverage may lapse during extended periods of unemployment. For these reasons, the construction industry has one of the highest proportions of workers without health insurance.

The second type of insurance is workers' compensation, which covers injuries and illnesses that occur as a result of work.

OCCUPATIONAL MEDICINE: State of the Art Reviews—
Vol. 10, No. 2, April 1995. Philadelphia, Hanley & Belfus, Inc.

435

TABLE 1.   Ten Leading Diagnoses on Workers' Compensation Claims among 5,839
Construction Laborers, Washington State, 1990 and 1991

Diagnostic Category	Percentage of Total
Diseases of the musculoskeletal system and connective tissue	20
Sprains and strains of joints and adjacent muscles	9
Open wounds	9
Dislocations	8
Contusions with intact skin surface	8
Symptoms, signs, and ill-defined conditions	5
Fractures	5
Hereditary and degenerative diseases of the central nervous system	5
Certain traumatic complications and unspecified injuries	3
Superficial injury	3

Note: The diagnostic categories are based on the *International Classification of Diseases, Ninth Revision*
(ICD-9).
From the Washington State Department of Labor and Industries.

Although each state has its own workers' compensation program, they have
several common elements. If a worker is injured on the job or has a work-related
condition or disease, he or she must submit a claim to the workers' compensation
agency and, if it is approved, the agency will pay for the medical care until the at-
tending physician or insurance carrier or agency determines that no further care is
required. A worker with a medical problem that is not job-related submits claims for
care under conventional medical insurance.

As might be expected, these two sources pay for treatment of quite different
kinds of medical problems (Tables 1 and 2). Although the composition of the groups
of laborers in the two tables is not identical, the comparison of these diagnostic distributions is typical. Almost 40% of the diagnoses among claims to the workers' compensation agency represented musculoskeletal injuries, while almost 25% of those
submitted to the health insurance plan were respiratory or nervous system problems.

TABLE 2.   Ten Leading Diagnoses on Health Insurance Claims among 7,311 Construction
Laborers, Washington State, 1989

Diagnostic Category	Percentage of Total
Diseases of the respiratory system	13
Diseases of the nervous system	11
Diseases of the musculoskeletal system	10
Symptoms, signs, and poorly defined conditions	8
Dislocations	7
Mental disorders	5
Sprains and strains of joints, and adjacent conditions	5
Diseases of the genitourinary system	5
Diseases of the skin and subcutaneous tissue	5
Diseases of the digestive system	4

Note: The diagnostic categories are based on the *International Classification of Diseases, Ninth Revision*
(ICD-9)
From the Northwest Laborers Health and Security Trust.

HEALTH INSURANCE IN THE CONSTRUCTION INDUSTRY

Health insurance for construction workers is mainly limited to union members and is provided through health and welfare funds. This benefit system has developed over 40 years in response to the peculiar nature of construction employment.

The plans are multiemployer trust funds. Each trust fund collects contributions per hour per worker from employers based on rates that are negotiated in collective bargaining agreements. The unions currently have about 1,250 health and welfare trust funds. An average trust fund covers approximately 2,500 workers and their dependents, but the funds vary greatly in size, from covering fewer than 100 union members to 40,000 or more members. These plans provide health coverage to approximately 4 million construction workers and their dependents, or a total of more than 10 million people.

To continue providing benefits to workers during temporary unemployment, the health and welfare trusts have established "hour banks." Workers are employed for certain periods (defined as hours, weeks, or months) during which employers contribute to the trust—based on hours worked—before the worker becomes eligible for benefits. The worker can then use the reserves in his or her "bank account" when they are unemployed, until the bank is exhausted, or until the worker's account is depleted. The bank can carry a worker for as much as a year of unemployment.

The average contribution rate for health and welfare coverage in 1992 was $3.02 per hour worked, up from $1 in 1982 and $2 in 1988. The explosion in cost is accounted for by major three factors: medical inflation, cost shifting, and paying for unemployed workers who are eligible for health insurance benefits.

Although benefits provided by health and welfare trust funds include health insurance, life insurance, disability insurance, and annuities, most of the expenditures are for health insurance.

The health insurance benefits rarely differ from what would be found in any group health insurance plan: hospitalization, major medical, and prescription drugs. There is rarely a particular provision for occupational medical services or preventive services other than an ill-defined "annual physical examination."

The health and welfare funds may self-insure for health care, or they may buy group insurance from a health insurance provider. They may also be self-administered and handle all claims processing, or they may contract with an administrative service provider.

OCCUPATIONAL MEDICINE FOR CONSTRUCTION WORKERS

The role of occupational medicine in the construction industry in the U.S. has been quite limited. Not a single construction employer in the U.S. employs an occupational health physician, but then again, few employers in any discipline have any specialized occupational safety and health staff. Most occupational medical services have focused on performing medical surveys, especially for asbestos disease in different construction trades.

Some European countries provide more comprehensive occupational medical care to construction workers than does the U.S.

France. National law has required routine examinations since World War II. The main objective has been to screen workers for fitness for work. Large occupational health centers have been developed for this purpose, and most of them are operated under joint agreements between labor and management. In urban areas there may be specific health centers for construction; otherwise, health centers may serve several different trades. Records of such examinations are maintained in occupational

TABLE 3.   Legally Mandated Medical Monitoring for German Workers

Substance	First Follow-up (Months)	Next Follow-up (Months)	Monthly Interval for Subsequent Follow-ups (for Carcinogen Exposure)
Asbestos	12–36	12–36	12–36*
Benzene	2	3–6	≤ 60
Isocyanate	3–6	12–24	—
Lead			
in air > 75 µg/m³			
in blood 50–60 µg/100 mL	12,[†] 6[‡]	12,[†] 6[‡]	—
in air 75–100 µg/m³			
in blood ≤ 50 µg/100 mL	12,[†] 6[‡]	12,[†] 12[‡]	—
in blood 60–70 µg/mL	immed.,[†] 6[‡]	12,[†] 6[‡]	—
Nickel	36–60	36–60	36–60

German law specifies medical monitoring for dozens of potentially toxic substances from acrylamide to zinchromate. Check-ups are required before work is begun, at specified intervals, and after known exposure to carcinogenic substances. The preemployment check-up provides a baseline for future examinations. The required intervals for medical follow-ups for some substances believed to be in the work environment are listed below for some substances common to construction.
* Depending on the type of asbestos exposure: for latency under 15 years, 36; for a latency of more than 15 years, 12–36 months.
† Medical examination.
‡ Blood-lead test.
Note: All intervals are in months. The eight Bau-Berufsgenossenschaften (professional associations for construction) provide such check-ups in their medical clinics. The OSHA interim lead standard for construction requires medical removal from lead exposure at 50 µg/dL for blood lead and sets an exposure limit of 30 µg/m³ for air.
From Gerda Linke-Kaiser, MD, Bau-Berufsgenossenschaften.

health centers, and there is a growing body of epidemiologic studies and administrative reports based on the collected data.

Germany.   Safety and health and workers' compensation in the construction industry are provided by the Bau-Berufsgenossenschaften (BBGs). These eight private foundations are jointly governed by labor and management and exist pursuant to statutory requirement. They provide comprehensive services to all employers and employees. In terms of occupational medicine, the BBGs operate occupational health clinics where they offer periodic examinations, including those required by law for exposure to particular toxic substances (Table 3). The German associations also operate acute care and rehabilitation centers, including specialized centers for workers with traumatic spinal and other injuries. In addition, the BBGs assess the work-relatedness of medical conditions. The associations recently have begun to perform statistical analyses of data from health examinations.

The Netherlands.   Stichting Arbouw, a joint union-employer safety and health organization, offers health examinations through participating clinical centers with which it contracts. It collects data from these centers in a uniform system and performs epidemiologic studies.

Sweden.   In the late 1960s the unions and employers negotiated agreements to establish Bygghälsan, a joint union-employer safety and health organization that provided comprehensive services to employers and workers. It included a standardized occupational health examination that was provided by staff physicians and nurses in stationary clinics or in mobile units. This negotiated capitation-based financing system ended in 1993. Bygghälsan performed extensive epidemiologic

TABLE 4.   Standardized Mortality Ratios for Nonparticipants and Participants (Plumbers, Insulators, and Painters) of a Swedish Construction Industry Preventive Health Program, 1971–79[5]

Causes of Death	Standardized Mortality Ratio		Nonparticipants/ Participants	Confidence Intervals (95%)
	Nonparticipants	Participants		
All causes	1.29	0.75	1.71	1.52, 1.80
Alcoholism	2.24	0.38	5.92	3.41, 10.80
Liver cirrhosis	2.17	0.70	3.08	2.16, 4.45
Violent death	1.49	0.71	2.11	1.78, 2.51
All cancers	1.24	0.93	1.34	1.21, 1.48
Laryngeal	3.12	1.11	2.81	0.92, 10.20
Pleural	2.60	2.34	1.11	0.46, 2.63
Esophageal	1.29	0.94	1.37	0.68, 2.78
Liver	1.28	0.78	1.62	0.76, 3.57

Note: Standardized mortality ratios are based on comparison with white male Swedish population. Numbers reflect deaths recorded from 1971–1979; nonparticipant deaths totaled 3,506 and participants 2,299.

analysis and has been the prime center for data on the morbidity patterns of construction workers (see chapter 2). One longitudinal study of mortality rates for three trades shows that self-selection may significantly affect conclusions derived from clinical examination studies and that nonparticipants may be the individuals most in need of preventive services (Table 4).

RECENT DEVELOPMENTS IN HEALTH CARE DELIVERY
In the U.S., many health and welfare funds offer some preventive services as benefits. These often are coupled with cost-control measures such as the use of primary care providers as gatekeepers. The trend of the past half decade toward the use of preferred provider organizations and health maintenance organizations as a means to control costs has special potential to improve continuity of care, targeted preventive care, and consultation patterns.

Better Continuity of Care.   A key criterion for quality of health care and improved outcomes is continuity of care. Yet, according to anecdotal evidence, episodic care characterizes the patterns of health care use and delivery for construction workers. The opportunity to create systems with continuity between episodes of care and, also, levels of care within a particular episode, should be seized upon. HMOs and PPOs can serve as vehicles for improved structuring of health care delivery.

Targeted Preventive Care.   Preventive examinations currently provided for as an annual physical could easily be defined in terms of protocols for particular trades. These protocols could include detailed occupational histories and emphasize trade-specific problems, such as pulmonary disease, musculoskeletal disorders, skin diseases, and central and peripheral nervous system disorders. Providers in a PPO could be identified to carry out such examinations based on their expertise and interest.

Improved Consultation Patterns.   The limited availability of worker-oriented occupational medical expertise could best be used in contractual arrangements with health systems, to train primary care providers, to perform quality control review, to consult on particular cases, and to collect and analyze data.

A health and security fund of the Laborers' International Union N.A. has attempted to structure care within a PPO in Washington State (Box 1).

An Example of Preventive Medicine in Managed Care Organizations

In 1993, the trustees of the Northwest Laborers' Health and Security Fund agreed to establish a periodic preventive or occupational health examination for participants.

Services provided. Using recommendations in the report of Public Health Service Preventive Services Task Force as a guide, a protocol was created by the medical advisor to the Health and Security Fund, which included the following: personal and family medical history, occupational exposures history, social history, physical examination, audiometry, vision tests, and laboratory tests (cholesterol, blood sugar, urinalysis). When indicated, other tests were performed, including mammogram, chest x-ray, electrocardiogram, spirometry, and Papanicolaou smears and pelvic examination. Immunization boosters were given when required.

Delivery system. The Health and Security Fund contracted with an outpatient preferred provider organization covering Washington State. With assistance from the medical director of the PPO network, physicians were selected from the PPO network based on certain characteristics: an interest in preventive medicine for workers, experience in pulmonary medicine, and willingness to fill out reporting forms and participate in a structured health program. Care was taken to assure geographic coverage. The PPO medical director was responsible for quality control and for assuring that participating medical providers reported back findings according to the protocol. The findings were collected in a data system at the Health and Security Fund Administrative Office.

Approach. Plan participants were informed about the service and encouraged to make use of it. They were given a list of approved providers. When they made appointments for examinations, the providers would verify eligibility with the Health and Security Fund Administrative Office. Once the examinations were concluded, the providers would be reimbursed when a completed report of findings was submitted to the aministrative office. Abnormalities were followed up in two ways:
- *Nonoccupational abnormalities* were referred back to the person's usual physician or treated by the examining physician.
- *Occupational abnormalities*, such as clear-cut noise-induced hearing loss or pulmonary asbestosis were referred for care funded by workers' compensation.

Initial findings. After having the program in place for 1 year, the following observations can be made:
- The program is popular among construction workers.
- However, only 10% of those eligible took advantage of the program in the first year.
- Health care providers like the clinical protocol.

Finklea reviewed 64 randomly selected examination reports provided by the Health and Security Fund office. They show:
- Health providers generally fill out the forms and comply with the program.
- Health providers need clear guidelines for follow-up of abnormal findings.
- Primary care providers frequently fail to recognize the need to follow-up on occupational health risks reported in the history form.

BOX 1

Psychological Considerations

A traumatic injury or fatality on the job has severe repercussions, not just for the victim and the victim's family, but for coworkers. A report from Bygghälsan in Sweden has stressed the importance of psychosocial counseling for work teams in construction when there has been a traumatic injury to one or more coworkers.[10]

THE WORKERS' COMPENSATION SYSTEM

Workers' compensation is a major issue for the construction industry. Although construction employs 5–6% of the U.S. work force, it accounts for more than 30% of all workers' compensation expenditures. A study being performed by the Center to Protect Workers' Rights based on data from Washington State has found that 34.7% of construction laborers had one or more claims with workers' compensation during a 2-year period. Workers' compensation arose from reform movements early in the 20th century. Currently, many of the basic ideas are being reconsidered in light of problems that have emerged in the system, as follows.[9]

First, the costs are growing out of control. Costs in the U.S. have grown from $2 billion in 1960 to more than $60 billion today. The average workers' compensation premium for three key trades—carpenters, bricklayers, and structural ironworkers—is 28.6% of payroll.[8] In other words, if a worker earns $20 an hour, the employer pays an additional $5.72 per hour for workers' compensation alone. That is twice what the employer pays for health insurance coverage, if it is provided.

Second, the system is extremely inefficient. According to data from Oregon, overhead amounts to 27.1% of the costs. A significant portion of costs of overhead results from legal proceedings. Workers' compensation overhead is almost equal to the cash benefits paid to disabled workers (Fig. 1).

Third, the system is state-based, and costs and benefits differ greatly among states. Construction workers and contractors often travel across state lines in search of work and may thus be affected by the vagaries of state statutes. The lack of uniformity among state programs is especially burdensome to highly mobile occupations such as construction.

Fourth, the system does not adequately cover nonacute conditions. Such nonacute conditions, including many musculoskeletal disorders and most occupational diseases, are now the most common occupationally related conditions (Table 1). A study in New York State suggests that the workers' compensation system is incapable of addressing these conditions in an orderly manner. The study estimates that about 40,000 people in the U.S. die each year from occupationally related cancers. Yet, the system as a whole probably compensates fewer than 300 such cases annually.[6] Few

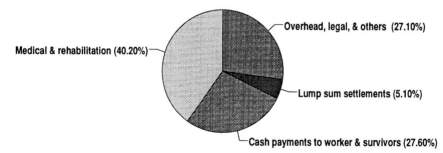

FIGURE 1. Where workers' compensation premiums go. Source: Oregon Department of Finance, Annual Report 1992.

claims are filed because the medical profession does not recognize the relationship of cancer to work. Claims that are filed are typically contested, because, for most chronic diseases, there are many different potential causes, only some of which are work-related.[9]

Fifth, the system leads to many disputes. In some jurisdictions more than half of all closed claims for lost-time injuries involve a legal proceeding. These legal proceedings contribute greatly to the overall inefficiencies of workers' compensation.

Sixth, workers' expectations have changed. When workers' compensation was in its infancy, there were few medical choices. It was assumed that the employer would assure proper care for an injured worker in return for being protected from tort suits. Today, workers make extensive choices about medical care delivery and can have access to the best medical care available.

An Alternative to the Present System

In 1992, under a then-new Massachusetts Law, the Pioneer Valley Building Trades entered into a collective bargaining agreement with the Bechtel Construction Company to jointly manage the workers' compensation system on a medium-size construction project (Box 2). This approach is rapidly gaining in acceptance in the unionized construction industry and could eventually lead to nationally negotiated agreements with uniformity in benefits and costs across the states. Enabling legislation similar to that in Massachusetts has been passed in California, Florida, and other states.[2] Such agreements open the door for a much more active role by worker-oriented occupational medical providers in the design of more effective health systems for workers who are injured on the job, including a greater emphasis on preventive services.

Rehabilitation and Return to Work

A main objective of workers' compensation is to rehabilitate injured workers so they can return to their usual occupations. Effective rehabilitation is not only a public health objective; it is in everyone's economic interest. Returning workers to employment saves insurance costs for the employer, and workers who are employed earn wages that typically exceed workers' compensation benefits by at least twice.[7]

Despite these incentives, rehabilitation and return to work generally do not function well.[1] A study of construction workers with low back problems, conducted by the Columbia Health Group, a major provider of rehabilitation in Ontario, found an average duration of disability of 46 days. In reviewing many cases, the group concluded that 20 days of the delay was the result of inefficiencies in the system, such as failure to schedule workers, workers getting lost in the referral between providers, and a lack of communication between providers and employers about opportunities for early return to work. In other words, about 43% of the lost time was due to poor case management.

Making rehabilitation and return to work more effective in construction is not easy. As with much contingent work, any employer is likely to be reluctant to take on a worker who needs light duty if the worker's injury was caused in employment with another employer. Also, most construction employers are small and do not have the capacity to offer light-duty assignments. Union jurisdiction is another obstacle. In construction, there are 15 unions representing the different crafts. For an injured ironworker to be assigned to serve as a flagman during recuperation would be to usurp a laborer's jurisdiction. The jurisdiction for the job of flagman belongs to the members of the laborers' union; therefore, the ironworker would fill a slot designated for a laborer.

The Pioneer Valley Agreement

In 1992, the Pioneer Valley Building Trades in western Massachusetts entered into a collective bargaining agreement with the Bechtel Construction Company on workers' compensation. The agreement covered the last 8 months of a construction project on a cogeneration plant begun in 1991 and completed in 1993. It involved 300 workers.

The negotiated agreement ended up covering the last 8 months of the project. The agreement listed five goals: improved safety, improved access to high-quality health care, accelerated delivery of benefits, reduced costs, and reduced or eliminated adversarial disputes requiring legal proceedings. The agreement put in place the following program:

Governance. A committee with equal labor-management representation developed and oversaw the program. John Lewis, an attorney based in Boca Raton, Florida, helped the parties design the agreement.

Medical providers. Jay Himmelstein, MD, of the University of Massachusetts Medical Center was retained to establish a network of medical providers. An injured worker could select any provider in the network. A nurse was designated to act as case manager and patient advocate for all injuries. The physicians in the network determined disability. The employer or a worker could demand one change of provider annually.

Dispute resolution. There were three stages through which to resolve disputes. Ground rules established that no dispute would take more than 65 days to be resolved (compared with an average 1.5 years in the Massachusetts compensation system).

- *Stage 1: ombudsman.* A Bechtel nurse was designated to hear all complaints. The nurse had a limit of 5 days to resolve them or refer them to stage two.
- *Stage 2: mediation.* A mediator agreed to by the governing committee was to be assigned to hear any cases not resolved in stage one. The mediation process was to be nonlegal (neither party could have legal representation) and nonbinding. Mediation had to be settled in less than 30 days.
- *Stage 3: legal arbitration.* Any case not settled in mediation was to be referred to binding arbitration. The arbitrator was to be selected jointly by the governing committee. This stage allowed legal representation. The case had to be settled within 30 days.

Data collection and analysis. This was done by Bechtel's insurance department.

Pioneer Valley Agreement Results

	8 months before	8 months after
Number of claims	38	22
Lost-time claims	11	2
Litigated cases	8	0
Costs	$480,000	$220,000
Hours worked	217,117	223,744
Lost-time injury rate/200 hours worked	10.12	1.78
Reported costs per hour	$2.21	$0.98

Source: Bechtel Construction Co.

The numbers are small, the agreement was short-lived, and—as with most experiments—the parties were anxious to demonstrate success. Nonetheless, compared with the preceding 8 months, the 8 months of the agreement showed remarkable progress.

BOX 2

There has been only one documented attempt in Canada or the U.S. to create a system to address these problems. In Hamilton, Ontario, the unions negotiated an agreement with the employers to set up a rehabilitation center and to override the employer and union jurisdiction obstacles. The agreement provided that one large employer, a utility, would designate slots on its maintenance work force for workers during the early stages of return to work. In turn, workers normally assigned to such work would be given regular construction jobs by other employers. The case management would be carried out jointly by the union hiring halls and the rehabilitation center to assure that workers were employed in jobs suitable to their physical abilities. Unfortunately, implementation of this program has been delayed by the severe economic depression that has hit construction in Ontario.

CONCLUSION

In the current health care system, the delivery of occupational health services is not consistent for all worker groups, and these preventive services are seldom integrated into or coordinated closely with clinical preventive services and therapeutic services provided by primary care physicians. This is especially true for construction workers, who move frequently from one job or employer to another as jobs are completed. It is not unusual for construction workers, often with their families in tow, to move from one locality to another so that they can keep working. Contractors and subcontractors often employ a small number of workers, if any, and it would be rare for a contractor to have a company–owned clinic. Occupational health services are lacking or are generally limited to those required by state law: contract services for acute trauma provided by industrial clinics or community hospitals.

Newly emerging opportunities, such as those created by the use of managed-care systems for health care cost control or collectively bargained workers' compensation programs, could significantly alter the market for occupational medicine, especially for worker-oriented occupational medical providers.

REFERENCES

1. Atherley GS: Department of Community Medicine, University of Toronto, Toronto, Ontario, personal communication.
2. Coye S, Grob H: Collective Bargaining on Workers' Compensation in the Construction Industry: A Manual. Washington, DC: The Center to Protect Workers' Rights (in press).
3. Craig JL: Mobilized occupational health services: The TVA experience. J Occup Med 10:179–184, 1968.
4. Craig JL: A practical approach to cost analysis of an occupational health program. J Occup Med 16:445–448, 1974.
5. Englund A, Engholm G, Michaels D, Ringen K: Twenty years of follow-up of mortality and cancer incidence in Swedish construction workers. Presented at the 120th annual meeting of the American Public Health Association, Washington, DC, November 8–12, 1992.
6. Markowitz S, Fisher E, Fahs M, et al: Occupational disease in New York State: A comprehensive re-examination. Am J Ind Med 16:417–436, 1989.
7. Morrison MH: Rehabilitation and return to work: Do other countries succeed? Work 3:48–54, 1993.
8. Powers MB: Cost fever breaks. Engineering News Record 233(13): 40–41, 1994.
9. Spieler EA: Perpetuating risk? Workers' compensation and the persistence of occupational injuries. Houston Law Review 31:119–264, 1994.
10. Von Gerber C, Olsson S: After the accident: Support, strategies and development. Malmö, Sweden, Bygghälsan, 1993, mimeo.

KNUT RINGEN, DrPH
ANDERS ENGLUND, MD
LAURA WELCH, MD
JAMES L. WEEKS, ScD, CIH
JANE L. SEEGAL, MS

PERSPECTIVES ON THE FUTURE

From The Center to Protect
  Workers' Rights
Washington, DC (KR, JLS)
  and
Division of Occupational and
  Environmental Medicine
George Washington University
Washington, DC (LW, JLW)
  and
Department of Health and Social
  Affairs
National Board of Occupational
  Safety and Health
Solna, Sweden (AE)

Reprint requests to:
Jane L. Seegal, MS
The Center to Protect Workers'
  Rights
111 Massachusetts Ave. NW
Washington, DC 20001

The construction industry is in the throes of change arising from greater competition, the decline of union representation, and increased interest—among economists, management analysts, and others—in conditions in the industry. A number of factors fuel this change, including the following:

- Construction owners and contractors are increasingly concerned about skyrocketing insurance costs, largely tied to the rate of occupational injury in the industry.
- Construction contractors, who employ the workers, are slashing costs, largely by cutting or limiting wages and benefits.
- Workers are finding conditions in the industry less appealing; as a result, it is increasingly difficult to recruit high-quality workers into the industry and, equally important, more difficult to induce the best workers to make a career of construction work.
- The unions are trying to resist the push to cut wages and benefits but are trying to accommodate the need for cost containment.
- The potentially most lucrative cost-cutting source—improved safety and health and, thus, reduced insurance costs—is hampered by a lack of progress in safety and health. In 2 decades, the rates of lost-time injuries and lost work time per injury have remained fairly constant.[1,7]
- Research agencies and researchers are finding construction to be a largely unex-

OCCUPATIONAL MEDICINE: State of the Art Reviews—
Vol. 10, No. 2, April 1995. Philadelphia, Hanley & Belfus, Inc.

445

plored field and are responding to the opportunity to investigate, and shed light on, safety- and health-related conditions.

In an unusual way, safety and health finds itself in a favorable position. Construction owners and contractors are increasingly recognizing that improved safety practices yield lower costs. The unions have stepped up their long-time emphasis on safety and health in response to favorable recognition for this from their members and the employers.

One of the paradoxes of construction work is that, compared with assembly-line manufacturing, it provides workers much greater freedom and empowerment in job-related decisions, a pattern usually associated with white-collar occupations. For instance, during a construction project, it is not unusual for a tradesperson to challenge or change the architect's design. The construction trades, with their high level of skills training, are in that sense more akin to white-collar professions than are most workers in manufacturing. At the same time, construction work is so intermittent and insecure that it may impede healthful behavior.

An important role for occupational safety and health professionals is to better understand this paradox. They must encourage the industry to preserve organizational features that favor healthful employment and reduce those that induce risk taking. In this sense, the role of occupational health goes beyond traditional boundaries: we need to understand the industry, how the work is organized, and how construction workers' lives are intertwined with work organization.

A NATIONAL GOAL

We believe a new occupational safety and health standard for construction should be set, based on current performance of some of the most successful multinational contractors (Table 1). The proposed standard suggests that work-related fatalities and injuries could be reduced by more than 80% and that substantial amounts of money could be saved. This concept has limitations: it does not take into account occupational illnesses, it does not address the unique needs of various specialty contractors, and it carries the limitations imposed by inadequate safety and health data. Nonetheless, the proposal provides a starting point for defining what can and should be expected in safety and health performance for each work site, each employer, and the industry.

A Labor-Management Framework

To raise the standard, processes must be developed to enable gradual improvement in safety and health performance. These processes must be grounded in the main interest groups of the industry: construction employers and construction unions.

The reports of the Department of Labor-Department of Commerce Commission on the Future of Labor-Management Relations has made a compelling case for improved labor-management cooperation being essential to sustaining a fast pace of change consistent with creating "high performance workplaces and industries," which includes safety and health.[4] This view is especially relevant to the construction sector.

The Role of Construction Owners

Until the early 1990s, the owners who contract for construction have not legally been considered parties to safety and health. This is changing. In the European Union's directive on construction safety and health,[3] the owners are

TABLE 1.   Proposal for a Universal Occupational Safety and Health Standard for Construction

Construction is one of the most dangerous industries in terms of occupational safety and health. It is also the most difficult to monitor because of the many employers and worksites—and the temporary and constantly changing nature of the work. Sufficient data now exist to enable the establishment of a universal safety and health standard for the industry.

Performance Benchmark
The following levels appear to be technologically and economically feasible
   Deaths: < 3 cases per 200 million hours worked
   Lost-time injuries: < 1 case per 200,000 hours worked

Proposed Requirements
Employers would be required to have safety and health programs that include:
   Site safety and health plans
   Hazard identification and monitoring
   Training and orientation (including hazard communication) for workers
   Personal protective equipment as needed
   Medical testing as needed
   Recordkeeping and reporting

Implementation
Because deaths and injuries in the U.S. construction industry are 6 times above the proposed standard, implementation would be phased in over several years.

Justification
Impact. If fully complied with, the standard would achieve:
   Deaths: Reduced from 950 to 160 (790 cases saved)
   Injuries: Reduced from 226,000 to 38,000 (188,000 cases saved)

Feasibility. These levels are reached by certain countries (for instance, the Netherlands) and in the United States by some owners (the Army Corps of Engineers) and some contractor groups (members of the National Constructors Association).

Economic benefit. If fully complied with, the standard would reduce direct costs per worker per year from $3,500 to $584. Reduced indirect costs would double the total savings.

expected to include safety and health requirements in their bid solicitations and award procedures. In the United States, moves also are being made in this direction. The American National Standards Institute's A-10 Committee has recommended that this practice be adopted throughout the industry. On federally funded construction managed by the U.S. Army Corps of Engineers—acting essentially as owners—contractors have been required for many years to meet safety and health requirements, resulting in substantially lower rates of injury. Corps contractors' average lost-workday case rate in 1984–88 was 1.34–1.54 per 100 full-time workers; the national construction industry average was 6.8–6.9 per 100 full-time workers.[6] The Army Corps practice can be expected to be extended to construction contracted for by other federal agencies. Petrochemical companies have adopted their own requirements. Recently, the Chemical Manufacturers' Association proposed a uniform approach for the industry.[2]

PROMISING AREAS FOR FOCUS AND IMPROVEMENT

Traumatic Injuries

In late 1994, the Occupational Safety and Health Administration (OSHA) implemented a new focused inspection program for construction, with two aims. First, the program is intended to make the industry, including OSHA inspectors, pay attention to the four sources that account for more than 80% of serious injuries: falls, electrocutions, "caught between," and "struck by" (see chapter 4). Second, by having

OSHA inspectors use a triage system, the program is designed to enable OSHA to inspect more sites for serious problems. An inspector first determines if an employer has a comprehensive safety and health plan for a project and, then, whether evidence of the target hazards exists. If the employer has a comprehensive program and if the inspector knows of no evidence of the four key injury hazards on the project, the inspector assumes that the employer is in compliance with other safety and health requirements to the extent that a wall-to-wall inspection would be likely not to identify major safety and health violations. This allows the OSHA inspector to move to another work site without delay. We believe that this new approach by OSHA has great promise as it becomes refined and also expanded to health hazards.

Construction Ergonomics

Musculoskeletal disorders have emerged as the most widespread and costly problem in the industry. Finding a niche for addressing them within the paradigms of occupational safety and health has not been easy. Unfortunately, the field of ergonomics, which has grown from problems related to industrial and office work, has had little experience in construction.

Construction injuries are often different than those in other industries. Most musculoskeletal disorders in construction do not arise from "repetitive motions" in the conventional sense. Many are caused by awkward postures, working for hours reaching above shoulder level or kneeling or bending; some problems caused by heavy lifting may be a response to just a few episodes; other problems result from attempts to compensate for slips and trips. At the same time, most musculoskeletal problems that result in workers' compensation claims are acute in their manifestation if not in their etiology. Developing ways to address these problems in a way that is acceptable to the industry will be a major challenge. Three areas are emerging as vehicles for change.

Materials Handling. In 1992 the European Union issued a directive requiring construction sites to consider carefully how materials are moved about the site, at the same time placing restrictions on lifting and other manual tasks. Subsequently, the Health and Safety Executive of the United Kingdom issued guidance based on the European Union directive.[5] Although the National Institute for Occupational Safety and Health (NIOSH) in the U.S. has long had recommendations on manual lifting limitations, no requirements or industrywide practices exist for their implementation. In addition, unlike in Europe, the NIOSH requirements have been limited mainly to weight, with little consideration of shapes or ways to design materials to make them easier to handle.

Site Safety and Health Plans. The OSHA standard for hazardous waste operations (CFR 1926.120) first codified requirements for site safety and health plans. This approach is gradually being extended to all construction, as is exemplified in the new focused inspection program.

Exposure Assessment. With its constantly changing work sites, construction challenges traditional industrial hygiene approaches. Unlike in stationary industry, construction's hazardous exposures tend to be unanticipated, short-term, and high-level. Therefore, a new paradigm of industrial hygiene geared toward the construction workplace is being developed at the Center to Protect Workers' Rights. Known as task-based exposure assessment monitoring (T-BEAM), the approach is taking into account two general categories of exposure.

First, to determine what kind of protective measures should be taken, construction work is broken down into defined tasks with *anticipated exposures*. Likely exposure levels can be predicted based on empirical studies of such tasks. For instance, in maintenance of coal-fired utility boilers, workers are at risk of exposure to arsenic if certain types of coal, such as anthracite, have been used. In such cases, a contractor is required to provide workers with respirators and suits and to monitor the exposure level to ensure that the OSHA permissible exposure limit has not been exceeded.

Unanticipated exposures may either involve workers handling hazardous substances or bystanders from a different trade. One example might be a change of wind during torching of a metal railing covered with lead-based paint. Such exposures are common enough to be a serious health threat. The hope is that workers will be trained and thus able to identify potential hazards so that they can halt work and seek expert evaluations by an industrial hygienist. This is necessary because it is impractical to have industrial hygienists on all work sites at all times.

THE ROLE OF OCCUPATIONAL AND PREVENTIVE MEDICINE

Occupational physicians and nurses have played a minimal role in the construction industry in the U.S., but there are three reasons why we expect that to change. The industry faces new regulatory requirements involving safety and health, increasing preventive coverage in health insurance plans, and the financial crisis facing workers' compensation.

First, a growing number of regulations, notably related to environmental cleanup of toxic hazards, lead removal, and asbestos removal, require periodic monitoring for health outcomes. There is a great need for standardized protocols and continuity of delivery. Since few good models are available for validated tests or approaches to delivery, occupational medicine faces a huge challenge: to define medical protocols that can capture the health consequences of intermittent, short-term, high-level exposures; to provide these in a system that offers continuity for workers as they regularly change work sites and employers; and to capture data from these examinations in a way that they can be analyzed epidemiologically.

Second, preventive medicine is increasingly included as a covered benefit under health insurance plans that are provided as part of health and welfare trusts for construction workers and their families. Much of this trend is tied to the greater acceptance of managed care programs for all sectors, mainly health maintenance organizations or preferred provider networks. This change provides an opportunity to structure medical care delivery to emphasize primary care, which means that occupational medicine can play a central role should its practitioners choose to do so.

Third, managed care rooted in occupational medicine is receiving an added boost—from the nearly universal agreement that workers' compensation must change. For workers' compensation for construction, occupational medicine will need to respond with development of (1) more objective disability determinations, particularly for occupational diseases, including the less acute musculoskeletal disorders; (2) protocols or models for the earliest return to work of injured workers; and (3) effective feedback on ways to prevent safety and health problems, feedback based on medical surveillance and epidemiologic analyses.

New paradigms are needed if occupational medicine is to successfully meet these opportunities. The role of the physician may be less than it has been typically. Extensive evidence exists that nurses may be better equipped than physicians to communicate effectively with workers. Also, approaches that rely on multidisciplinary teams need to be given more attention. Such teams may include physicians, nurses, physical therapists, industrial hygienists, (safety) engineers, and social workers or psychologists.

RESEARCH NEEDS

We still know far too little about the safety and health risks associated with construction, and we know very little about the long-term health consequences of working a lifetime in the industry. Much of what we know comes from the long-term follow-up of the Swedish cohorts (see chapter 2).

The Swedish data suggest striking contrasts when the cohorts are subdivided into workers who have participated in health programs and those who have not. Those who participate have favorable health profiles compared with the general population. This finding suggests a "healthy worker effect," that these workers who are recruited into and stay in the industry have good health patterns and maintain them. Yet, construction workers who do not participate in the health programs have significantly poorer health profiles than the general population. This suggests the converse of the "healthy worker effect."

Although some construction research should focus on new problems, it is much more important that better methods to prevent the known occupational safety and health problems in the industry be developed and evaluated. Such intervention research should evaluate methods to overcome the barriers to better safety and health programs and to demonstrate how new technologies and better safety programs can reduce the risk of injury and illness on the construction site. These intervention programs must be cost-effective, and their implementation must be feasible in a variety of types of construction settings.

Examples of the types of needed research include:

- Development of surveillance data systems that provide useful data for construction managers
- Use of current surveillance data to better describe and set priorities for addressing health risks for construction workers
- Evaluation of the benefits and costs of construction safety training programs
- Development of construction planning technologies that incorporate occupational safety and health requirements
- Development of new tools and other technologies to reduce the risk of work-related musculoskeletal disorders

SUMMARY

There is a growing trend toward new forms of labor-management cooperation, through negotiated agreements involving job-site safety and health, workers' compensation, and preventive medicine (see chapter 14). These developments are likely to change safety and health in the industry. At the same time, they provide opportunities for practitioners and researchers in occupational safety and health.

If we can venture to express a professional wish, it would be to find answers to the following: How can we, as the professions concerned with the well being of workers, help preserve the characteristics of construction work that are positive while reducing the aspects of the industry's functioning that are so deleterious to health? How do we preserve the crafts with their fostering of self-esteem: through individual freedom on the job, team work, or empowerment? Meanwhile, how do we reduce the destructive patterns of work, not just on the work site, but also involving the pressures and lifestyle associated with intermittent and uncertain employment?

The rewards for safety and health professionals in the construction industry are immediate and striking. Whether through the practice of safety and health or through research, results can be measured in short order. That is a professional benefit afforded by few other industries.

To structure occupational safety and health programs for construction workers, the safety and health professions need to engage in the labor-management processes that are changing the industry. In construction, it is not enough to think about what needs to be done in individual workplaces. In construction, we must think industry-wide, because that is how workers are employed. This need for a new approach is one that the professions have not faced, which may be one reason why so few of us have attempted to provide professional services to this industry. Luckily, this seems to be changing.

REFERENCES

1. Bureau of Labor Statistics: Workplace injuries and illnesses in 1993. Washington, DC, December 21, 1994.
2. Chemical Manufacturers' Association: Managers' Guide to Implementing a Contractor Safety and Health Program [draft 3]. Washington, DC, American Petroleum Institute and Chemical Manufacturers' Association, October 1994.
3. Commission of the European Communities: Safety and health in the construction sector. Luxembourg, Directorate-General for Employment, Industrial Relations and Social Affairs, Health and Safety Directorate, 1993.
4. Dunlop JT: Report and recommendations. Washington, DC, Commission on the Future of Worker-Management Relations, US Depts. of Labor and Commerce, December 1994.
5. Health and Safety Executive: Manual handling: Guidance on regulations. London, 1992.
6. Meridian Research: Worker protection programs in construction: Final report. Silver Spring, MD, Meridian Research, 1994, OSHA contract J-9-F-1-0019.
7. Weeks JL: Lost-Time Injury Rates in Construction, 1975-90. Washington, DC, Center to Protect Workers' Rights, 1993.

ANNEX

Mortality and Cancer Incidence in Various Groups of Construction Workers

Göran Engholm, MSc, and Anders Englund, MD

The workers studied were first examined by Bygghälsan in Sweden during 1971–1979. Follow-up reported here is through 1987 for cancer incidence and through 1988 for mortality.

The following tables provide results whenever the expected number of cases exceeds 0.75 and, at the same time, the observed number of cases is greater than 0.

Mortality by cause of death in asphalt workers

Follow-up from first checkup (1971-1979) to 1988.

Cause of death	Obs	Exp	SMR	(95 % C. I.)	Rel risk
All causes (001-999)	144	208.1	0.69	(0.58- 0.81)	0.93
All cancers (140-209)	42	47.9	0.88	(0.63- 1.18)	0.99
Lip etc (140-149)	2	1.2	1.69	(0.21- 6.12)	3.23
Oesophageal cancer (150)	1	1.2	0.85	(0.02- 4.72)	1.33
Stomach cancer (151)	6	3.7	1.62	(0.60- 3.53)	1.65
Colon cancer (153)	1	3.3	0.30	(0.01- 1.69)	0.37
Rectal cancer (154)	0	1.9	0.00	(0.00- 1.91)	0.00
Liver cancer (155.0)	1	1.0	0.96	(0.02- 5.36)	1.34
Gall bladder (156.0)	0	.8	0.00	(0.00- 4.39)	0.00
Pancreatic cancer (157)	2	3.4	0.59	(0.07- 2.14)	0.71
Lung (162.0-162.1)	8	10.1	0.79	(0.34- 1.55)	0.84
Malign melanoma (172)	3	1.4	2.08	(0.43- 6.09)	2.45
Prostate cancer (185)	3	3.7	0.81	(0.17- 2.37)	0.85
Bladder cancer (188)	0	1.2	0.00	(0.00- 3.10)	0.00
Kidney cancer (189)	5	2.5	1.98	(0.64- 4.61)	2.39
Urinary org (188-189)	5	3.7	1.34	(0.44- 3.14)	1.64
Brain cancer (191)	1	2.3	0.43	(0.01- 2.38)	0.44
Oth lymph tissue (202)	2	1.5	1.29	(0.16- 4.66)	1.28
Mult myeloma (203)	0	.9	0.00	(0.00- 3.97)	0.00
Leukaemia (204-207)	2	2.0	0.98	(0.12- 3.54)	1.08
Diabetes (250)	2	2.9	0.69	(0.08- 2.48)	1.73
Alcoholism (303)	2	4.6	0.43	(0.05- 1.57)	0.87
Circul system (390-458)	51	88.8	0.57	(0.43- 0.76)	0.77
Isch heart dis (410-414)	44	64.9	0.68	(0.49- 0.91)	0.88
Cerebrovasc dis (430-438)	2	11.2	0.18	(0.02- 0.65)	0.26
Arteries etc (440-448)	2	3.5	0.57	(0.07- 2.05)	0.87
Respiratory syst (460-519)	3	8.5	0.35	(0.07- 1.03)	0.67
Bronchitis etc (490-493)	1	3.6	0.28	(0.01- 1.57)	0.54
Chronic bronchitis (491)	0	1.2	0.00	(0.00- 3.05)	0.00
Pneumonia (480-486)	2	4.0	0.50	(0.06- 1.82)	1.01
Digestive system (520-577)	5	9.9	0.51	(0.16- 1.18)	0.92
Oes., stom, duod (530-537)	0	1.5	0.00	(0.00- 2.49)	0.00
Liver cirrhosis (571)	3	5.9	0.51	(0.11- 1.49)	0.93
Genito-urin syst (580-607)	1	1.4	0.69	(0.02- 3.87)	1.50
Nephritis&nephrosis (580-4)	1	.6	1.56	(0.04- 8.71)	2.98
Violent death (800-999)	32	35.0	0.91	(0.63- 1.29)	1.18
Traffic accidents (800-845)	10	6.6	1.52	(0.73- 2.80)	1.74
Accidental falls (880-887)	2	2.5	0.82	(0.10- 2.95)	0.82
Suicide (950-959)	10	13.5	0.74	(0.35- 1.36)	0.99
Homicide (960-969)	0	.8	0.00	(0.00- 4.55)	0.00
Water transp acc (830-838)	1	.9	1.11	(0.03- 6.19)	1.19
Drowning (910-915)	1	1.6	0.63	(0.02- 3.53)	0.91
Other accidents (916-929)	2	1.3	1.57	(0.19- 5.69)	1.21

Cancer incidence by site of cancer in asphalt workers

Follow-up from first checkup (1971-1979) to 1987.

Site of cancer	Obs	Exp	SIR	(95 % C. I.)	Rel risk
All cancers (140-209)	72	87.9	0.82	(0.64- 1.03)	0.86
Lip (140)	1	.9	1.15	(0.03- 6.40)	0.96
Lip etc (140-149)	4	3.2	1.25	(0.34- 3.19)	1.46
Digest ca (150-154)	13	16.0	0.81	(0.43- 1.39)	0.85
Oesophagus (150)	0	1.1	0.00	(0.00- 3.24)	0.00
Stomach (151)	8	4.4	1.80	(0.78- 3.55)	1.72
Intestines (152-153)	5	6.3	0.79	(0.26- 1.85)	0.85
Colon (153)	5	5.7	0.87	(0.28- 2.04)	0.94
Rectum (154)	0	4.1	0.00	(0.00- 0.90)	0.00
Liver (155.0)	1	1.1	0.91	(0.02- 5.07)	1.32
Pancreas (157)	2	2.9	0.69	(0.08- 2.50)	0.83
Larynx (161)	0	1.2	0.00	(0.00- 3.02)	0.00
Lung etc (162)	9	10.2	0.88	(0.40- 1.68)	0.92
Resp ca (160-164)	9	12.1	0.75	(0.34- 1.42)	0.80
Lung (162.1)	9	9.8	0.92	(0.42- 1.75)	0.98
Prostate (177)	12	11.0	1.09	(0.56- 1.91)	1.08
Testis (178)	2	1.9	1.04	(0.13- 3.76)	1.16
Bladder (181)	5	6.2	0.81	(0.26- 1.90)	0.84
Kidney (180)	7	4.5	1.55	(0.62- 3.18)	1.72
Lymph&blood (200-209)	7	9.1	0.77	(0.31- 1.58)	0.76
Nhl (200)	3	3.3	0.90	(0.19- 2.63)	0.87
Hodgkin's (201)	1	1.1	0.92	(0.02- 5.11)	0.90
Mult myeloma (203)	0	1.3	0.00	(0.00- 2.75)	0.00
Oth ly&blood (202, 204-209)	3	3.4	0.89	(0.18- 2.59)	0.92
Melanoma (190)	1	4.6	0.22	(0.01- 1.20)	0.24
Other skin (191)	0	2.3	0.00	(0.00- 1.58)	0.00
Nervous system (193)	1	4.6	0.22	(0.01- 1.22)	0.23

Two-sided p-values: * = p<0.05, ** = p<0.01, *** = p<0.001

Mortality by cause of death in rock workers

Follow-up from first checkup (1971-1979) to 1988.

Cause of death	Obs	Exp	SMR	(95 % C. I.)	Rel risk
All causes (001-999)	410	427.3	0.96	(0.87- 1.06)	1.30***
All cancers (140-209)	104	104.2	1.00	(0.82- 1.21)	1.13
Lip etc (140-149)	1	2.4	0.42	(0.01- 2.34)	0.78
Oesophageal cancer (150)	0	2.6	0.00	(0.00- 1.41)	0.00
Stomach cancer (151)	5	8.6	0.58	(0.19- 1.35)	0.58
Colon cancer (153)	4	7.3	0.55	(0.15- 1.41)	0.67
Rectal cancer (154)	2	4.4	0.45	(0.05- 1.63)	0.49
Liver cancer (155.0)	4	2.3	1.72	(0.47- 4.40)	2.44
Gall bladder (156.0)	2	1.9	1.05	(0.13- 3.80)	1.20
Pancreatic cancer (157)	7	7.5	0.93	(0.37- 1.92)	1.12
Laryngeal cancer (161)	1	.7	1.52	(0.04- 8.44)	2.25
Lung (162.0-162.1)	22	22.3	0.98	(0.62- 1.49)	1.05
Pleura (163.0)	0	.8	0.00	(0.00- 4.79)	0.00
Malign melanoma (172)	1	2.3	0.43	(0.01- 2.37)	0.49
Prostate cancer (185)	20	10.4	1.92	(1.17- 2.96)	2.05**
Bladder cancer (188)	2	3.0	0.67	(0.08- 2.42)	0.83
Kidney cancer (189)	8	5.4	1.49	(0.64- 2.93)	1.80
Urinary org (188-189)	10	8.4	1.20	(0.57- 2.20)	1.46
Brain cancer (191)	8	3.9	2.05	(0.88- 4.03)	2.19*
Lymphosarcoma (200.0-200.1)	1	.3	2.86	(0.07- 15.92)	2.94
Oth lymph tissue (202)	6	3.1	1.94	(0.71- 4.23)	1.95
Mult myeloma (203)	4	2.2	1.86	(0.51- 4.76)	1.96
Leukaemia (204-207)	3	3.8	0.79	(0.16- 2.32)	0.87
Diabetes (250)	1	5.2	0.19	(0.00- 1.06)	0.47
Alcoholism (303)	10	6.2	1.62	(0.78- 2.98)	3.37***
Circul system (390-458)	191	209.4	0.91	(0.79- 1.05)	1.24**
Isch heart dis (410-414)	145	154.1	0.94	(0.79- 1.11)	1.23*
Cerebrovasc dis (430-438)	24	26.7	0.90	(0.58- 1.34)	1.30
Arteries etc (440-448)	6	8.8	0.68	(0.25- 1.49)	1.06
Respiratory syst (460-519)	10	19.6	0.51	(0.25- 0.94)	0.97
Bronchitis etc (490-493)	2	8.4	0.24	(0.03- 0.86)	0.45
Chronic bronchitis (491)	1	3.2	0.32	(0.01- 1.76)	0.58
Pneumoconiosis (515-516.2)	2	.3	6.90	(0.84- 24.91)	5.94
Pneumonia (480-486)	6	8.9	0.67	(0.25- 1.46)	1.36
Digestive system (520-577)	15	17.8	0.84	(0.47- 1.39)	1.54
Oes., stom, duod (530-537)	3	3.2	0.93	(0.19- 2.71)	2.08
Liver cirrhosis (571)	8	9.7	0.82	(0.36- 1.63)	1.51
Genito-urin syst (580-607)	2	3.5	0.56	(0.07- 2.04)	1.22
Nephritis&nephrosis (580-4)	0	1.4	0.00	(0.00- 2.69)	0.00
Oth urinary syst (590-599)	2	1.8	1.10	(0.13- 3.97)	2.72
Violent death (800-999)	69	44.9	1.54	(1.20- 1.95)	2.02***
Traffic accidents (800-845)	14	8.3	1.69	(0.92- 2.83)	1.94*
Accidental falls (880-887)	7	4.1	1.70	(0.68- 3.51)	1.74
Suicide (950-959)	17	16.6	1.02	(0.60- 1.64)	1.38
Homicide (960-969)	3	.9	3.41	(0.70- 9.96)	6.53**
Water transp acc (830-838)	6	1.1	5.41	(1.98- 11.77)	6.23***
Drowning (910-915)	4	2.2	1.80	(0.49- 4.61)	2.66
Other accidents (916-929)	10	1.6	6.10	(2.92- 11.21)	4.97***

Cancer incidence by site of cancer in rock workers

Follow-up from first checkup (1971-1979) to 1987.

Site of cancer	Obs	Exp	SIR	(95 % C. I.)	Rel risk
All cancers (140-209)	182	183.0	0.99	(0.86- 1.15)	1.05
Lip (140)	3	1.9	1.60	(0.33- 4.69)	1.34
Lip etc (140-149)	6	6.2	0.96	(0.35- 2.10)	1.13
Digest ca (150-154)	29	35.3	0.82	(0.55- 1.18)	0.86
Oesophagus (150)	1	2.5	0.39	(0.01- 2.18)	0.59
Stomach (151)	9	10.2	0.88	(0.40- 1.67)	0.83
Intestines (152-153)	11	13.5	0.82	(0.41- 1.46)	0.88
Colon (153)	11	12.4	0.89	(0.44- 1.59)	0.96
Rectum (154)	8	9.1	0.88	(0.38- 1.74)	0.93
Liver (155.0)	5	2.5	1.98	(0.64- 4.61)	2.95*
Gall bladder (155.1)	1	1.0	1.02	(0.03- 5.69)	1.20
Pancreas (157)	5	6.5	0.77	(0.25- 1.79)	0.91
Larynx (161)	3	2.5	1.19	(0.24- 3.47)	1.46
Lung etc (162)	24	22.2	1.08	(0.69- 1.61)	1.13
Resp ca (160-164)	27	26.1	1.03	(0.68- 1.50)	1.11
Lung (162.1)	23	21.5	1.07	(0.68- 1.61)	1.15
Pleura (162.2)	1	.7	1.47	(0.04- 8.19)	0.94
Prostate (177)	33	30.6	1.08	(0.74- 1.52)	1.07
Testis (178)	1	1.8	0.55	(0.01- 3.06)	0.61
Bladder (181)	14	13.3	1.05	(0.58- 1.77)	1.09
Kidney (180)	14	9.0	1.55	(0.85- 2.60)	1.74
Lymph&blood (200-209)	20	16.8	1.19	(0.73- 1.84)	1.18
Nhl (200)	6	6.0	1.00	(0.37- 2.17)	0.96
Hodgkin's (201)	2	1.5	1.36	(0.16- 4.91)	1.34
Mult myeloma (203)	5	2.9	1.72	(0.56- 4.02)	1.67
Oth ly&blood (202, 204-209)	7	6.4	1.09	(0.44- 2.25)	1.14
Melanoma (190)	5	6.9	0.72	(0.23- 1.69)	0.82
Other skin (191)	3	5.3	0.56	(0.12- 1.64)	0.62
Nervous system (193)	12	7.2	1.68	(0.87- 2.93)	1.83

Two-sided p-values: * = p<0.05, ** = p<0.01, *** = p<0.001

Mortality by cause of death in concrete workers

Follow-up from first checkup (1971-1979) to 1988.

Cause of death	Obs	Exp	SMR	(95 % C. I.)	Rel risk
All causes (001-999)	4153	5224.5	0.79	(0.77- 0.82)	1.09***
All cancers (140-209)	1209	1275.3	0.95	(0.90- 1.00)	1.10**
Lip cancer (140)	1	.6	1.82	(0.05- 10.13)	0.00 ND
Lip etc (140-149)	13	27.3	0.48	(0.25- 0.82)	0.87
Oesophageal cancer (150)	26	31.5	0.83	(0.54- 1.21)	1.40
Stomach cancer (151)	136	109.4	1.24	(1.04- 1.47)	1.36**
Sm intestines (152)	6	4.5	1.34	(0.49- 2.92)	1.32
Colon cancer (153)	72	89.9	0.80	(0.63- 1.01)	0.97
Rectal cancer (154)	63	55.2	1.14	(0.88- 1.46)	1.34
Liver cancer (155.0)	21	28.8	0.73	(0.45- 1.11)	1.01
Gall bladder (156.0)	16	23.6	0.68	(0.39- 1.10)	0.72
Pancreatic cancer (157)	82	92.1	0.89	(0.71- 1.11)	1.10
Peritoneum (158)	3	3.9	0.76	(0.16- 2.23)	0.72
Nose, nasal cav (160)	2	1.9	1.08	(0.13- 3.88)	2.04
Laryngeal cancer (161)	6	7.9	0.76	(0.28- 1.65)	1.13
Lung (162.0-162.1)	296	269.2	1.10	(0.98- 1.23)	1.23**
Pleura (163.0)	14	9.1	1.53	(0.84- 2.57)	1.17
Bone (170)	4	4.6	0.86	(0.24- 2.21)	1.29
Connect tissue (171)	5	5.7	0.87	(0.28- 2.04)	1.24
Malign melanoma (172)	20	24.9	0.80	(0.49- 1.24)	0.92
Other skin (173)	0	2.9	0.00	(0.00- 1.28)	0.00
Prostate cancer (185)	132	145.2	0.91	(0.76- 1.08)	0.94
Testis cancer (186)	1	3.5	0.29	(0.01- 1.61)	0.48
Bladder cancer (188)	33	38.7	0.85	(0.59- 1.20)	1.08
Kidney cancer (189)	56	63.4	0.88	(0.67- 1.15)	1.07
Urinary org (188-189)	89	102.2	0.87	(0.70- 1.07)	1.07
Brain cancer (191)	34	41.8	0.81	(0.56- 1.14)	0.82
Oth endocr glands (194)	2	1.8	1.09	(0.13- 3.95)	1.68
Thyroid cancer (193)	1	4.8	0.21	(0.01- 1.17)	0.26
Lymphosarcoma (200.0-200.1)	4	4.3	0.93	(0.25- 2.39)	0.91
Hodgkins" disease (201)	9	7.8	1.16	(0.53- 2.19)	1.82
Oth lymph tissue (202)	34	36.3	0.94	(0.65- 1.31)	0.91
Mult myeloma (203)	30	26.8	1.12	(0.75- 1.60)	1.21
Leukaemia (204-207)	42	44.5	0.94	(0.68- 1.28)	1.05
Diabetes (250)	20	61.6	0.32	(0.20- 0.50)	0.77
Alcoholism (303)	36	58.2	0.62	(0.43- 0.86)	1.30
Circul system (390-458)	2048	2678.6	0.76	(0.73- 0.80)	1.04
Isch heart dis (410-414)	1530	1954.3	0.78	(0.74- 0.82)	1.03
Cerebrovasc dis (430-438)	265	353.9	0.75	(0.66- 0.84)	1.10
Arteries etc (440-448)	71	117.7	0.60	(0.47- 0.76)	0.91
Respiratory syst (460-519)	156	257.5	0.61	(0.51- 0.71)	1.20
Bronchitis etc (490-493)	64	108.7	0.59	(0.45- 0.75)	1.18
Chronic bronchitis (491)	32	43.0	0.74	(0.51- 1.05)	1.54
Pneumoconiosis (515-516.2)	3	4.0	0.75	(0.16- 2.20)	0.54
Pneumonia (480-486)	71	119.6	0.59	(0.46- 0.75)	1.26
Digestive system (520-577)	127	201.0	0.63	(0.53- 0.75)	1.18
Oes., stom, duod (530-537)	16	40.3	0.40	(0.23- 0.64)	0.84
Liver cirrhosis (571)	66	101.1	0.65	(0.50- 0.83)	1.24
Genito-urin syst (580-607)	31	48.9	0.63	(0.43- 0.90)	1.53
Male genital (600-607)	4	5.7	0.70	(0.19- 1.80)	1.81
Nephritis&nephrosis (580-4)	11	17.2	0.64	(0.32- 1.15)	1.27
Oth urinary syst (590-599)	16	26.0	0.61	(0.35- 1.00)	1.73
Violent death (800-999)	413	449.4	0.92	(0.83- 1.01)	1.23***
Traffic accidents (800-845)	75	86.0	0.87	(0.69- 1.09)	0.99

Mortality by cause of death in concrete workers

Follow-up from first checkup (1971-1979) to 1988.

Cause of death	Obs	Exp	SMR	(95 % C. I.)	Rel risk
Accidental falls (880-887)	67	47.0	1.43	(1.11- 1.81)	1.61**
Suicide (950-959)	142	162.0	0.88	(0.74- 1.03)	1.21*
Homicide (960-969)	7	8.1	0.86	(0.35- 1.77)	1.66
Water transp acc (830-838)	11	10.8	1.02	(0.51- 1.82)	1.10
Drowning (910-915)	26	23.0	1.13	(0.74- 1.66)	1.85**
Other accidents (916-929)	25	16.4	1.53	(0.99- 2.25)	1.21
Traffic accidents (800-845)	75	86.0	0.87	(0.69- 1.09)	0.99
Accidental falls (880-887)	67	47.0	1.43	(1.11- 1.81)	1.61**
Suicide (950-959)	142	162.0	0.88	(0.74- 1.03)	1.21*
Homicide (960-969)	7	8.1	0.86	(0.35- 1.77)	1.66
Water transp acc (830-838)	11	10.8	1.02	(0.51- 1.82)	1.10
Drowning (910-915)	26	23.0	1.13	(0.74- 1.66)	1.85**
Other accidents (916-929)	25	16.4	1.53	(0.99- 2.25)	1.21

Cancer incidence by site of cancer in concrete workers

Follow-up from first checkup (1971-1979) to 1987.

Site of cancer	Obs	Exp	SIR	(95 % C. I.)	Rel risk
All cancers (140-209)	2082	2199.8	0.95	(0.91- 0.99)	1.00
Lip (140)	41	22.4	1.83	(1.31- 2.48)	1.77**
Lip etc (140-149)	69	70.7	0.98	(0.76- 1.23)	1.18
Digest ca (150-154)	416	432.1	0.96	(0.87- 1.06)	1.01
Oesophagus (150)	22	30.7	0.72	(0.45- 1.09)	1.12
Stomach (151)	152	127.4	1.19	(1.01- 1.40)	1.18
Intestines (152-153)	137	163.9	0.84	(0.70- 0.99)	0.87
Colon (153)	126	150.8	0.84	(0.70- 1.00)	0.88
Rectum (154)	105	110.1	0.95	(0.78- 1.15)	1.00
Liver (155.0)	19	31.8	0.60	(0.36- 0.93)	0.83
Gall bladder (155.1)	7	12.4	0.56	(0.23- 1.16)	0.60
Pancreas (157)	70	79.7	0.88	(0.68- 1.11)	1.06
Nose (160)	2	5.2	0.39	(0.05- 1.39)	0.39
Larynx (161)	34	29.1	1.17	(0.81- 1.63)	1.61*
Lung etc (162)	278	264.7	1.05	(0.93- 1.18)	1.13
Resp ca (160-164)	326	310.4	1.05	(0.94- 1.17)	1.16*
Lung (162.1)	264	256.2	1.03	(0.91- 1.16)	1.13
Pleura (162.2)	13	7.8	1.66	(0.88- 2.84)	1.08
Prostate (177)	385	413.0	0.93	(0.84- 1.03)	0.90
Testis (178)	7	16.5	0.42	(0.17- 0.87)	0.44*
Bladder (181)	147	159.4	0.92	(0.78- 1.08)	0.94
Kidney (180)	96	103.3	0.93	(0.75- 1.14)	1.04
Lymph&blood (200-209)	191	193.0	0.99	(0.85- 1.14)	0.98
Nhl (200)	69	67.8	1.02	(0.79- 1.29)	0.98
Hodgkin's (201)	15	15.6	0.96	(0.54- 1.59)	0.93
Mult myeloma (203)	37	35.0	1.06	(0.75- 1.46)	1.02
Oth ly&blood (202, 204-209)	70	74.7	0.94	(0.73- 1.18)	0.97
Melanoma (190)	53	70.5	0.75	(0.56- 0.98)	0.83
Other skin (191)	62	68.2	0.91	(0.70- 1.17)	1.00
Nervous system (193)	64	75.6	0.85	(0.65- 1.08)	0.89

Two-sided p-values: * = p<0.05, ** = p<0.01, *** = p<0.001

Mortality by cause of death in wood workers/carpenters

Follow-up from first checkup (1971-1979) to 1988.

Cause of death	Obs	Exp	SMR	(95 % C. I.)	Rel risk
All causes (001-999)	3543	5257.5	0.67	(0.65- 0.70)	0.89***
All cancers (140-209)	988	1243.1	0.79	(0.75- 0.85)	0.88***
Lip etc (140-149)	9	26.0	0.35	(0.16- 0.66)	0.59
Oesophageal cancer (150)	13	30.0	0.43	(0.23- 0.74)	0.63
Stomach cancer (151)	88	105.5	0.83	(0.67- 1.03)	0.81
Sm intestines (152)	5	4.4	1.15	(0.37- 2.68)	1.07
Colon cancer (153)	72	87.0	0.83	(0.65- 1.04)	1.01
Rectal cancer (154)	55	53.1	1.04	(0.78- 1.35)	1.17
Liver cancer (155.0)	12	27.9	0.43	(0.22- 0.75)	0.54
Gall bladder (156.0)	15	22.7	0.66	(0.37- 1.09)	0.70
Pancreatic cancer (157)	60	88.1	0.68	(0.52- 0.88)	0.78
Peritoneum (158)	5	4.0	1.25	(0.41- 2.92)	1.33
Nose, nasal cav (160)	2	1.9	1.06	(0.13- 3.84)	2.02
Laryngeal cancer (161)	5	7.5	0.67	(0.22- 1.56)	0.96
Lung (162.0-162.1)	169	257.3	0.66	(0.56- 0.76)	0.65***
Pleura (163.0)	7	9.0	0.78	(0.31- 1.61)	0.52
Bone (170)	3	5.3	0.57	(0.12- 1.66)	0.77
Connect tissue (171)	3	6.2	0.48	(0.10- 1.41)	0.60
Malign melanoma (172)	24	25.7	0.93	(0.60- 1.39)	1.11
Other skin (173)	5	2.9	1.71	(0.56- 4.00)	3.16
Prostate cancer (185)	144	141.0	1.02	(0.86- 1.20)	1.10
Testis cancer (186)	2	5.4	0.37	(0.04- 1.33)	0.60
Bladder cancer (188)	26	37.3	0.70	(0.46- 1.02)	0.84
Kidney cancer (189)	54	60.4	0.89	(0.67- 1.17)	1.09
Urinary org (188-189)	80	97.7	0.82	(0.65- 1.02)	0.99
Brain cancer (191)	46	42.9	1.07	(0.78- 1.43)	1.16
Oth endocr glands (194)	1	1.9	0.53	(0.01- 2.98)	0.68
Thyroid cancer (193)	4	4.6	0.87	(0.24- 2.22)	1.40
Lymphosarcoma (200.0-200.1)	7	4.2	1.68	(0.67- 3.46)	2.03
Hodgkins" disease (201)	4	8.8	0.45	(0.12- 1.16)	0.57
Oth lymph tissue (202)	34	36.3	0.94	(0.65- 1.31)	0.91
Mult myeloma (203)	17	25.8	0.66	(0.38- 1.06)	0.63
Leukaemia (204-207)	52	46.8	1.11	(0.83- 1.46)	1.30
Diabetes (250)	29	64.3	0.45	(0.30- 0.65)	1.16
Alcoholism (303)	30	64.2	0.47	(0.32- 0.67)	0.92
Circul system (390-458)	1755	2592.2	0.68	(0.65- 0.71)	0.89***
Isch heart dis (410-414)	1330	1876.3	0.71	(0.67- 0.75)	0.91**
Cerebrovasc dis (430-438)	219	348.3	0.63	(0.55- 0.72)	0.88
Arteries etc (440-448)	61	115.3	0.53	(0.40- 0.68)	0.77
Respiratory syst (460-519)	100	255.5	0.39	(0.32- 0.48)	0.70***
Bronchitis etc (490-493)	42	106.1	0.40	(0.29- 0.54)	0.72
Chronic bronchitis (491)	13	41.8	0.31	(0.17- 0.53)	0.51*
Pneumoconiosis (515-516.2)	1	3.9	0.26	(0.01- 1.43)	0.17
Pneumonia (480-486)	47	120.5	0.39	(0.29- 0.52)	0.74
Digestive system (520-577)	108	199.6	0.54	(0.44- 0.65)	0.97
Oes., stom, duod (530-537)	28	39.2	0.71	(0.47- 1.03)	1.85*
Liver cirrhosis (571)	48	99.7	0.48	(0.35- 0.64)	0.85
Genito-urin syst (580-607)	17	48.5	0.35	(0.20- 0.56)	0.71
Male genital (600-607)	1	5.6	0.18	(0.00- 0.99)	0.32

Mortality by cause of death in wood workers/carpenters

Follow-up from first checkup (1971-1979) to 1988.

Cause of death	Obs	Exp	SMR	(95 % C. I.)		Rel risk
Nephritis&nephrosis (580-4)	8	17.1	0.47	(0.20-	0.92)	0.85
Oth urinary syst (590-599)	8	25.8	0.31	(0.13-	0.61)	0.70
Violent death (800-999)	419	583.4	0.72	(0.65-	0.79)	0.91
Traffic accidents (800-845)	100	121.0	0.83	(0.67-	1.00)	0.92
Accidental falls (880-887)	50	50.0	1.00	(0.74-	1.32)	1.01
Suicide (950-959)	158	214.9	0.74	(0.62-	0.86)	0.98
Homicide (960-969)	2	12.5	0.16	(0.02-	0.58)	0.24
Water transp acc (830-838)	19	14.7	1.29	(0.78-	2.02)	1.53
Drowning (910-915)	19	27.8	0.68	(0.41-	1.07)	0.98
Other accidents (916-929)	19	21.1	0.90	(0.54-	1.41)	0.64

Cancer incidence by site of cancer in wood workers/carpenters

Follow-up from first checkup (1971-1979) to 1987.

Site of cancer	Obs	Exp	SIR	(95 % C. I.)		Rel risk
All cancers (140-209)	1891	2171.9	0.87	(0.83-	0.91)	0.90***
Lip (140)	19	21.5	0.88	(0.53-	1.38)	0.69
Lip etc (140-149)	47	68.5	0.69	(0.50-	0.91)	0.76
Digest ca (150-154)	392	416.8	0.94	(0.85-	1.04)	0.98
Oesophagus (150)	14	29.0	0.48	(0.26-	0.81)	0.68
Stomach (151)	135	122.6	1.10	(0.92-	1.30)	1.06
Intestines (152-153)	141	159.5	0.88	(0.74-	1.04)	0.94
Colon (153)	128	146.7	0.87	(0.73-	1.04)	0.92
Rectum (154)	102	105.7	0.96	(0.79-	1.17)	1.02
Liver (155.0)	13	31.0	0.42	(0.22-	0.72)	0.55
Gall bladder (155.1)	10	11.9	0.84	(0.40-	1.54)	0.97
Pancreas (157)	48	75.9	0.63	(0.47-	0.84)	0.71*
Nose (160)	11	5.0	2.20	(1.10-	3.93)	4.08***
Larynx (161)	13	27.5	0.47	(0.25-	0.81)	0.52*
Lung etc (162)	163	251.8	0.65	(0.55-	0.75)	0.63***
Resp ca (160-164)	194	295.4	0.66	(0.57-	0.76)	0.65***
Lung (162.1)	159	243.4	0.65	(0.56-	0.76)	0.65***
Pleura (162.2)	3	7.8	0.38	(0.08-	1.12)	0.21**
Prostate (177)	416	397.3	1.05	(0.95-	1.15)	1.04
Testis (178)	26	30.8	0.84	(0.55-	1.24)	0.92
Bladder (181)	119	153.5	0.78	(0.64-	0.93)	0.76**
Kidney (180)	78	98.9	0.79	(0.62-	0.98)	0.85
Lymph&blood (200-209)	201	198.3	1.01	(0.88-	1.16)	1.01
Nhl (200)	70	68.6	1.02	(0.80-	1.29)	0.98
Hodgkin's (201)	21	20.1	1.05	(0.65-	1.60)	1.03
Mult myeloma (203)	25	33.5	0.75	(0.48-	1.10)	0.67
Oth ly&blood (202, 204-209)	85	76.2	1.12	(0.89-	1.38)	1.21
Melanoma (190)	57	76.9	0.74	(0.56-	0.96)	0.82
Other skin (191)	56	67.4	0.83	(0.63-	1.08)	0.89
Nervous system (193)	88	81.8	1.08	(0.86-	1.32)	1.20

Two-sided p-values: * = p<0.05, ** = p<0.01, *** = p<0.001

Mortality by cause of death in brick layers

Follow-up from first checkup (1971-1979) to 1988.

Cause of death	Obs	Exp	SMR	(95 % C. I.)	Rel risk
All causes (001-999)	908	1273.7	0.71	(0.67- 0.76)	0.96
All cancers (140-209)	244	308.7	0.79	(0.69- 0.90)	0.89
Lip etc (140-149)	3	6.5	0.46	(0.10- 1.35)	0.86
Oesophageal cancer (150)	10	7.5	1.33	(0.64- 2.44)	2.20*
Stomach cancer (151)	17	26.6	0.64	(0.37- 1.02)	0.64
Sm intestines (152)	4	1.1	3.74	(1.02- 9.57)	3.97*
Colon cancer (153)	14	21.7	0.64	(0.35- 1.08)	0.78
Rectal cancer (154)	6	13.4	0.45	(0.16- 0.98)	0.48
Liver cancer (155.0)	6	7.0	0.86	(0.32- 1.88)	1.21
Gall bladder (156.0)	9	5.7	1.58	(0.72- 2.99)	1.87
Pancreatic cancer (157)	12	22.1	0.54	(0.28- 0.95)	0.64
Peritoneum (158)	3	1.0	3.13	(0.64- 9.13)	3.49
Laryngeal cancer (161)	3	1.9	1.58	(0.33- 4.61)	2.47
Lung (162.0-162.1)	50	64.7	0.77	(0.57- 1.02)	0.82
Pleura (163.0)	0	2.2	0.00	(0.00- 1.67)	0.00
Bone (170)	0	1.1	0.00	(0.00- 3.24)	0.00
Connect tissue (171)	1	1.4	0.72	(0.02- 4.01)	0.97
Malign melanoma (172)	5	6.0	0.83	(0.27- 1.94)	0.97
Prostate cancer (185)	30	35.9	0.84	(0.56- 1.19)	0.87
Testis cancer (186)	1	.9	1.09	(0.03- 6.06)	2.00
Bladder cancer (188)	5	9.4	0.53	(0.17- 1.24)	0.65
Kidney cancer (189)	12	15.1	0.79	(0.41- 1.38)	0.94
Urinary org (188-189)	17	24.6	0.69	(0.40- 1.11)	0.83
Brain cancer (191)	12	10.0	1.20	(0.62- 2.09)	1.27
Thyroid cancer (193)	1	1.1	0.87	(0.02- 4.84)	1.32
Lymphosarcoma (200.0-200.1)	0	1.0	0.00	(0.00- 3.62)	0.00
Hodgkins" disease (201)	3	1.9	1.56	(0.32- 4.57)	2.27
Oth lymph tissue (202)	7	8.8	0.79	(0.32- 1.64)	0.78
Mult myeloma (203)	8	6.5	1.23	(0.53- 2.43)	1.30
Leukaemia (204-207)	7	10.9	0.64	(0.26- 1.32)	0.69
Diabetes (250)	2	15.2	0.13	(0.02- 0.48)	0.32
Alcoholism (303)	12	14.1	0.85	(0.44- 1.49)	1.76
Circul system (390-458)	462	652.0	0.71	(0.65- 0.78)	0.95
Isch heart dis (410-414)	348	474.0	0.73	(0.66- 0.82)	0.96
Cerebrovasc dis (430-438)	48	87.1	0.55	(0.41- 0.73)	0.78
Arteries etc (440-448)	22	29.0	0.76	(0.48- 1.15)	1.18
Respiratory syst (460-519)	42	63.4	0.66	(0.48- 0.90)	1.28
Bronchitis etc (490-493)	17	26.5	0.64	(0.37- 1.03)	1.25
Chronic bronchitis (491)	4	10.6	0.38	(0.10- 0.97)	0.68
Pneumoconiosis (515-516.2)	2	1.0	2.02	(0.24- 7.30)	1.67
Pneumonia (480-486)	15	29.6	0.51	(0.28- 0.83)	1.02
Digestive system (520-577)	25	48.2	0.52	(0.34- 0.77)	0.93
Oes., stom, duod (530-537)	3	9.8	0.31	(0.06- 0.90)	0.66
Liver cirrhosis (571)	11	23.8	0.46	(0.23- 0.83)	0.83
Genito-urin syst (580-607)	2	12.1	0.17	(0.02- 0.60)	0.34
Male genital (600-607)	1	1.4	0.69	(0.02- 3.87)	1.55
Nephritis&nephrosis (580-4)	1	4.2	0.24	(0.01- 1.33)	0.44
Oth urinary syst (590-599)	0	6.5	0.00	(0.00- 0.57)	0.00

Mortality by cause of death in brick layers

Follow-up from first checkup (1971-1979) to 1988.

Cause of death	Obs	Exp	SMR	(95 % C. I.)	Rel risk
Violent death (800-999)	92	112.5	0.82	(0.66- 1.00)	1.06
Traffic accidents (800-845)	21	21.7	0.97	(0.60- 1.48)	1.10
Accidental falls (880-887)	11	11.5	· 0.96	(0.48- 1.71)	0.97
Suicide (950-959)	34	40.8	0.83	(0.58- 1.17)	1.12
Homicide (960-969)	1	2.1	0.47	(0.01- 2.62)	0.83
Water transp acc (830-838)	4	2.7	1.46	(0.40- 3.74)	1.60
Drowning (910-915)	7	5.7	1.23	(0.50- 2.54)	1.83
Other accidents (916-929)	1	4.1	0.24	(0.01- 1.36)	0.18

Cancer incidence by site of cancer in brick layers

Follow-up from first checkup (1971-1979) to 1987.

Site of cancer	Obs	Exp	SIR	(95 % C. I.)	Rel risk
All cancers (140-209)	468	532.4	0.88	(0.80- 0.96)	0.93
Lip (140)	5	5.4	0.93	(0.30- 2.17)	0.76
Lip etc (140-149)	17	16.8	1.01	(0.59- 1.62)	1.19
Digest ca (150-154)	86	104.2	0.83	(0.66- 1.02)	0.86
Oesophagus (150)	9	7.3	1.23	(0.56- 2.33)	1.96
Stomach (151)	23	30.8	0.75	(0.47- 1.12)	0.70
Intestines (152-153)	35	39.6	0.88	(0.62- 1.23)	0.95
Colon (153)	31	36.4	0.85	(0.58- 1.21)	0.91
Rectum (154)	19	26.5	0.72	(0.43- 1.12)	0.74
Liver (155.0)	6	7.7	0.78	(0.28- 1.69)	1.13
Gall bladder (155.1)	4	3.0	1.32	(0.36- 3.39)	1.60
Pancreas (157)	11	19.1	0.57	(0.29- 1.03)	0.67
Peritoneum (158)	2	.2	12.50	(1.51- 45.15)	13.37**
Nose (160)	1	1.2	0.81	(0.02- 4.49)	0.93
Larynx (161)	4	6.9	0.58	(0.16- 1.49)	0.70
Lung etc (162)	56	63.3	0.88	(0.67- 1.15)	0.92
Resp ca (160-164)	61	74.2	0.82	(0.63- 1.06)	0.87
Lung (162.1)	56	61.3	0.91	(0.69- 1.19)	0.98
Pleura (162.2)	0	1.9	0.00	(0.00- 1.93)	0.00
Prostate (177)	95	101.4	0.94	(0.76- 1.15)	0.92
Testis (178)	6	4.5	1.33	(0.49- 2.89)	1.49
Bladder (181)	35	38.3	0.91	(0.64- 1.27)	0.94
Kidney (180)	23	24.6	0.94	(0.59- 1.40)	1.04
Lymph&blood (200-209)	40	46.8	0.86	(0.61- 1.16)	0.84
Nhl (200)	10	16.3	0.61	(0.29- 1.13)	0.58
Hodgkin's (201)	5	3.9	1.27	(0.41- 2.96)	1.26
Mult myeloma (203)	11	8.4	1.31	(0.65- 2.35)	1.27
Oth ly&blood (202, 204-209)	14	18.1	0.77	(0.42- 1.30)	0.80
Melanoma (190)	14	17.1	0.82	(0.45- 1.37)	0.93
Other skin (191)	11	16.7	0.66	(0.33- 1.18)	0.71
Nervous system (193)	18	18.3	0.98	(0.58- 1.55)	1.06

Two-sided p-values: * = p<0.05, ** = p<0.01, *** = p<0.001

Mortality by cause of death in machine operators

Follow-up from first checkup (1971-1979) to 1988.

Cause of death	Obs	Exp	SMR	(95 % C. I.)	Rel risk
All causes (001-999)	394	499.1	0.79	(0.71- 0.87)	1.06
All cancers (140-209)	96	113.8	0.84	(0.68- 1.03)	0.96
Lip etc (140-149)	3	2.8	1.06	(0.22- 3.09)	2.02
Oesophageal cancer (150)	0	2.8	0.00	(0.00- 1.32)	0.00
Stomach cancer (151)	10	8.6	1.16	(0.55- 2.13)	1.18
Colon cancer (153)	10	7.8	1.29	(0.62- 2.36)	1.59
Rectal cancer (154)	3	4.5	0.66	(0.14- 1.93)	0.72
Liver cancer (155.0)	2	2.5	0.81	(0.10- 2.94)	1.13
Gall bladder (156.0)	2	2.0	1.02	(0.12- 3.69)	1.16
Pancreatic cancer (157)	7	7.9	0.88	(0.35- 1.81)	1.06
Lung (162.0-162.1)	16	24.1	0.67	(0.38- 1.08)	0.71
Pleura (163.0)	0	.9	0.00	(0.00- 3.92)	0.00
Connect tissue (171)	0	.8	0.00	(0.00- 4.73)	0.00
Malign melanoma (172)	3	3.6	0.84	(0.17- 2.44)	0.97
Prostate cancer (185)	11	8.3	1.33	(0.66- 2.38)	1.41
Testis cancer (186)	1	.8	1.19	(0.03- 6.63)	2.19
Bladder cancer (188)	1	2.8	0.36	(0.01- 2.02)	0.45
Kidney cancer (189)	3	6.0	0.50	(0.10- 1.45)	0.59
Urinary org (188-189)	4	8.8	0.45	(0.12- 1.16)	0.55
Brain cancer (191)	6	5.8	1.04	(0.38- 2.26)	1.09
Thyroid cancer (193)	1	.4	2.27	(0.06- 12.66)	3.56
Lymphosarcoma (200.0-200.1)	2	.4	5.13	(0.62- 18.52)	5.55
Hodgkins" disease (201)	1	1.1	0.87	(0.02- 4.84)	1.20
Oth lymph tissue (202)	3	3.8	0.80	(0.16- 2.34)	0.79
Mult myeloma (203)	2	2.2	0.91	(0.11- 3.30)	0.94
Leukaemia (204-207)	4	5.0	0.80	(0.22- 2.06)	0.88
Diabetes (250)	3	7.1	0.42	(0.09- 1.24)	1.06
Alcoholism (303)	4	11.8	0.34	(0.09- 0.87)	0.67
Circul system (390-458)	189	207.6	0.91	(0.79- 1.05)	1.23**
Isch heart dis (410-414)	142	151.7	0.94	(0.79- 1.10)	1.23*
Cerebrovasc dis (430-438)	27	26.0	1.04	(0.68- 1.51)	1.51*
Arteries etc (440-448)	8	8.1	0.99	(0.43- 1.95)	1.54
Respiratory syst (460-519)	9	19.9	0.45	(0.21- 0.86)	0.86
Bronchitis etc (490-493)	4	8.3	0.48	(0.13- 1.23)	0.92
Chronic bronchitis (491)	2	2.8	0.73	(0.09- 2.63)	1.35
Pneumonia (480-486)	5	9.4	0.53	(0.17- 1.25)	1.08
Digestive system (520-577)	8	24.0	0.33	(0.14- 0.66)	0.60
Oes., stom, duod (530-537)	0	3.5	0.00	(0.00- 1.05)	0.00
Liver cirrhosis (571)	5	14.5	0.34	(0.11- 0.80)	0.62
Genito-urin syst (580-607)	0	3.3	0.00	(0.00- 1.11)	0.00
Nephritis&nephrosis (580-4)	0	1.5	0.00	(0.00- 2.43)	0.00
Oth urinary syst (590-599)	0	1.5	0.00	(0.00- 2.38)	0.00
Violent death (800-999)	72	89.3	0.81	(0.63- 1.02)	1.04
Traffic accidents (800-845)	16	16.7	0.96	(0.55- 1.55)	1.09
Accidental falls (880-887)	3	6.0	0.50	(0.10- 1.45)	0.50

Mortality by cause of death in machine operators

Follow-up from first checkup (1971-1979) to 1988.

Cause of death	Obs	Exp	SMR	(95 % C. I.)	Rel risk
Suicide (950-959)	31	34.6	0.90	(0.61- 1.27)	1.21
Homicide (960-969)	0	2.1	0.00	(0.00- 1.74)	0.00
Water transp acc (830-838)	1	2.3	0.43	(0.01- 2.40)	0.45
Drowning (910-915)	1	4.0	0.25	(0.01- 1.40)	0.35
Other accidents (916-929)	17	3.2	5.28	(3.08- 8.45)	4.48***

Cancer incidence by site of cancer in machine operators

Follow-up from first checkup (1971-1979) to 1987.

Site of cancer	Obs	Exp	SIR	(95 % C. I.)	Rel risk
All cancers (140-209)	204	210.4	0.97	(0.84- 1.11)	1.02
Lip (140)	2	2.1	0.96	(0.12- 3.47)	0.80
Lip etc (140-149)	7	7.8	0.90	(0.36- 1.85)	1.05
Digest ca (150-154)	41	37.8	1.08	(0.78- 1.47)	1.14
Oesophagus (150)	1	2.7	0.37	(0.01- 2.06)	0.56
Stomach (151)	14	10.4	1.34	(0.73- 2.25)	1.28
Intestines (152-153)	18	15.0	1.20	(0.71- 1.90)	1.30
Colon (153)	16	13.6	1.17	(0.67- 1.91)	1.27
Rectum (154)	8	9.7	0.82	(0.36- 1.63)	0.86
Liver (155.0)	1	2.6	0.39	(0.01- 2.16)	0.55
Gall bladder (155.1)	1	1.0	1.03	(0.03- 5.74)	1.21
Pancreas (157)	6	6.8	0.88	(0.32- 1.91)	1.05
Larynx (161)	2	2.9	0.69	(0.08- 2.48)	0.83
Lung etc (162)	19	24.2	0.78	(0.47- 1.23)	0.82
Resp ca (160-164)	21	28.7	0.73	(0.45- 1.12)	0.78
Lung (162.1)	19	23.3	0.82	(0.49- 1.28)	0.87
Pleura (162.2)	0	.9	0.00	(0.00- 4.10)	0.00
Prostate (177)	34	24.8	1.37	(0.95- 1.92)	1.36
Testis (178)	3	5.1	0.59	(0.12- 1.74)	0.65
Bladder (181)	16	14.6	1.09	(0.62- 1.77)	1.13
Kidney (180)	7	10.9	0.64	(0.26- 1.32)	0.71
Lymph&blood (200-209)	24	22.3	1.08	(0.69- 1.60)	1.07
Nhl (200)	10	8.1	1.23	(0.59- 2.26)	1.19
Hodgkin's (201)	2	2.8	0.73	(0.09- 2.63)	0.71
Mult myeloma (203)	2	3.2	0.63	(0.08- 2.26)	0.59
Oth ly&blood (202, 204-209)	10	8.2	1.22	(0.58- 2.24)	1.28
Melanoma (190)	9	11.7	0.77	(0.35- 1.46)	0.88
Other skin (191)	7	5.5	1.28	(0.52- 2.64)	1.42
Nervous system (193)	9	11.3	0.79	(0.36- 1.51)	0.85

Two-sided p-values: * = p<0.05, ** = p<0.01, *** = p<0.001

Mortality by cause of death in drivers

Follow-up from first checkup (1971-1979) to 1988.

Cause of death	Obs	Exp	SMR	(95 % C. I.)	Rel risk
All causes (001-999)	324	380.2	0.85	(0.76- 0.95)	1.15*
All cancers (140-209)	79	91.7	0.86	(0.68- 1.07)	0.98
Lip etc (140-149)	2	2.1	0.94	(0.11- 3.39)	1.78
Oesophageal cancer (150)	1	2.3	0.43	(0.01- 2.42)	0.68
Stomach cancer (151)	7	7.5	0.94	(0.38- 1.93)	0.95
Colon cancer (153)	6	6.4	0.94	(0.35- 2.05)	1.16
Rectal cancer (154)	4	3.9	1.03	(0.28- 2.65)	1.13
Liver cancer (155.0)	2	2.0	0.98	(0.12- 3.54)	1.37
Gall bladder (156.0)	0	1.7	0.00	(0.00- 2.22)	0.00
Pancreatic cancer (157)	5	6.6	0.76	(0.25- 1.77)	0.91
Lung (162.0-162.1)	23	19.6	1.17	(0.74- 1.76)	1.26
Pleura (163.0)	2	.7	2.90	(0.35- 10.47)	2.17
Connect tissue (171)	1	.5	2.04	(0.05- 11.37)	2.85
Malign melanoma (172)	1	2.2	0.45	(0.01- 2.52)	0.52
Prostate cancer (185)	5	8.7	0.57	(0.19- 1.34)	0.60
Bladder cancer (188)	1	2.5	0.39	(0.01- 2.18)	0.48
Kidney cancer (189)	5	4.8	1.05	(0.34- 2.45)	1.26
Urinary org (188-189)	6	7.3	0.82	(0.30- 1.78)	0.99
Brain cancer (191)	2	3.6	0.55	(0.07- 1.98)	0.57
Oth lymph tissue (202)	0	2.8	0.00	(0.00- 1.32)	0.00
Mult myeloma (203)	7	1.9	3.72	(1.50- 7.67)	4.04***
Leukaemia (204-207)	1	3.4	0.29	(0.01- 1.62)	0.32
Diabetes (250)	5	4.8	1.05	(0.34- 2.45)	2.68
Alcoholism (303)	2	6.1	0.33	(0.04- 1.18)	0.65
Circul system (390-458)	178	181.2	0.98	(0.84- 1.14)	1.33***
Isch heart dis (410-414)	139	133.4	1.04	(0.88- 1.23)	1.37***
Cerebrovasc dis (430-438)	21	22.9	0.92	(0.57- 1.40)	1.33
Arteries etc (440-448)	5	7.5	0.67	(0.22- 1.56)	1.03
Respiratory syst (460-519)	5	17.0	0.29	(0.10- 0.69)	0.56
Bronchitis etc (490-493)	3	7.3	0.41	(0.08- 1.20)	0.79
Chronic bronchitis (491)	1	2.7	0.37	(0.01- 2.06)	0.68
Pneumonia (480-486)	2	7.8	0.26	(0.03- 0.93)	0.51
Digestive system (520-577)	7	16.2	0.43	(0.17- 0.89)	0.78
Oes., stom, duod (530-537)	2	2.8	0.71	(0.09- 2.57)	1.58
Liver cirrhosis (571)	4	9.0	0.44	(0.12- 1.14)	0.80
Genito-urin syst (580-607)	4	3.0	1.33	(0.36- 3.41)	2.95
Male genital (600-607)	2	.3	6.90	(0.84- 24.91)	17.95***
Nephritis&nephrosis (580-4)	0	1.2	0.00	(0.00- 3.10)	0.00
Oth urinary syst (590-599)	2	1.5	1.32	(0.16- 4.75)	3.27
Violent death (800-999)	34	45.1	0.75	(0.52- 1.05)	0.97
Traffic accidents (800-845)	8	8.4	0.95	(0.41- 1.87)	1.08
Accidental falls (880-887)	4	3.8	1.06	(0.29- 2.70)	1.07
Suicide (950-959)	12	16.9	0.71	(0.37- 1.24)	0.95

Mortality by cause of death in drivers

Follow-up from first checkup (1971-1979) to 1988.

Cause of death	Obs	Exp	SMR	(95 % C. I.)	Rel risk
Homicide (960-969)	0	.9	0.00	(0.00- 3.88)	0.00
Water transp acc (830-838)	1	1.1	0.88	(0.02- 4.89)	0.94
Drowning (910-915)	2	2.2	0.92	(0.11- 3.33)	1.33
Other accidents (916-929)	2	1.6	1.23	(0.15- 4.43)	0.94

Cancer incidence by site of cancer in drivers

Follow-up from first checkup (1971-1979) to 1987.

Site of cancer	Obs	Exp	SIR	(95 % C. I.)	Rel risk
All cancers (140-209)	152	162.8	0.93	(0.79- 1.09)	0.99
Lip (140)	6	1.6	3.64	(1.33- 7.91)	3.12*
Lip etc (140-149)	9	5.6	1.60	(0.73- 3.05)	1.90
Digest ca (150-154)	23	31.0	0.74	(0.47- 1.11)	0.78
Oesophagus (150)	1	2.2	0.45	(0.01- 2.49)	0.67
Stomach (151)	7	8.9	0.79	(0.32- 1.63)	0.75
Intestines (152-153)	5	11.9	0.42	(0.14- 0.98)	0.45
Colon (153)	4	10.9	0.37	(0.10- 0.94)	0.39
Rectum (154)	10	8.0	1.25	(0.60- 2.30)	1.32
Liver (155.0)	2	2.2	0.90	(0.11- 3.27)	1.31
Gall bladder (155.1)	0	.9	0.00	(0.00- 4.34)	0.00
Pancreas (157)	5	5.7	0.88	(0.28- 2.04)	1.05
Larynx (161)	0	2.3	0.00	(0.00- 1.64)	0.00
Lung etc (162)	22	19.6	1.12	(0.70- 1.70)	1.18
Resp ca (160-164)	24	23.1	1.04	(0.67- 1.55)	1.12
Lung (162.1)	20	18.9	1.06	(0.65- 1.63)	1.13
Pleura (162.2)	2	.6	3.23	(0.39- 11.65)	2.11
Prostate (177)	25	25.8	0.97	(0.63- 1.43)	0.95
Testis (178)	1	2.1	0.48	(0.01- 2.67)	0.53
Bladder (181)	7	11.7	0.60	(0.24- 1.23)	0.61
Kidney (180)	8	8.1	0.99	(0.43- 1.95)	1.10
Lymph&blood (200-209)	19	15.4	1.24	(0.74- 1.93)	1.23
Nhl (200)	4	5.5	0.72	(0.20- 1.85)	0.69
Hodgkin's (201)	0	1.5	0.00	(0.00- 2.53)	0.00
Mult myeloma (203)	7	2.6	2.73	(1.10- 5.63)	2.69*
Oth ly&blood (202, 204-209)	8	5.8	1.37	(0.59- 2.71)	1.44
Melanoma (190)	6	6.7	0.90	(0.33- 1.96)	1.03
Other skin (191)	5	4.7	1.08	(0.35- 2.51)	1.19
Nervous system (193)	8	6.8	1.18	(0.51- 2.32)	1.27

Two-sided p-values: * = p<0.05, ** = p<0.01, *** = p<0.001

Mortality by cause of death in glass workers

Follow-up from first checkup (1971-1979) to 1988.

Cause of death	Obs	Exp	SMR	(95 % C. I.)	Rel risk
All causes (001-999)	89	107.5	0.83	(0.67- 1.02)	1.12
All cancers (140-209)	27	23.7	1.14	(0.75- 1.66)	1.29
Lip etc (140-149)	1	.5	1.89	(0.05- 10.51)	3.57
Stomach cancer (151)	2	1.9	1.06	(0.13- 3.82)	1.07
Colon cancer (153)	2	1.6	1.23	(0.15- 4.43)	1.50
Rectal cancer (154)	0	1.0	0.00	(0.00- 3.84)	0.00
Liver cancer (155.0)	1	.5	1.92	(0.05- 10.71)	2.68
Pancreatic cancer (157)	2	1.6	1.24	(0.15- 4.49)	1.50
Lung (162.0-162.1)	4	4.8	0.84	(0.23- 2.14)	0.89
Malign melanoma (172)	1	.6	1.54	(0.04- 8.57)	1.79
Prostate cancer (185)	6	2.2	2.70	(0.99- 5.88)	2.86*
Bladder cancer (188)	3	.6	4.76	(0.98- 13.92)	6.04**
Kidney cancer (189)	0	1.2	0.00	(0.00- 3.15)	0.00
Urinary org (188-189)	3	1.8	1.67	(0.34- 4.87)	2.03
Brain cancer (191)	2	1.1	1.87	(0.23- 6.75)	1.97
Oth lymph tissue (202)	1	.8	1.33	(0.03- 7.43)	1.32
Leukaemia (204-207)	0	1.1	0.00	(0.00- 3.48)	0.00
Diabetes (250)	0	1.5	0.00	(0.00- 2.49)	0.00
Alcoholism (303)	2	2.0	0.99	(0.12- 3.58)	1.99
Circul system (390-458)	41	46.3	0.88	(0.63- 1.20)	1.19
Isch heart dis (410-414)	30	33.1	0.91	(0.61- 1.29)	1.18
Cerebrovasc dis (430-438)	3	6.3	0.48	(0.10- 1.39)	0.69
Arteries etc (440-448)	5	2.0	2.49	(0.81- 5.81)	3.87**
Respiratory syst (460-519)	3	4.8	0.63	(0.13- 1.83)	1.19
Bronchitis etc (490-493)	1	1.9	0.52	(0.01- 2.92)	1.01
Chronic bronchitis (491)	1	.7	1.45	(0.04- 8.07)	2.69
Pneumonia (480-486)	1	2.3	0.43	(0.01- 2.38)	0.86
Digestive system (520-577)	2	4.6	0.43	(0.05- 1.57)	0.79
Oes., stom, duod (530-537)	1	.8	1.30	(0.03- 7.24)	2.87
Liver cirrhosis (571)	1	2.5	0.40	(0.01- 2.20)	0.72
Genito-urin syst (580-607)	0	.9	0.00	(0.00- 4.19)	0.00
Violent death (800-999)	12	18.9	0.64	(0.33- 1.11)	0.82
Traffic accidents (800-845)	2	4.0	0.50	(0.06- 1.82)	0.57
Accidental falls (880-887)	1	1.3	0.79	(0.02- 4.42)	0.80
Suicide (950-959)	5	7.2	0.70	(0.23- 1.62)	0.93
Drowning (910-915)	1	.8	1.22	(0.03- 6.79)	1.76
Other accidents (916-929)	2	.7	2.94	(0.36- 10.62)	2.28

Cancer incidence by site of cancer in glass workers

Follow-up from first checkup (1971-1979) to 1987.

Site of cancer	Obs	Exp	SIR	(95 % C. I.)	Rel risk
All cancers (140-209)	45	43.3	1.04	(0.76- 1.39)	1.10
Lip etc (140-149)	3	1.5	2.05	(0.42- 6.00)	2.41
Digest ca (150-154)	6	7.8	0.77	(0.28- 1.67)	0.81
Stomach (151)	2	2.2	0.90	(0.11- 3.24)	0.85
Intestines (152-153)	4	3.1	1.30	(0.35- 3.33)	1.40
Colon (153)	4	2.8	1.42	(0.39- 3.63)	1.53
Rectum (154)	0	2.0	0.00	(0.00- 1.87)	0.00
Liver (155.0)	1	.6	1.79	(0.05- 9.95)	2.59
Pancreas (157)	1	1.4	0.72	(0.02- 4.01)	0.86
Lung etc (162)	4	4.7	0.84	(0.23- 2.16)	0.88
Resp ca (160-164)	4	5.6	0.71	(0.19- 1.83)	0.76
Lung (162.1)	4	4.6	0.88	(0.24- 2.25)	0.94
Prostate (177)	10	6.2	1.62	(0.78- 2.98)	1.60
Testis (178)	0	1.2	0.00	(0.00- 3.07)	0.00
Bladder (181)	8	2.9	2.73	(1.18- 5.38)	2.84**
Kidney (180)	2	2.0	0.98	(0.12- 3.54)	1.09
Lymph&blood (200-209)	3	4.5	0.67	(0.14- 1.95)	0.66
Nhl (200)	3	1.6	1.92	(0.40- 5.62)	1.86
Oth ly&blood (202, 204-209)	0	1.7	0.00	(0.00- 2.20)	0.00
Melanoma (190)	1	2.2	0.47	(0.01- 2.59)	0.53
Other skin (191)	2	1.2	1.61	(0.20- 5.83)	1.78
Nervous system (193)	2	2.2	0.92	(0.11- 3.31)	0.99

Two-sided p-values: * = p<0.05, ** = p<0.01, *** = p<0.001

Mortality by cause of death in insulators

Follow-up from first checkup (1971-1979) to 1988.

Cause of death	Obs	Exp	SMR	(95 % C. I.)	Rel risk
All causes (001-999)	98	96.9	1.01	(0.82- 1.23)	1.36**
All cancers (140-209)	25	21.7	1.15	(0.75- 1.70)	1.31
Stomach cancer (151)	2	1.7	1.20	(0.15- 4.33)	1.21
Colon cancer (153)	0	1.5	0.00	(0.00- 2.49)	0.00
Rectal cancer (154)	1	.9	1.16	(0.03- 6.48)	1.27
Liver cancer (155.0)	1	.5	2.13	(0.05- 11.85)	2.97
Gall bladder (156.0)	1	.4	2.70	(0.07- 15.06)	3.09
Pancreatic cancer (157)	1	1.5	0.67	(0.02- 3.74)	0.81
Peritoneum (158)	2	.1	22.22	(2.69- 80.27)	24.48***
Lung (162.0-162.1)	12	4.5	2.67	(1.38- 4.67)	2.88***
Prostate cancer (185)	0	1.7	0.00	(0.00- 2.18)	0.00
Kidney cancer (189)	0	1.1	0.00	(0.00- 3.32)	0.00
Urinary org (188-189)	0	1.6	0.00	(0.00- 2.24)	0.00
Brain cancer (191)	0	1.1	0.00	(0.00- 3.42)	0.00
Oth lymph tissue (202)	1	.7	1.41	(0.04- 7.85)	1.39
Leukaemia (204-207)	0	1.0	0.00	(0.00- 3.76)	0.00
Diabetes (250)	0	1.4	0.00	(0.00- 2.71)	0.00
Alcoholism (303)	0	2.1	0.00	(0.00- 1.72)	0.00
Circul system (390-458)	34	40.1	0.85	(0.59- 1.19)	1.15
Isch heart dis (410-414)	26	29.1	0.89	(0.58- 1.31)	1.17
Cerebrovasc dis (430-438)	3	5.2	0.58	(0.12- 1.70)	0.84
Arteries etc (440-448)	2	1.6	1.24	(0.15- 4.49)	1.92
Respiratory syst (460-519)	5	3.9	1.28	(0.42- 2.98)	2.44
Bronchitis etc (490-493)	1	1.6	0.61	(0.02- 3.42)	1.18
Chronic bronchitis (491)	1	.6	1.82	(0.05- 10.13)	3.38
Pneumoconiosis (515-516.2)	2	.1	40.00	(4.84-144.49)	34.94***
Pneumonia (480-486)	1	1.9	0.54	(0.01- 3.01)	1.09
Digestive system (520-577)	6	4.4	1.35	(0.49- 2.93)	2.45
Liver cirrhosis (571)	4	2.6	1.53	(0.42- 3.91)	2.80
Violent death (800-999)	23	18.3	1.26	(0.80- 1.89)	1.63*
Traffic accidents (800-845)	6	3.7	1.62	(0.60- 3.53)	1.85
Accidental falls (880-887)	1	1.2	0.85	(0.02- 4.76)	0.86
Suicide (950-959)	11	7.0	1.56	(0.78- 2.80)	2.11*
Homicide (960-969)	1	.4	2.22	(0.06- 12.38)	4.04
Drowning (910-915)	0	.8	0.00	(0.00- 4.61)	0.00
Other accidents (916-929)	1	.7	1.52	(0.04- 8.44)	1.17

Cancer incidence by site of cancer in insulators

Follow-up from first checkup (1971-1979) to 1987.

Site of cancer	Obs	Exp	SIR	(95 % C. I.)	Rel risk
All cancers (140-209)	38	40.2	0.95	(0.67- 1.30)	1.00
Lip etc (140-149)	0	1.4	0.00	(0.00- 2.58)	0.00
Digest ca (150-154)	3	7.2	0.42	(0.09- 1.22)	0.44
Stomach (151)	1	2.0	0.50	(0.01- 2.79)	0.47
Intestines (152-153)	1	2.8	0.35	(0.01- 1.96)	0.38
Colon (153)	1	2.6	0.39	(0.01- 2.15)	0.41
Rectum (154)	1	1.8	0.55	(0.01- 3.04)	0.57
Liver (155.0)	2	.5	4.00	(0.48- 14.45)	5.87*
Gall bladder (155.1)	1	.2	5.26	(0.13- 29.32)	6.27
Pancreas (157)	1	1.3	0.78	(0.02- 4.35)	0.93
Peritoneum (158)	2	.0	200.00	(24.2-722.47)	224.00***
Lung etc (162)	11	4.5	2.44	(1.22- 4.37)	2.57**
Resp ca (160-164)	11	5.3	2.06	(1.03- 3.69)	2.22*
Lung (162.1)	10	4.3	2.31	(1.11- 4.26)	2.49**
Pleura (162.2)	1	.2	5.88	(0.15- 32.77)	3.83
Prostate (177)	3	5.0	0.60	(0.12- 1.75)	0.59
Testis (178)	2	1.1	1.79	(0.22- 6.45)	1.99
Bladder (181)	3	2.8	1.09	(0.22- 3.19)	1.13
Kidney (180)	2	2.0	1.00	(0.12- 3.61)	1.11
Lymph&blood (200-209)	3	4.3	0.70	(0.14- 2.05)	0.70
Nhl (200)	1	1.5	0.66	(0.02- 3.67)	0.63
Oth ly&blood (202, 204-209)	2	1.6	1.27	(0.15- 4.57)	1.32
Melanoma (190)	2	2.2	0.92	(0.11- 3.31)	1.05
Other skin (191)	2	1.1	1.87	(0.23- 6.75)	2.06
Nervous system (193)	0	2.2	0.00	(0.00- 1.71)	0.00

Two-sided p-values: * = p<0.05, ** = p<0.01, *** = p<0.001

Mortality by cause of death in plumbers

Follow-up from first checkup (1971-1979) to 1988.

Cause of death	Obs	Exp	SMR	(95 % C. I.)	Rel risk
All causes (001-999)	1094	1450.9	0.75	(0.71- 0.80)	1.02
All cancers (140-209)	340	336.7	1.01	(0.91- 1.12)	1.15*
Lip etc (140-149)	6	7.7	0.78	(0.28- 1.69)	1.49
Oesophageal cancer (150)	8	8.2	0.98	(0.42- 1.92)	1.58
Stomach cancer (151)	27	27.1	0.99	(0.66- 1.45)	1.01
Sm intestines (152)	0	1.2	0.00	(0.00- 3.00)	0.00
Colon cancer (153)	21	23.3	0.90	(0.56- 1.38)	1.11
Rectal cancer (154)	10	13.9	0.72	(0.34- 1.32)	0.77
Liver cancer (155.0)	4	7.4	0.54	(0.15- 1.38)	0.73
Gall bladder (156.0)	6	6.0	1.00	(0.37- 2.18)	1.15
Pancreatic cancer (157)	24	23.7	1.01	(0.65- 1.51)	1.24
Peritoneum (158)	1	1.2	0.83	(0.02- 4.60)	0.81
Laryngeal cancer (161)	2	2.0	0.99	(0.12- 3.58)	1.47
Lung (162.0-162.1)	100	70.4	1.42	(1.16- 1.73)	1.57***
Pleura (163.0)	10	2.6	3.88	(1.86- 7.13)	3.22***
Bone (170)	1	1.6	0.62	(0.02- 3.46)	0.87
Connect tissue (171)	3	2.0	1.52	(0.31- 4.43)	2.21
Malign melanoma (172)	5	8.7	0.57	(0.19- 1.34)	0.65
Other skin (173)	0	.8	0.00	(0.00- 4.50)	0.00
Prostate cancer (185)	37	31.4	1.18	(0.83- 1.62)	1.26
Testis cancer (186)	1	2.0	0.51	(0.01- 2.81)	0.89
Bladder cancer (188)	7	9.1	0.77	(0.31- 1.58)	0.95
Kidney cancer (189)	10	17.1	0.58	(0.28- 1.08)	0.69
Urinary org (188-189)	17	26.3	0.65	(0.38- 1.04)	0.78
Brain cancer (191)	13	14.3	0.91	(0.48- 1.55)	0.95
Oth endocr glands (194)	2	.6	3.39	(0.41- 12.25)	6.04
Thyroid cancer (193)	1	1.3	0.78	(0.02- 4.35)	1.18
Lymphosarcoma (200.0-200.1)	0	1.2	0.00	(0.00- 3.18)	0.00
Hodgkins" disease (201)	1	2.9	0.35	(0.01- 1.93)	0.46
Oth lymph tissue (202)	10	10.4	0.96	(0.46- 1.77)	0.95
Mult myeloma (203)	5	6.7	0.74	(0.24- 1.73)	0.76
Leukaemia (204-207)	15	13.7	1.10	(0.61- 1.81)	1.22
Diabetes (250)	12	19.1	0.63	(0.32- 1.10)	1.63
Alcoholism (303)	12	25.7	0.47	(0.24- 0.82)	0.93
Circul system (390-458)	469	659.2	0.71	(0.65- 0.78)	0.96
Isch heart dis (410-414)	354	479.2	0.74	(0.66- 0.82)	0.96
Cerebrovasc dis (430-438)	60	85.9	0.70	(0.53- 0.90)	1.01
Arteries etc (440-448)	18	27.7	0.65	(0.39- 1.03)	1.00
Respiratory syst (460-519)	44	64.1	0.69	(0.50- 0.92)	1.33
Bronchitis etc (490-493)	10	26.7	0.37	(0.18- 0.69)	0.71
Chronic bronchitis (491)	7	9.7	0.72	(0.29- 1.48)	1.35
Pneumoconiosis (515-516.2)	4	.9	4.40	(1.20- 11.25)	4.06*
Pneumonia (480-486)	26	30.2	0.86	(0.56- 1.26)	1.81**
Digestive system (520-577)	40	62.7	0.64	(0.46- 0.87)	1.17
Oes., stom, duod (530-537)	3	10.6	0.28	(0.06- 0.83)	0.61
Liver cirrhosis (571)	30	35.0	0.86	(0.58- 1.22)	1.62*
Genito-urin syst (580-607)	4	11.6	0.35	(0.09- 0.89)	0.73
Male genital (600-607)	1	1.1	0.87	(0.02- 4.84)	1.96
Nephritis&nephrosis (580-4)	2	4.6	0.44	(0.05- 1.57)	0.81
Oth urinary syst (590-599)	1	5.8	0.17	(0.00- 0.96)	0.40

Mortality by cause of death in plumbers

Follow-up from first checkup (1971-1979) to 1988.

Cause of death	Obs	Exp	SMR	(95 % C. I.)	Rel risk
Violent death (800-999)	142	211.1	0.67	(0.57- 0.79)	0.86
Traffic accidents (800-845)	33	41.8	0.79	(0.54- 1.11)	0.89
Accidental falls (880-887)	6	15.7	0.38	(0.14- 0.83)	0.37*
Suicide (950-959)	50	80.0	0.62	(0.46- 0.82)	0.83
Homicide (960-969)	4	4.8	0.84	(0.23- 2.14)	1.55
Water transp acc (830-838)	5	5.4	0.93	(0.30- 2.16)	0.99
Drowning (910-915)	7	9.6	0.73	(0.29- 1.50)	1.05
Other accidents (916-929)	7	7.7	0.92	(0.37- 1.89)	0.69

Cancer incidence by site of cancer in plumbers

Follow-up from first checkup (1971-1979) to 1987.

Site of cancer	Obs	Exp	SIR	(95 % C. I.)	Rel risk
All cancers (140-209)	631	604.7	1.04	(0.96- 1.13)	1.11*
Lip (140)	3	6.0	0.50	(0.10- 1.46)	0.40
Lip etc (140-149)	12	20.8	0.58	(0.30- 1.01)	0.66
Digest ca (150-154)	110	112.5	0.98	(0.80- 1.18)	1.03
Oesophagus (150)	9	7.9	1.14	(0.52- 2.16)	1.80
Stomach (151)	30	32.1	0.93	(0.63- 1.33)	0.88
Intestines (152-153)	49	43.8	1.12	(0.83- 1.48)	1.22
Colon (153)	46	40.1	1.15	(0.84- 1.53)	1.25
Rectum (154)	22	28.7	0.77	(0.48- 1.16)	0.80
Liver (155.0)	5	8.0	0.62	(0.20- 1.45)	0.89
Gall bladder (155.1)	3	3.0	0.98	(0.20- 2.87)	1.16
Pancreas (157)	23	20.4	1.13	(0.71- 1.69)	1.37
Peritoneum (158)	1	.2	5.00	(0.13- 27.86)	3.96
Nose (160)	2	1.5	1.29	(0.16- 4.66)	1.54
Larynx (161)	7	8.0	0.87	(0.35- 1.80)	1.07
Lung etc (162)	105	69.9	1.50	(1.23- 1.82)	1.63***
Resp ca (160-164)	117	82.6	1.42	(1.17- 1.70)	1.57***
Lung (162.1)	90	67.4	1.34	(1.07- 1.64)	1.46***
Pleura (162.2)	15	2.4	6.33	(3.54- 10.44)	5.07***
Prostate (177)	102	90.6	1.13	(0.92- 1.37)	1.12
Testis (178)	14	11.5	1.21	(0.66- 2.04)	1.38
Bladder (181)	45	42.4	1.06	(0.77- 1.42)	1.10
Kidney (180)	29	29.5	0.98	(0.66- 1.41)	1.09
Lymph&blood (200-209)	57	59.7	0.95	(0.72- 1.24)	0.94
Nhl (200)	21	21.2	0.99	(0.61- 1.51)	0.95
Hodgkin's (201)	5	6.8	0.74	(0.24- 1.72)	0.71
Mult myeloma (203)	8	9.3	0.86	(0.37- 1.70)	0.82
Oth ly&blood (202, 204-209)	23	22.5	1.02	(0.65- 1.54)	1.07
Melanoma (190)	27	27.4	0.99	(0.65- 1.44)	1.14
Other skin (191)	13	17.2	0.76	(0.40- 1.29)	0.82
Nervous system (193)	25	27.7	0.90	(0.58- 1.33)	0.97

Two-sided p-values: * = p<0.05, ** = p<0.01, *** = p<0.001

Mortality by cause of death in painters

Follow-up from first checkup (1971-1979) to 1988.

Cause of death	Obs	Exp	SMR	(95 % C. I.)		Rel risk
All causes (001-999)	1405	1945.8	0.72	(0.68-	0.76)	0.97
All cancers (140-209)	392	459.6	0.85	(0.77-	0.94)	0.96
Lip etc (140-149)	6	9.7	0.62	(0.23-	1.35)	1.18
Oesophageal cancer (150)	11	11.0	1.00	(0.50-	1.78)	1.63
Stomach cancer (151)	32	39.1	0.82	(0.56-	1.16)	0.82
Sm intestines (152)	1	1.6	0.62	(0.02-	3.48)	0.56
Colon cancer (153)	29	32.2	0.90	(0.60-	1.30)	1.11
Rectal cancer (154)	21	19.6	1.07	(0.66-	1.64)	1.18
Liver cancer (155.0)	6	10.3	0.58	(0.21-	1.27)	0.79
Gall bladder (156.0)	7	8.4	0.84	(0.34-	1.72)	0.95
Pancreatic cancer (157)	33	32.5	1.02	(0.70-	1.43)	1.25
Peritoneum (158)	0	1.5	0.00	(0.00-	2.46)	0.00
Laryngeal cancer (161)	2	2.8	0.72	(0.09-	2.62)	1.06
Lung (162.0-162.1)	91	95.1	0.96	(0.77-	1.17)	1.02
Pleura (163.0)	5	3.3	1.50	(0.49-	3.50)	1.11
Bone (170)	3	2.0	1.54	(0.32-	4.50)	2.42
Connect tissue (171)	2	2.3	0.87	(0.10-	3.13)	1.19
Malign melanoma (172)	9	9.6	0.93	(0.43-	1.77)	1.09
Other skin (173)	1	1.1	0.93	(0.02-	5.16)	1.20
Prostate cancer (185)	43	51.8	0.83	(0.60-	1.12)	0.86
Testis cancer (186)	1	2.0	0.50	(0.01-	2.77)	0.88
Bladder cancer (188)	10	13.7	0.73	(0.35-	1.34)	0.90
Kidney cancer (189)	14	22.4	0.62	(0.34-	1.05)	0.73
Urinary org (188-189)	24	36.1	0.66	(0.43-	0.99)	0.79
Brain cancer (191)	19	16.1	1.18	(0.71-	1.85)	1.26
Thyroid cancer (193)	1	1.7	0.58	(0.01-	3.26)	0.86
Lymphosarcoma (200.0-200.1)	0	1.6	0.00	(0.00-	2.36)	0.00
Hodgkins" disease (201)	0	3.3	0.00	(0.00-	1.12)	0.00
Oth lymph tissue (202)	10	13.5	0.74	(0.36-	1.37)	0.72
Mult myeloma (203)	6	9.5	0.63	(0.23-	1.37)	0.63
Leukaemia (204-207)	16	17.4	0.92	(0.53-	1.50)	1.02
Diabetes (250)	9	24.0	0.37	(0.17-	0.71)	0.93
Alcoholism (303)	9	24.4	0.37	(0.17-	0.70)	0.73
Circul system (390-458)	674	956.8	0.70	(0.65-	0.76)	0.95
Isch heart dis (410-414)	491	692.5	0.71	(0.65-	0.77)	0.92
Cerebrovasc dis (430-438)	82	128.6	0.64	(0.51-	0.79)	0.91
Arteries etc (440-448)	33	42.5	0.78	(0.53-	1.09)	1.22
Respiratory syst (460-519)	67	94.3	0.71	(0.55-	0.90)	1.39*
Bronchitis etc (490-493)	27	39.1	0.69	(0.45-	1.00)	1.37
Chronic bronchitis (491)	10	15.4	0.65	(0.31-	1.19)	1.22
Pneumoconiosis (515-516.2)	1	1.4	0.69	(0.02-	3.87)	0.53
Pneumonia (480-486)	31	44.5	0.70	(0.47-	0.99)	1.45
Digestive system (520-577)	49	74.8	0.66	(0.48-	0.87)	1.20
Oes., stom, duod (530-537)	7	14.6	0.48	(0.19-	0.99)	1.06
Liver cirrhosis (571)	19	37.6	0.51	(0.30-	0.79)	0.91
Genito-urin syst (580-607)	6	17.9	0.33	(0.12-	0.73)	0.70
Male genital (600-607)	0	2.1	0.00	(0.00-	1.76)	0.00
Nephritis&nephrosis (580-4)	3	6.3	0.47	(0.10-	1.39)	0.88

Mortality by cause of death in painters

Follow-up from first checkup (1971-1979) to 1988.

Cause of death	Obs	Exp	SMR	(95 % C. I.)	Rel risk
Oth urinary syst (590-599)	3	9.5	0.32	(0.07- 0.92)	0.74
Violent death (800-999)	149	217.2	0.69	(0.58- 0.81)	0.88
Traffic accidents (800-845)	24	44.4	0.54	(0.35- 0.80)	0.59*
Accidental falls (880-887)	13	18.7	0.70	(0.37- 1.19)	0.69
Suicide (950-959)	63	80.3	0.78	(0.60- 1.00)	1.06
Homicide (960-969)	7	4.7	1.50	(0.60- 3.09)	3.07*
Water transp acc (830-838)	4	5.5	0.73	(0.20- 1.87)	0.77
Drowning (910-915)	7	10.3	0.68	(0.27- 1.40)	0.97
Other accidents (916-929)	6	7.8	0.77	(0.28- 1.67)	0.57

Cancer incidence by site of cancer in painters

Follow-up from first checkup (1971-1979) to 1987.

Site of cancer	Obs	Exp	SIR	(95 % C. I.)	Rel risk
All cancers (140-209)	785	804.1	0.98	(0.91- 1.05)	1.03
Lip (140)	4	8.0	0.50	(0.14- 1.28)	0.40
Lip etc (140-149)	20	25.5	0.78	(0.48- 1.21)	0.91
Digest ca (150-154)	166	154.2	1.08	(0.92- 1.25)	1.14
Oesophagus (150)	11	10.7	1.03	(0.51- 1.84)	1.63
Stomach (151)	38	45.4	0.84	(0.59- 1.15)	0.78
Intestines (152-153)	69	59.0	1.17	(0.91- 1.48)	1.28
Colon (153)	63	54.3	1.16	(0.89- 1.48)	1.28
Rectum (154)	48	39.1	1.23	(0.90- 1.63)	1.32
Liver (155.0)	4	11.4	0.35	(0.10- 0.90)	0.48
Gall bladder (155.1)	4	4.4	0.90	(0.25- 2.32)	1.06
Pancreas (157)	31	28.0	1.11	(0.75- 1.57)	1.36
Nose (160)	0	1.9	0.00	(0.00- 1.97)	0.00
Larynx (161)	6	10.2	0.59	(0.22- 1.28)	0.70
Lung etc (162)	99	93.3	1.06	(0.86- 1.29)	1.12
Resp ca (160-164)	108	109.4	0.99	(0.81- 1.19)	1.06
Lung (162.1)	92	90.1	1.02	(0.82- 1.25)	1.10
Pleura (162.2)	7	2.9	2.41	(0.97- 4.96)	1.62
Prostate (177)	156	145.8	1.07	(0.91- 1.25)	1.06
Testis (178)	12	11.3	1.06	(0.55- 1.85)	1.19
Bladder (181)	60	56.8	1.06	(0.81- 1.36)	1.10
Kidney (180)	26	36.8	0.71	(0.46- 1.03)	0.77
Lymph&blood (200-209)	73	73.7	0.99	(0.78- 1.25)	0.98
Nhl (200)	28	25.5	1.10	(0.73- 1.59)	1.06
Hodgkin's (201)	5	7.5	0.67	(0.22- 1.56)	0.64
Mult myeloma (203)	15	12.4	1.21	(0.68- 1.99)	1.17
Oth ly&blood (202, 204-209)	25	28.3	0.88	(0.57- 1.30)	0.92
Melanoma (190)	22	28.9	0.76	(0.48- 1.15)	0.86
Other skin (191)	16	24.9	0.64	(0.37- 1.04)	0.69
Nervous system (193)	31	30.6	1.01	(0.69- 1.44)	1.10

Two-sided p-values: * = p<0.05, ** = p<0.01, *** = p<0.001

Mortality by cause of death in sheet metal workers

Follow-up from first checkup (1971-1979) to 1988.

Cause of death	Obs	Exp	SMR	(95 % C. I.)	Rel risk
All causes (001-999)	294	382.8	0.77	(0.68- 0.86)	1.03
All cancers (140-209)	93	84.2	1.10	(0.89- 1.35)	1.26*
Lip etc (140-149)	2	1.9	1.05	(0.13- 3.78)	1.99
Oesophageal cancer (150)	0	2.0	0.00	(0.00- 1.87)	0.00
Stomach cancer (151)	8	6.6	1.21	(0.52- 2.38)	1.23
Colon cancer (153)	2	5.7	0.35	(0.04- 1.26)	0.42
Rectal cancer (154)	6	3.4	1.78	(0.65- 3.88)	1.97
Liver cancer (155.0)	2	1.8	1.09	(0.13- 3.93)	1.52
Gall bladder (156.0)	1	1.4	0.69	(0.02- 3.87)	0.79
Pancreatic cancer (157)	3	5.7	0.52	(0.11- 1.53)	0.63
Lung (162.0-162.1)	29	17.1	1.70	(1.14- 2.44)	1.84**
Pleura (163.0)	3	.7	4.55	(0.94- 13.28)	3.47
Malign melanoma (172)	6	2.4	2.47	(0.91- 5.37)	2.97*
Other skin (173)	1	.2	4.55	(0.12- 25.33)	6.27
Prostate cancer (185)	4	7.3	0.55	(0.15- 1.40)	0.57
Bladder cancer (188)	3	2.2	1.38	(0.29- 4.04)	1.74
Kidney cancer (189)	3	4.2	0.72	(0.15- 2.10)	0.86
Urinary org (188-189)	6	6.3	0.94	(0.35- 2.06)	1.15
Brain cancer (191)	9	4.0	2.25	(1.03- 4.27)	2.41*
Hodgkins" disease (201)	1	.9	1.11	(0.03- 6.19)	1.55
Oth lymph tissue (202)	5	2.7	1.82	(0.59- 4.26)	1.83
Mult myeloma (203)	1	1.6	0.61	(0.02- 3.42)	0.63
Leukaemia (204-207)	3	3.9	0.77	(0.16- 2.25)	0.85
Diabetes (250)	1	5.3	0.19	(0.00- 1.04)	0.46
Alcoholism (303)	4	7.7	0.52	(0.14- 1.34)	1.05
Circul system (390-458)	120	159.6	0.75	(0.62- 0.90)	1.01
Isch heart dis (410-414)	91	114.7	0.79	(0.64- 0.97)	1.04
Cerebrovasc dis (430-438)	19	21.2	0.90	(0.54- 1.40)	1.30
Arteries etc (440-448)	5	6.7	0.75	(0.24- 1.74)	1.15
Respiratory syst (460-519)	5	16.0	0.31	(0.10- 0.73)	0.59
Bronchitis etc (490-493)	2	6.6	0.30	(0.04- 1.10)	0.58
Chronic bronchitis (491)	1	2.3	0.43	(0.01- 2.41)	0.80
Pneumonia (480-486)	2	7.7	0.26	(0.03- 0.94)	0.52
Digestive system (520-577)	14	16.6	0.85	(0.46- 1.42)	1.54
Oes., stom, duod (530-537)	1	2.6	0.38	(0.01- 2.11)	0.83
Liver cirrhosis (571)	7	9.3	0.75	(0.30- 1.55)	1.38
Genito-urin syst (580-607)	2	2.9	0.70	(0.08- 2.53)	1.52
Nephritis&nephrosis (580-4)	2	1.2	1.69	(0.21- 6.12)	3.28
Oth urinary syst (590-599)	0	1.4	0.00	(0.00- 2.62)	0.00
Violent death (800-999)	50	73.1	0.68	(0.51- 0.90)	0.88
Traffic accidents (800-845)	8	15.6	0.51	(0.22- 1.01)	0.57
Accidental falls (880-887)	11	4.5	2.42	(1.21- 4.34)	2.52**
Suicide (950-959)	15	27.9	0.54	(0.30- 0.89)	0.72

Mortality by cause of death in sheet metal workers

Follow-up from first checkup (1971-1979) to 1988.

Cause of death	Obs	Exp	SMR	(95 % C. I.)	Rel risk
Homicide (960-969)	0	1.8	0.00	(0.00- 2.02)	0.00
Water transp acc (830-838)	1	1.9	0.52	(0.01- 2.92)	0.55
Drowning (910-915)	1	3.2	0.32	(0.01- 1.76)	0.45
Other accidents (916-929)	1	2.6	0.38	(0.01- 2.12)	0.29

Cancer incidence by site of cancer in sheet metal workers

Follow-up from first checkup (1971-1979) to 1987.

Site of cancer	Obs	Exp	SIR	(95 % C. I.)	Rel risk
All cancers (140-209)	175	156.4	1.12	(0.96- 1.30)	1.19*
Lip (140)	1	1.5	0.68	(0.02- 3.76)	0.56
Lip etc (140-149)	8	5.3	1.51	(0.65- 2.97)	1.78
Digest ca (150-154)	31	27.8	1.12	(0.76- 1.58)	1.17
Oesophagus (150)	2	1.9	1.05	(0.13- 3.78)	1.60
Stomach (151)	13	7.9	1.65	(0.88- 2.83)	1.58
Intestines (152-153)	6	11.0	0.54	(0.20- 1.19)	0.58
Colon (153)	6	10.1	0.60	(0.22- 1.30)	0.64
Rectum (154)	10	7.0	1.42	(0.68- 2.61)	1.50
Liver (155.0)	1	2.0	0.50	(0.01- 2.80)	0.72
Pancreas (157)	2	4.9	0.41	(0.05- 1.47)	0.48
Larynx (161)	1	2.0	0.51	(0.01- 2.83)	0.61
Lung etc (162)	29	17.0	1.70	(1.14- 2.44)	1.80**
Resp ca (160-164)	31	20.2	1.54	(1.04- 2.18)	1.66**
Lung (162.1)	26	16.4	1.59	(1.04- 2.33)	1.71**
Pleura (162.2)	3	.6	4.76	(0.98- 13.92)	3.17
Prostate (177)	17	21.2	0.80	(0.47- 1.28)	0.79
Testis (178)	3	4.8	0.62	(0.13- 1.83)	0.69
Bladder (181)	14	10.5	1.33	(0.73- 2.23)	1.38
Kidney (180)	3	7.4	0.41	(0.08- 1.18)	0.45
Lymph&blood (200-209)	19	16.6	1.15	(0.69- 1.79)	1.14
Nhl (200)	10	5.8	1.73	(0.83- 3.19)	1.69
Hodgkin's (201)	2	2.4	0.84	(0.10- 3.05)	0.82
Mult myeloma (203)	2	2.3	0.88	(0.11- 3.17)	0.84
Oth ly&blood (202, 204-209)	5	6.2	0.81	(0.26- 1.89)	0.84
Melanoma (190)	9	8.2	1.10	(0.50- 2.09)	1.26
Other skin (191)	5	4.3	1.15	(0.37- 2.68)	1.27
Nervous system (193)	13	8.2	1.58	(0.84- 2.70)	1.72

Two-sided p-values: * = p<0.05, ** = p<0.01, *** = p<0.001

Mortality by cause of death in electricians

Follow-up from first checkup (1971-1979) to 1988.

Cause of death	Obs	Exp	SMR	(95 % C. I.)	Rel risk
All causes (001-999)	707	1064.7	0.66	(0.62- 0.71)	0.89**
All cancers (140-209)	223	232.2	0.96	(0.84- 1.10)	1.09
Lip etc (140-149)	5	5.5	0.91	(0.29- 2.11)	1.75
Oesophageal cancer (150)	5	5.5	0.91	(0.29- 2.11)	1.44
Stomach cancer (151)	13	17.5	0.74	(0.40- 1.27)	0.75
Sm intestines (152)	2	.9	2.30	(0.28- 8.30)	2.23
Colon cancer (153)	16	15.6	1.02	(0.59- 1.66)	1.26
Rectal cancer (154)	7	9.1	0.77	(0.31- 1.58)	0.83
Liver cancer (155.0)	7	5.1	1.39	(0.56- 2.86)	1.99
Gall bladder (156.0)	6	3.9	1.52	(0.56- 3.31)	1.78
Pancreatic cancer (157)	13	15.8	0.82	(0.44- 1.41)	0.99
Peritoneum (158)	1	.9	1.05	(0.03- 5.86)	1.05
Laryngeal cancer (161)	1	1.3	0.75	(0.02- 4.16)	1.09
Lung (162.0-162.1)	43	47.5	0.90	(0.65- 1.22)	0.97
Pleura (163.0)	3	1.9	1.61	(0.33- 4.71)	1.20
Bone (170)	0	1.5	0.00	(0.00- 2.53)	0.00
Connect tissue (171)	2	1.7	1.16	(0.14- 4.20)	1.63
Malign melanoma (172)	6	7.3	0.83	(0.30- 1.80)	0.96
Other skin (173)	1	.6	1.64	(0.04- 9.13)	2.20
Prostate cancer (185)	19	17.9	1.06	(0.64- 1.66)	1.12
Testis cancer (186)	2	2.3	0.87	(0.11- 3.14)	1.63
Bladder cancer (188)	13	5.7	2.30	(1.22- 3.93)	3.06***
Kidney cancer (189)	12	11.8	1.02	(0.53- 1.78)	1.23
Urinary org (188-189)	25	17.5	1.43	(0.93- 2.11)	1.79**
Brain cancer (191)	13	11.9	1.10	(0.58- 1.87)	1.16
Thyroid cancer (193)	0	.9	0.00	(0.00- 4.19)	0.00
Lymphosarcoma (200.0-200.1)	1	.7	1.39	(0.04- 7.74)	1.40
Hodgkins" disease (201)	3	2.6	1.16	(0.24- 3.40)	1.66
Oth lymph tissue (202)	6	7.9	0.76	(0.28- 1.65)	0.74
Mult myeloma (203)	3	4.4	0.68	(0.14- 1.98)	0.70
Leukaemia (204-207)	12	11.0	1.09	(0.56- 1.90)	1.21
Diabetes (250)	3	15.0	0.20	(0.04- 0.58)	0.49
Alcoholism (303)	7	23.8	0.29	(0.12- 0.61)	0.57
Circul system (390-458)	288	425.1	0.68	(0.60- 0.76)	0.91
Isch heart dis (410-414)	216	306.8	0.70	(0.61- 0.80)	0.92
Cerebrovasc dis (430-438)	32	54.8	0.58	(0.40- 0.82)	0.84
Arteries etc (440-448)	9	17.3	0.52	(0.24- 0.99)	0.80
Respiratory syst (460-519)	20	42.3	0.47	(0.29- 0.73)	0.90
Bronchitis etc (490-493)	7	17.5	0.40	(0.16- 0.83)	0.77
Chronic bronchitis (491)	1	5.8	0.17	(0.00- 0.95)	0.31
Pneumoconiosis (515-516.2)	1	.6	1.82	(0.05- 10.13)	1.47
Pneumonia (480-486)	7	20.2	0.35	(0.14- 0.71)	0.69
Digestive system (520-577)	14	47.6	0.29	(0.16- 0.49)	0.52*
Oes., stom, duod (530-537)	1	7.0	0.14	(0.00- 0.79)	0.30
Liver cirrhosis (571)	9	27.9	0.32	(0.15- 0.61)	0.57
Genito-urin syst (580-607)	6	7.1	0.85	(0.31- 1.84)	1.87
Nephritis&nephrosis (580-4)	3	3.2	0.95	(0.20- 2.77)	1.84
Oth urinary syst (590-599)	3	3.4	0.89	(0.18- 2.61)	2.23

Mortality by cause of death in electricians

Follow-up from first checkup (1971-1979) to 1988.

Cause of death	Obs	Exp	SMR	(95 % C. I.)		Rel risk
Violent death (800-999)	124	221.0	0.56	(0.47-	0.67)	0.71***
Traffic accidents (800-845)	32	46.1	0.69	(0.47-	0.98)	0.77
Accidental falls (880-887)	8	13.0	0.62	(0.27-	1.21)	0.61
Suicide (950-959)	45	85.5	0.53	(0.38-	0.70)	0.69*
Homicide (960-969)	3	5.6	0.53	(0.11-	1.55)	0.94
Water transp acc (830-838)	2	5.8	0.35	(0.04-	1.25)	0.35
Drowning (910-915)	7	9.4	0.75	(0.30-	1.54)	1.08
Other accidents (916-929)	10	7.8	1.28	(0.61-	2.35)	0.98

Cancer incidence by site of cancer in electricians

Follow-up from first checkup (1971-1979) to 1987.

Site of cancer	Obs	Exp	SIR	(95 % C. I.)		Rel risk
All cancers (140-209)	438	437.2	1.00	(0.91-	1.10)	1.06
Lip (140)	2	4.1	0.49	(0.06-	1.76)	0.40
Lip etc (140-149)	14	15.3	0.91	(0.50-	1.53)	1.07
Digest ca (150-154)	83	76.2	1.09	(0.87-	1.35)	1.15
Oesophagus (150)	4	5.3	0.75	(0.20-	1.93)	1.15
Stomach (151)	24	21.0	1.14	(0.73-	1.70)	1.09
Intestines (152-153)	38	30.4	1.25	(0.88-	1.71)	1.36
Colon (153)	34	27.7	1.23	(0.85-	1.71)	1.34
Rectum (154)	17	19.5	0.87	(0.51-	1.40)	0.92
Liver (155.0)	9	5.4	1.66	(0.76-	3.15)	2.53*
Gall bladder (155.1)	3	2.0	1.53	(0.32-	4.47)	1.84
Pancreas (157)	10	13.5	0.74	(0.35-	1.36)	0.88
Nose (160)	0	1.1	0.00	(0.00-	3.29)	0.00
Larynx (161)	4	5.6	0.71	(0.19-	1.82)	0.86
Lung etc (162)	41	47.7	0.86	(0.62-	1.17)	0.90
Resp ca (160-164)	46	56.5	0.81	(0.60-	1.09)	0.87
Lung (162.1)	40	45.7	0.87	(0.62-	1.19)	0.93
Pleura (162.2)	0	1.8	0.00	(0.00-	2.06)	0.00
Prostate (177)	49	52.9	0.93	(0.68-	1.22)	0.91
Testis (178)	13	15.2	0.86	(0.46-	1.47)	0.94
Bladder (181)	39	29.3	1.33	(0.95-	1.82)	1.39
Kidney (180)	22	21.2	1.04	(0.65-	1.57)	1.16
Lymph&blood (200-209)	55	47.6	1.15	(0.87-	1.50)	1.15
Nhl (200)	16	16.8	0.95	(0.54-	1.55)	0.91
Hodgkin's (201)	8	7.0	1.14	(0.49-	2.25)	1.13
Mult myeloma (203)	8	6.3	1.27	(0.55-	2.50)	1.23
Oth ly&blood (202, 204-209)	23	17.5	1.31	(0.83-	1.97)	1.39
Melanoma (190)	21	24.8	0.85	(0.52-	1.30)	0.96
Other skin (191)	8	11.6	0.69	(0.30-	1.36)	0.75
Nervous system (193)	24	24.6	0.98	(0.63-	1.45)	1.05

Two-sided p-values: * = p<0.05, ** = p<0.01, *** = p<0.001

Mortality by cause of death in the total cohort

Follow-up from first checkup (1971-1979) to 1988.

Cause of death	Obs	Exp	SMR	(95 % C. I.)
All causes (001-999)	18659	25129.3	0.74***	(0.73- 0.75)
All cancers (140-209)	5257	5958.6	0.88***	(0.86- 0.91)
Lip cancer (140)	1	2.4	0.41	(0.01- 2.31)
Lip etc (140-149)	70	130.9	0.53***	(0.42- 0.68)
Oesophageal cancer (150)	93	145.5	0.64***	(0.52- 0.78)
Stomach cancer (151)	489	495.7	0.99	(0.90- 1.08)
Sm intestines (152)	23	21.2	1.08	(0.69- 1.63)
Colon cancer (153)	340	415.5	0.82***	(0.73- 0.91)
Rectal cancer (154)	231	252.1	0.92	(0.80- 1.04)
Liver cancer (155.0)	96	132.9	0.72***	(0.58- 0.88)
Gall bladder (156.0)	95	108.0	0.88	(0.71- 1.08)
Pancreatic cancer (157)	351	423.5	0.83***	(0.74- 0.92)
Peritoneum (158)	20	19.9	1.00	(0.61- 1.55)
Nose, nasal cav (160)	6	9.5	0.63	(0.23- 1.38)
Laryngeal cancer (161)	25	36.3	0.69	(0.45- 1.02)
Lung (162.0-162.1)	1168	1248.1	0.94*	(0.88- 0.99)
Pleura (163.0)	60	44.2	1.36*	(1.04- 1.75)
Bone (170)	18	25.5	0.71	(0.42- 1.12)
Connect tissue (171)	23	31.2	0.74	(0.47- 1.11)
Malign melanoma (172)	116	134.6	0.86	(0.71- 1.03)
Other skin (173)	11	14.0	0.79	(0.39- 1.40)
Prostate cancer (185)	593	624.3	0.95	(0.87- 1.03)
Testis cancer (186)	15	26.6	0.56*	(0.32- 0.93)
Bladder cancer (188)	138	172.0	0.80**	(0.67- 0.95)
Kidney cancer (189)	249	297.5	0.84**	(0.74- 0.95)
Urinary org (188-189)	387	469.7	0.82***	(0.74- 0.91)
Brain cancer (191)	213	222.9	0.96	(0.83- 1.09)
Oth endocr glands (194)	7	9.5	0.74	(0.30- 1.52)
Thyroid cancer (193)	15	22.3	0.67	(0.38- 1.11)
Lymphosarcoma (200.0-200.1)	20	19.9	1.01	(0.61- 1.55)
Hodgkins" disease (201)	32	44.0	0.73	(0.50- 1.03)
Oth lymph tissue (202)	180	177.8	1.01	(0.87- 1.17)
Mult myeloma (203)	118	122.2	0.97	(0.80- 1.16)
Leukaemia (204-207)	206	226.9	0.91	(0.79- 1.04)
Diabetes (250)	126	314.3	0.40***	(0.33- 0.48)
Alcoholism (303)	180	360.0	0.50***	(0.43- 0.58)
Circul system (390-458)	8977	12112.8	0.74***	(0.73- 0.76)
Isch heart dis (410-414)	6748	8811.7	0.77***	(0.75- 0.78)
Cerebrovasc dis (430-438)	1106	1594.0	0.69***	(0.65- 0.74)
Arteries etc (440-448)	340	523.6	0.65***	(0.58- 0.72)
Respiratory syst (460-519)	618	1175.4	0.53***	(0.49- 0.57)
Bronchitis etc (490-493)	256	492.5	0.52***	(0.46- 0.59)
Chronic bronchitis (491)	102	188.4	0.54***	(0.44- 0.66)
Pneumoconiosis (515-516.2)	22	17.5	1.26	(0.79- 1.90)
Pneumonia (480-486)	274	550.4	0.50***	(0.44- 0.56)
Digestive system (520-577)	560	1012.5	0.55***	(0.51- 0.60)
Oes., stom, duod (530-537)	85	186.7	0.46***	(0.36- 0.56)
Liver cirrhosis (571)	294	534.9	0.55***	(0.49- 0.62)
Genito-urin syst (580-607)	101	217.5	0.46***	(0.38- 0.56)
Male genital (600-607)	11	23.7	0.46**	(0.23- 0.83)

Mortality by cause of death in the total cohort

Follow-up from first checkup (1971-1979) to 1988.

Cause of death	Obs	Exp	SMR	(95 % C. I.)
Nephritis&nephrosis (580-4)	43	80.6	0.53***	(0.39- 0.72)
Oth urinary syst (590-599)	47	113.3	0.41***	(0.30- 0.55)
Violent death (800-999)	2302	2976.9	0.77***	(0.74- 0.81)
Traffic accidents (800-845)	520	590.3	0.88**	(0.81- 0.96)
Accidental falls (880-887)	246	248.6	0.99	(0.87- 1.12)
Suicide (950-959)	827	1109.6	0.75***	(0.70- 0.80)
Homicide (960-969)	36	64.1	0.56***	(0.39- 0.78)
Water transp acc (830-838)	70	74.9	0.93	(0.73- 1.18)
Drowning (910-915)	98	140.9	0.70***	(0.56- 0.85)
Other accidents (916-929)	140	107.7	1.30**	(1.09- 1.53)

Cancer incidence by site of cancer in asphalt workers

Follow-up from first checkup (1971-1979) to 1987.
Total cohort

Site of cancer	Obs	Exp	SIR	(95 % C. I.)
All cancers (140-209)	9940	10500.0	0.95***	(0.93- 0.97)
Lip (140)	126	104.8	1.20*	(1.00- 1.43)
Lip etc (140-149)	296	345.8	0.86**	(0.76- 0.96)
Digest ca (150-154)	1905	2000.7	0.95*	(0.91- 1.00)
Oesophagus (150)	93	141.1	0.66***	(0.53- 0.81)
Stomach (151)	612	580.9	1.05	(0.97- 1.14)
Intestines (152-153)	715	768.9	0.93	(0.86- 1.00)
Colon (153)	655	705.5	0.93	(0.86- 1.00)
Rectum (154)	485	509.8	0.95	(0.87- 1.04)
Liver (155.0)	101	145.8	0.69***	(0.56- 0.84)
Gall bladder (155.1)	48	56.1	0.86	(0.63- 1.13)
Pancreas (157)	306	365.3	0.84**	(0.75- 0.94)
Peritoneum (158)	5	3.4	1.48	(0.48- 3.46)
Nose (160)	22	25.5	0.86	(0.54- 1.31)
Larynx (161)	113	137.6	0.82*	(0.68- 0.99)
Lung etc (162)	1177	1231.2	0.96	(0.90- 1.01)
Resp ca (160-164)	1352	1447.6	0.93*	(0.88- 0.99)
Lung (162.1)	1113	1188.9	0.94*	(0.88- 0.99)
Pleura (162.2)	61	39.2	1.56**	(1.19- 2.00)
Prostate (177)	1810	1784.2	1.01	(0.97- 1.06)
Testis (178)	136	150.8	0.90	(0.76- 1.07)
Bladder (181)	723	745.8	0.97	(0.90- 1.04)
Kidney (180)	449	497.8	0.90*	(0.82- 0.99)
Lymph&blood (200-209)	989	981.4	1.01	(0.95- 1.07)
Nhl (200)	359	345.6	1.04	(0.93- 1.15)
Hodgkin's (201)	101	99.0	1.02	(0.83- 1.24)
Mult myeloma (203)	170	162.9	1.04	(0.89- 1.21)
Oth ly&blood (202, 204-209)	359	374.1	0.96	(0.86- 1.06)
Melanoma (190)	357	407.4	0.88*	(0.79- 0.97)
Other skin (191)	285	313.7	0.91	(0.81- 1.02)
Nervous system (193)	393	422.7	0.93	(0.84- 1.03)

Two-sided p-values: * = p<0.05, ** = p<0.01, *** = p<0.001

INDEX

Entries in **boldface type** indicate complete chapters.

Abrasive-blasting workers. *See* Sandblasting workers
Acetone, as respiratory hazard, 321–322, 328, 340
Acids, as lung cancer risk factor, 321–322
Acromioclavicular joint, osteoarthritis of, 296, 306, 307, 308
Adhesives, 313, 341, 342
Administrative controls, 411, 417
  for asbestos exposure, 414
  for ergonomic risk factors, 388
  for vibration exposure, 375
AFL–CIO, 281
African-American construction workers, mortality patterns of, 274, 275–276, 278, 279
Airborne hazards, 407
  environmental controls for, 412
Air compressors, noise control regulations for, 365, 368
Airway obstruction and diseases, 326–328, 408
Alcohol abuse, 263, 267, 275, 276, 407, 439
Alkalis, as lung cancer risk factor, 321–322
Allergic diseases and reactions, 336
  dust exposure-related, 429
  epoxy resin products-related, 347, 348
Aluminum, as respiratory hazard, 314, 316
American Association of Occupational Health Nurses, code of ethics of, 423
American College of Occupational and Environmental Medicine, code of ethics of, 423–424
American Conference of Governmental Industrial Hygienists, vibration exposure limits of, 373, 376
American National Standard for Construction and Demolition Operations, 397
American National Standards Institute
  construction safety standards of, 397, 398, 447
  ergonomic risk factor reduction standards of, 392
  vibration exposure standards of, 373, 374, 376
Americans with Disabilities Act, 370, 392, 425
American Thoracic Society, pulmonary function test standards of, 429–430
Aminoglycoside antibiotics, as hearing loss risk factor, 429
Amyl acetate, as respiratory irritant, 328
Antihypertensive agents, as hearing loss risk factor, 429
Apophyseal joints, osteoarthritis of, 303
Arsenic
  exposure limits for, 315

Arsenic *(cont.)*
  neurotoxicity of, 276
  OSHA compliance monitoring of, 320
  as respiratory hazard, 314, 315, 320
Arthritis, spinal, vibration-related, 373–374
Articular disorders, pathophysiology of, 301–302
Asbestos exposure
  as bronchitis risk factor, 326
  controls for, 414–415, 418
  exposure limits for, 315, 414, 320, 325
  exposure sources of, 324, 414–415
  as lung cancer risk factor, 321–322
  medical surveillance of, 432, 438
  OSHA compliance monitoring of, 320, 325
  removal of, 414
  as respiratory hazard, 313, 321–322, 326
  in specific construction trades, 408
  substitutes for, 415, 418
Asbestos insulation workers
  asbestosis in, 325, 408
  lung cancer in, 322, 408
  mesothelioma in, 408
Asbestosis, 256, 324–325, 308
  proportionate mortality rate of, 274, 275, 320–321, 322
Asbestos-related cancer, standardized mortality and incidence rates of, 268
Asphalt fumes, as respiratory hazard, 314, 316, 330
Asphalt workers
  lung cancer in, 323
  standardized mortality and incidence rates in, 263–264
Associated General Contractors, construction safety code of, 397, 398
Association of Occupational and Environmental Clinics, Patient Bill of Rights of, 424
Asthma, occupational, 319, 327
  in atopic individuals, 430
  rate ratio of, 321
Atopy, 430
Audiometric testing, 369, 370–371
Azoles, as wood protectants, 343

Back injuries
  classification of, 385
  in masonry block layers, 390
  prediction of, 428–429
  vibration-related, 373–374, 375
Back pain, vibration-related, 300
Bats, as histoplasmosis vectors, 328